THE WORLD AT 18 000 BP

TITLES OF RELATED INTEREST

Animals into art
H. Morphy (ed.)

Archaeological approaches to cultural identity
S. J. Shennan (ed.)

Archaeological heritage management in the modern world
H. F. Cleere (ed.)

Centre and periphery: comparative studies in archaeology
T. C. Champion (ed.)

Chalcolithic, Bronze and Iron Age cultures in South Asia
M. Lal (ed.)

Conflict in the archaeology of living traditions
R. Layton (ed.)

Domination and resistance
D. Miller *et al.* (eds)

The excluded past: archaeology in education
P. Stone & R. MacKenzie (eds)

Food, metals and towns in African history: African adaptations in subsistence and technology
T. Shaw *et al.* (eds)

Foraging and farming: the evolution of plant exploitation
D. Harris & G. Hillman (eds)

From the Baltic to the Black Sea: studies in medieval archaeology
L. Alcock & D. Austin (eds)

Hominid evolution, behaviour and dispersal
M. H. Day *et al.* (eds)

Hunters of the recent past
L. Davis & B. O. K. Reeves (eds)

The meanings of things: material culture and symbolic expression
I. Hodder (ed.)

Pleistocene perspective: innovation, adaptation and human survival
A. M. ApSimon & S. Joyce (eds)

The politics of the past
P. Gathercole & D. Lowenthal (eds)

Signifying animals: human meaning in the natural world
R. G. Willis (ed.)

State and society: the emergence and development of social hierarchy and political centralization
J. Gledhill *et al.* (eds)

The walking larder: patterns of domestication, pastoralism, and predation
J. Clutton-Brock (ed.)

What is an animal?
T. Ingold (ed.)

What's new? A closer look at the process of innovation
S. E. van der Leeuw & R. Torrence (eds)

Who needs the past? Indigenous values and archaeology
R. Layton (ed.)

The world at 18 000 BP: high latitudes
O. Soffer & C. Gamble (eds)

THE WORLD AT 18 000 BP

Volume 2

Low latitudes

Edited by

Clive Gamble

Department of Archaeology, University of Southampton, UK

Olga Soffer

Department of Anthropology, University of Illinois at Urbana-Champaign, USA

London
UNWIN HYMAN
Boston   Sydney   Wellington

Published by the Academic Division of
Unwin Hyman Ltd
15/17 Broadwick Street, London W1V 1FP, UK

Unwin Hyman Inc.,
8 Winchester Place, Winchester, Mass. 01890, USA

Allen & Unwin (Australia) Ltd,
8 Napier Street, North Sydney, NSW 2060, Australia

Allen & Unwin (New Zealand) Ltd in association with the
Port Nicholson Press Ltd,
Compusales Building, 75 Ghuznee Street, Wellington 1, New Zealand

First published in 1990

British Library Cataloguing in Publication Data
The World at 18,000 BP.
  1. Pleistocene strata
  I. Gamble, Clive   II. Soffer, Olga   III. Series
  551.7'92

  ISBN 0-04-445126-1 v.1
  ISBN 0-04-445127-X v.2

Library of Congress Cataloging in Publication Data
The World at 18,000 BP / edited by Olga Soffer, Clive Gamble.
    p.   cm.
  Includes bibliographical references.
  Contents: v. 1. High latitudes – v. 2. Low latitudes.
  ISBN 0-04-445126-1 (v. 1): £40.00. – ISBN 0-04-445127-X (v. 2)
    1. Man, Prehistoric.   2. Paleoecology.   3. Paleogeography.
  I. Soffer, Olga.   II. Gamble, Clive.
  GN741.W67   1989
  930.1–dc20   89-16627
                    CIP

Typeset in 10 on 12 point Bembo by Computape (Pickering) Ltd,
North Yorkshire and printed in Great Britain by
the University Press, Cambridge

Contents

Contents of volume 1: high latitudes   page   xi

List of contributors   xiii

Acknowledgements   xvii

Introduction: Pleistocene polyphony: the diversity of human adaptations at
    the Last Glacial Maximum   Clive Gamble & Olga Soffer   1

    Introduction   1
    World prehistory and hunter–gatherers   1
    Review of the LGM volumes as a project framework   6
    Some problems with the LGM framework   15

1   The distribution of human settlement in the extra-tropical Old World:
    24 000–15 000 BP   Teresa Madeyska   24

    Introduction   24
    Settlement distributions   25
    Sahara   25
    Mediterranean   25
    Nile Valley   27
    Near East   28
    Central and southern Asia   29
    Far East   29
    Northern Asia   30
    Conclusion   33

NORTH AFRICA AND THE MIDDLE EAST

2   North Africa at 18 000 BP   Angela E. Close & Fred Wendorf   41

    Introduction   41
    Palaeoenvironment   41
    Human occupation of the Maghreb   42
    Human occupation of Cyrenaïca   47
    Human occupation of the Lower Nile Valley   49
    Conclusion   53

3   The Last Glacial Maximum in the Mediterranean Levant
    Ofer Bar-Yosef   58
    Introduction   58

Palaeoenvironments in the Levant   58
The definition of Epi-Palaeolithic entities   61
The Kebaran Complex   63
The Geometric Kebaran Complex   69
The Mushabian Complex and its contemporaries   71
Discussion   72

4   *The Last Glacial Maximum in the Jordanian desert*
    Brian F. Byrd & Andrew N. Garrard   78

Introduction   78
Environmental setting   79
Research design   81
Field methods   81
Preliminary results   83
Summary of Azraq Basin adaptations   92

5   *Kebaran occupation at the Last Glacial Maximum in Wadi*
    al-Hammeh, Jordan Valley   Phillip C. Edwards   97

Definition of the region and geology of Wadi al-Hammeh   98
Palaeoenvironmental reconstruction   103
The Kebaran sites   104
The archaeological landscape   107
Kebaran settlement patterns   108
Kebaran subsistence patterns   108
Measuring occupation intensity   111
Conclusions   114

SUB-SAHARAN AFRICA

6   *The Glacial Maximum in tropical Africa: 22 000–12 000 BP*
    Alison S. Brooks & Peter Robertshaw   121

Introduction   121
Palaeoclimatic reconstruction   130
Archaeological evidence for cultural complexity: 24 000–12 000 BP 138
Summary and discussion   158

7   *Changes in the archaeological record in South Africa at 18 000 BP*
    Janette Deacon   170

Introduction   170
Modern environments and the archaeological record   170
The palaeoclimatic record   173
The artefact record   175
Economy   181
Social correlates   182
Some conclusions   183

8   *A palaeoecological model for archaeological site distribution in*
    southern Africa during the Upper Pleniglacial and Late Glacial
    Peter Mitchell   189

    Introduction   189
    The nature and reliability of the evidence   190
    The Last Glacial Maximum palaeoenvironment and the distribution
        of archaeological sites   195
    A tentative ecological model of Last Glacial Maximum site distribution   198
    The distribution of archaeological sites in South Africa during the Late
        Glacial and Postglacial   201

9   *Zimbabwe at 18 000 BP*   Nick J. Walker   206

    Introduction   206
    Archaeological research   207
    Discussion and conclusions   210

10 *A view from the south: southern Africa before, during, and after the*
    Last Glacial Maximum   John Parkington   214

    Introduction   214
    Settlement histories   215
    Elands Bay Cave   216
    Caves elsewhere   220
    A general perspective   223

SOUTHERN ASIA, SUNDA AND AUSTRALIA

11 *South Asian climate and environment at c. 18 000 BP*
    D. P. Agrawal, Rekha Dodia & Mala Seth   231

    Introduction   231
    The Arabian Sea   231
    Rajasthan   232
    Kashmir   233
    Conclusion   235

12 *Hunter–gatherers of the terminal Pleistocene in Uttar Pradesh, India*
    Vidula Jayaswal   237

    Introduction   237
    Research history   237
    Pleistocene geology   238
    Upper Palaeolithic   238
    Settlement evidence   239
    Discussion   252

13   *From Late Pleistocene to Early Holocene in Sundaland*
        Peter Bellwood   255

        Introduction   255
        Equatorial rainforest exploitation   257
        The impact of the post 18 000 BP sea-level rise   260
        Post-18 000 BP lithic technology   260

14   *From Kakadu to Kutikina: the southern continent at 18 000 years ago*
        Rhys Jones   264

        Ice-Age climatic regime in the south   266
        Kakadu: the tropical savanna   268
        The arid zone   274
        Tasmania   275
        The Kutikina sequence   278
        Other sites in the Franklin catchment   284
        The Weld and the Florentine: new investigations   285
        Rock art   288
        Furthest south   290

15   *Environmental history in southwestern New South Wales during the*
        Late Pleistocene   Harry Allen   296

        Introduction   296
        The Willandra Lakes   296
        Archaeological sites in the Willandra Lakes area, 22 000–15 000 BP   299
        Discussion   312
        Revision of comparisons   315

Afterword: Minitime and megaspace in the Palaeolithic at 18 K and
        otherwise   H. Martin Wobst   322

        No change without change   322
        18 K hunter–gatherers   324
        18 K nature and culture   326
        Contemporaneity   327
        Peak form   329
        18 K panopticum   331

Indexes   335

Contents of volume 1: high latitudes

Introduction: *Pleistocene polyphony: the diversity of human adaptations at the Last Glacial Maximum* Clive Gamble & Olga Soffer

1 *Living in the last high glacial – an interdisciplinary challenge* T. H. van Andel

NORTHWESTERN EUROPE

2 *The last Pleniglacial in the Paris Basin (22 500–17 000 BP)* Béatrice Schmider

3 *The northwestern European Plain around 18 000 BP* Marcel Otte

4 *The last Pleniglacial in the south of France (24 000–14 000 years ago)* Jean-Philippe Rigaud & Jan F. Simek

SOUTHERN EUROPE

5 *The Last Glacial Maximum in Cantabrian Spain: the Solutrean* Lawrence Guy Straus

6 *The Portuguese Estremadura at 18 000 BP: the Solutrean* João Zilhão

7 *Continuity and change in Italy at the Last Glacial Maximum* Margherita Mussi

8 *The Balkans at 18 000 BP: the view from Epirus* Geoff Bailey & Clive Gamble

CENTRAL AND EASTERN EUROPE

9 *Germany at 18 000 BP* Gerd-C. Weniger

10 *Moravia during the Upper Pleniglacial* Jiří Svoboda

11 *Northern Central Europe c. 18 000 BP* Janusz K. Kozlowski

12   *The Russian Plain at the Last Glacial Maximum*   Olga Soffer

EASTERN EURASIA AND THE NEW WORLD

13   *Environmental conditions and human occupation of northern Eurasia during the Late Valdai*   A. A. Velichko & E. I. Kurenkova

14   *Central Asian hunter–gatherers at the Last Glacial Maximum*   Richard S. Davis

15   *China at the Last Glacial Maximum*   Chun Chen & John W. Olsen

16   *Japan and Korea at 18 000 BP*   T. E. G. Reynolds & S. C. Kaner

17   *New World palaeoecology at the Last Glacial Maximum and the implications for New World prehistory*   George C. Frison & Danny N. Walker

Afterword: Minitime and megaspace in the Palaeolithic at 18 K and otherwise   H. Martin Wobst

List of contributors

Names of contributors to this volume are printed in bold type.

D. P. Agrawal, Physical Research Laboratory, Navrangpura, Ahmedabad 380 0009 India.

Harry Allen, Department of Anthropology, University of Auckland, Private Bag, Auckland, New Zealand.

T. H. van Andel, Department of Earth Sciences, University of Cambridge, Downing Street, Cambridge CB2 3EQ, England.

Geoff Bailey, Department of Archaeology, University of Cambridge, Downing Street, Cambridge CB2 3DZ, England.

Ofer Bar-Yosef, Department of Anthropology, Harvard University, Cambridge, MA 02138, USA.

Peter Bellwood, Department of Anthropology, Research School of Pacific Studies, Australian National University, GPO Box 4, Canberra ACT 2601, Australia.

Alison S. Brooks, Department of Anthropology, Smithsonian Institution, Washington DC 20560, USA

Brian F. Byrd, Department of Anthropology, University of Wisconsin, Madison, 53706 USA.

Chun Chen, Department of Anthropology, McGill University, Montreal PO H3A 2TZ, Canada.

Angela E. Close, Department of Anthropology, Southern Methodist University, Dallas, Texas 75275, USA.

Richard S. Davis, Department of Anthropology, Bryn Mawr College, Bryn Mawr, PA 19010, USA.

Janette Deacon, Department of Archaeology, University of Stellenbosch, Stellenbosch 7600, South Africa.

Rekha Dodia, Physical Research Laboratory, Navrangpura, Ahmedabad 380009, India.

Phillip C. Edwards, Department of Archaeology, University of Sydney, New South Wales, 2006 Sydney, Australia.

George C. Frison, Department of Anthropology, University of Wyoming, Laramie, Wyoming 82071, USA.

Clive Gamble, Department of Archaeology, University of Southampton, Southampton SO9 5NH, England.

Andrew N. Garrard, British Institute at Amman for Archaeology and History, PO Box 925071, Amman, Jordan.

Vidula Jayaswal, Department of Ancient Indian History, Culture and Archaeology, Banaras Hindu University, Varanasi 221005, India.

Rhys Jones, Department of Prehistory, Research School of Pacific Studies, Australian National University, Canberra, ACT 2601, Australia.

S. C. Kaner, Department of Archaeology, University of Cambridge, Downing Street Cambridge CB2 3DZ, England.

Janusz K. Kozłowski, Instytut Archeologii, Universytet Jagiellonski, ul. Golebia, 11, 31–007 Kraków, Poland.

E. I. Kurenkova, Otdel Paleogeografii, Institut Geografii AN SSSR, Staromonetnii per., 29, Moscow 109017, USSR.

Teresa Madeyska, Warszawa Institute of Geological Sciences of the Polish Academy of Sciences, Al. Zwirki i Wigury 93, 02–089 Warszawa, Poland.

Peter Mitchell, Department of Ethnology and Prehistory, University of Oxford, 60 Banbury Road, Oxford, OX2 6PN, England.

Margherita Mussi, Dipartimento di Scienze dell' Antichità, Università di Roma 'La Sapienza', Via Palestro 63, I–00185 Roma, Italy.

John W. Olsen, Department of Anthropology, University of Arizona, Tucson AZ 85721, USA.

Marcel Otte, Service de Préhistoire, Université de Liège, Place du XX Août, 7 Batiment A1, B–4000 Liège, Belgium.

John Parkington, Spatial Archaeology Research Unit, Department of Archaeology, University of Cape Town, Rondebosch 7700, Cape Town, South Africa.

T. E. G. Reynolds, Department of Archaeology, University of Cambridge, Downing Street, Cambridge CB2 3DZ, England.

Jean-Philippe Rigaud, Direction des Antiquités Préhistorique d'Aquitaine, 28 Place Gambetta, Bordeaux, 33074, France.

Peter Robertshaw, Department of Anthropology, California State University, San Bernadino, CA 92407–2397, USA.

Béatrice Schmider, Laboratoire d'Ethnologie Préhistorique, 44 rue de l'Amiral-Mouchez, 75015 Paris, France.

Mala Seth, Gujarat University, Navrangpura, Ahmedabad 380009, India.

Jan F. Simek, Department of Anthropology, University of Tennessee, Knoxville, Tennessee 37996-0720, USA.

Olga Soffer, Department of Anthropology, University of Illinois at Urbana-Champaign, 109 Davenport Hall, 607 South Mathews Avenue, Urbana, IL 61801, USA.

Lawrence Guy Straus, Department of Anthropology, University of New Mexico, Albuquerque, New Mexico 87131, USA.

Jiří Svoboda, AUČSAV, Sady OSVobozeni 17/19, Brno 66203, Czechoslovakia.

A. A. Velichko, Otdel Paleogeografii, Institut Geografii AN SSSR, Staromonetnii per., 29, Moscow 109017, USSR.

Danny N. Walker, State Archaeologist's Office, Wyoming Recreation Commission, Department of Anthropology, University of Wyoming, Laramie, Wyoming 82071, USA.

Nick J. Walker, c/o National Museum, Post Bag 00114, Gabarone, Botswana.

Fred Wendorf, Department of Anthropology, Southern Methodist University, Dallas, Texas 75275, USA.

Gerd-C. Weniger, Deutsches Archäologisches Institut, Serrano 159, 28002 Madrid, Spain.

H. Martin Wobst, Department of Anthropology, Machmer Hall, University of Massachusetts, Amherst, MA 01003, USA.

João Zilhão, Instituto de Arqueologia da Faculdade de Letras de Lisboa, Cidade Universitária Campo Grande, 1699 Lisboa Codex, Portugal.

Acknowledgements

The core of these volumes first saw light as papers presented at the symposium 'Hunter–gatherers at the Last Glacial Maximum: the global record' held during the 52nd Annual Meeting of the Society for American Archaeology in Toronto, Canada in May 1987. Funding to help some participants come to Toronto and take part in the symposium was generously provided by IPS of the University of Illinois, IREX, the Society for American Archaeology, the University of Toronto, the Ford Foundation, the University of Southampton, the British Academy, and the Prehistoric Society.

Our very special thanks go to Dr Timothy Kaiser of the University of Toronto, programme chair for the SAA Annual Meeting, who, even though a Neolithic specialist, took his Palaeolithic colleagues under his most capable and hospitable wing and greatly helped ensure the success of their efforts. We also wish to express our gratitude to Dr Kenneth Jacobs of the University of Montreal, Dr Alice Kehoe of Marquette University, and Mr Tom Kehoe of the Milwaukee Public Museum, who kindly acted as our reception and transport committees in Montreal, Chicago, and Milwaukee.

Drafting and editorial assistance with the preparation of these volumes was provided by Ms Inne Choi and Ms Jolee West of the University of Illinois and Val Wilson, who also expertly compiled the index, and Kathryn Knowles of the University of Southampton.

We also gratefully acknowledge the assistance and encouragement during the planning and production of this project from Arthur ApSimon, Peter Ucko, Tjeerd van Andel, Paul Mellars, and the truly international community of prehistoric hunters and gatherers.

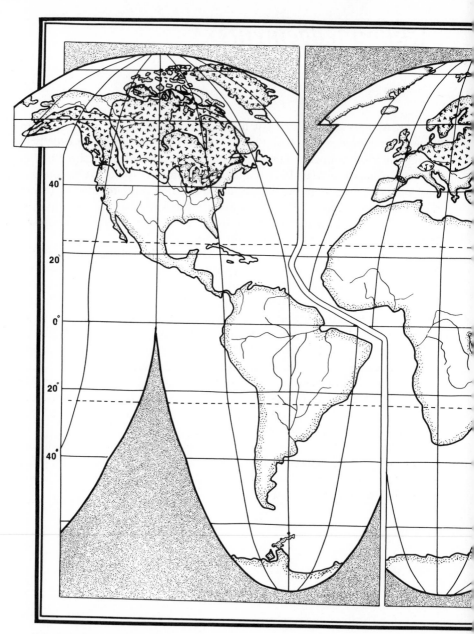

The world at 18 000 BP.

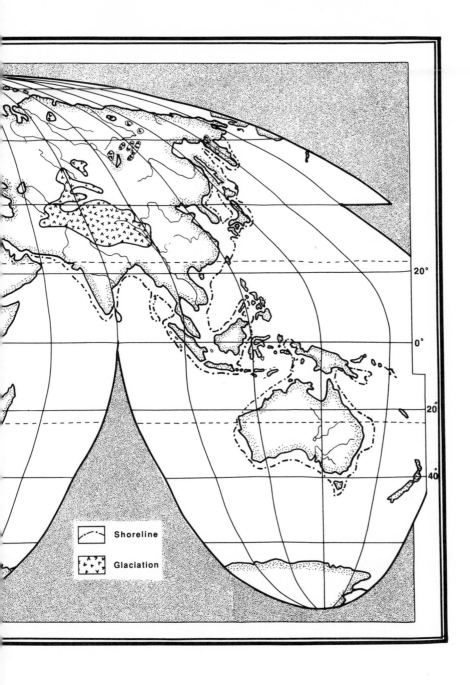

20°

0°

20°

40°

Shoreline

Glaciation

Radiocarbon dates

Throughout the text, BP refers to uncalibrated
radio carbon dates unless otherwise stated.

Introduction
Pleistocene polyphony: the diversity of human adaptations at the Last Glacial Maximum

CLIVE GAMBLE & OLGA SOFFER

Introduction

Investigating the global record at the Last Glacial Maximum (LGM), 18 000 years ago, is an exercise in a new approach to world prehistory. Our aim in these volumes is to show that it is appropriate and possible to assemble archaeological data on a global scale. The purpose of compiling such a record is to examine long-term human adaptation to a climatic minimum and investigate the trajectories of change among later prehistoric hunter-and-gatherer societies.

In order to meet this goal we have assembled chapters that provide summaries of the available data within five continents. The geographical scale and temporal range of these contributions varies considerably (see the table on pp. 10–11) and we are aware that the coverage we have obtained lacks standardization. This is hardly surprising given the history of research into the archaeology of the LGM on a world scale. However, we take it as an encouraging sign for the future development of global studies into prehistoric hunters and gatherers that such a comprehensive picture could be brought together within the short period that this project has been running. What may be lacking in uniformity of presentation is more than compensated for by diversity of approach and interpretation. This is what we would expect from a world prehistory and it must be welcomed as a sign of significant, and we hope lasting, international collaboration.

World prehistory and hunter–gatherers

The accepted format for writing a world prehistory has been a chronological narrative moving between important moments in the human story. In earlier examples by either single (Clark 1977, Wenke 1980) or multiauthors (Sherratt 1980), such overviews began with the origins and spread of early humans and then proceeded to the intensification of social and economic life that took place with increasing rapidity during the present interglacial. Such overviews are understandably dominated by later prehistory and by those areas of the world that show the most striking developments. Hence interest is focused on the varied trajectories that led in some parts of the world to the origin of states and the sources of social power from which the roots of the modern industrialized world can be traced (Gamble 1986a). The themes that emerge in these works include the explanation of local change and complexity, the loss of autonomy, and the growth of inequality.

The investigation of late glacial prehistoric hunters and gatherers forms the baseline for these narratives since they are held to represent the last universal adaptation. This exclusive but disjointed world system was finally replaced by one where such sociopolitical constructions formed a minor and increasingly peripheral component to the dominant and conjoined complex social formations.

These views have been questioned in recent years following a major change in the way that non–Western societies, past and present, are conceptualized (Wolf 1982). Far from being seen as simple and unspecialized, it is now more common to describe the archaeological remains from the late glacial hunter–gatherers as the result of complex adaptations (Price & Brown 1985, Zvelebil 1986, Soffer 1987). Expectations of uniform and unvarying lifestyles have been replaced by models of complex political geographies, where the intensification of social life is driven by its own internal dynamic to transform the means and relations of production. Nowhere is this more marked than in the study of Australian prehistory where the view of long-term, unchanging adaptations in desert and semiarid habitats (Allen 1972, Gould 1980) has been replaced by models of change that are linked to social rather than environmental variables (Lourandos 1987, Smith 1988, Allen, Vol. 2, Ch.15). The obvious target of many of these studies lies in the perspective such a change of emphasis brings to the study of the origins and dispersal of agriculture. The conclusion reached by some has been that the major watershed in prehistory should be located well before the traditional markers provided by the appearance of Neolithic pottery, domestic animals, and crops.

The study of intensification and complexity is an example of a thematic approach to world prehistory and is a welcome break from the culture histories contained in previous accounts.

A second theme which currently is enjoying a resurgence in interest on a global scale concerns the appearance of modern humans. Here the accent is on integrating the various lines of evidence from genetics, palaeobiology, and archaeology (Mellars & Stringer 1989). These three lines of enquiry currently provide their own definition of modern humans. Consequently, problems arise when an attempt is made to draw the various lines of evidence together into the familiar time and space framework that such origins research normally requires. In other words, trying to answer the question by stating when and where such origins took place in the expectation that this will point to why?

While definitions can be agreed by comparing earlier Neanderthal populations and their archaeological remains to those who came after them, little attempt has yet been made to examine the contexts where selection for these so-called modern traits – be they mitochondrial DNA, a reduced supra-orbital torus, or backed blades and figurines – took place. Notwithstanding this lacuna, it is generally agreed that Neanderthal societies differed from those which followed because they were smaller in social and spatial scale, relied on face-to-face contact, and lacked the social apparatus to intensify their food management strategies in the face of the worsening resources (Gamble 1986b, Soffer 1989).

The LGM as a theme and data base

These two themes provide much of the current focus for cross-cultural comparisons and they will continue to be important for prehistoric hunter–gatherer research. Where they differ from this project is that discussion of the questions, raised by these themes, tends to override methodological issues of how comparisons can be made. This is clearest in the debate concerning hunter–gatherer intensification, where the archaeological record is frequently interpreted at face-value and where just-so stories (e.g. Bender 1985) vie for our support. In the other theme we find interminable discussion of taxonomic issues (Wolpoff & Nkini 1985), which hopes that the 'true' story will emerge once these are worked out. These two themes have quite naturally come to set their own agendas and methods of discourse. In both cases the scenarios and debates are the very stuff of archaeological research, and in the following pages many familiar echoes from them can be heard.

By comparison, examining the archaeological record at 18 000 BP has no comparable thematic direction. It does, however, offer an opportunity to examine and evaluate several of the propositions and models that are put forward in the name of either intensification or sapienization. A global data base of human population at the LGM provides a means to investigate spatial variation in such important factors as technology, settlement organization, subsistence behaviour, social networking, and political complexity, without the need to view the outcome within a context of definitions linked to prior expectations. Furthermore, focusing on the LGM at 18 000 BP allows us to hold time constant and so allow an examination of the methodology of cross-cultural comparison – an area which is less apparent in the two other themes we have mentioned.

At the moment an LGM data base is obviously far from complete and details of what to record, the standardization of terms, and the frameworks for analysis are still under discussion. It is also, as we will explore below, an approach not free from its own procedural problems and a priori assumptions. From the experience of this pioneering project we look foward to the time when world prehistory will have a comparative basis for the discussion of essential issues in sociocultural evolution. Then the diversity of world prehistory, which we acknowledged earlier, will come into its own as the forum for debating ideas rather than the mechanics of observation.

Why the world at 18 000 BP?

It might be argued that existing themes could provide a similar focus for the development of collaborative research. It was felt, however, that progress towards the goals of the project would be made easier if a thematically more neutral research target was established. Undoubtedly, themes would emerge from compiling and discussing the data base and the most important criterion at the outset was to have an existing project as a 'role' model in order to channel interest.

In this project we settled on the LGM – a time-period that saw global climatic minima reached in the last full interglacial–glacial cycle. In selecting to pivot this project around environmental conditions at a particular point in time we in no way advocate the primacy of the natural environment in determining human adaptations. Rather, we argue that this important component of human adaptation has to be understood and controlled before other important components, such as economic or sociopolitical relationships, can be untangled.

The choice of the LGM as a collaborative research project was initially influenced by the success of the CLIMAP project (1976, 1981, Gates 1976, van Andel, Vol. 1, Ch. 1) in modelling the Earth's climate at 18 000 BP. However, the relevance of global maps of sea-surface temperatures, albedo, and ice extent (CLIMAP 1976, Fig 1) might well be questioned for the study of prehistoric human populations. Only occasionally, as Zilhão's (Vol. 1, Ch. 6) study of coastal Portugal shows, is there a direct relevance. The same question might also be raised for the reconstruction of continental conditions when presented on such a large scale (Peterson *et al.* 1979, COHMAP 1988, Figs 3 & 4). While global conditions might establish a temporal focus for examining survival strategies, adaptation is to the local and regional distribution of resources. Therefore we do not see our LGM project as filling in the archaeology for CLIMAP, and these volumes are not intended as an archaeological copy of this important project. While the environment is discussed by all contributors, only the chapters by van Andel, Velichko & Kurenkova, and Agrawal *et al.* deal with it in any detail.

Alternatively, it would have been possible to take other significant moments from the oceanic record, such as the last interglacial at 125 000 BP or the Holocene climatic optimum between 9000 and 6000 BP as shown by lake-level data (COHMAP 1988, Fig. 6). These were ruled out since we wished to limit the project to a period when *Homo sapiens sapiens* was universally distributed and when the assumptions of global hunter–gatherer adaptations were still justified.

The choice of 18 000 BP was dictated by archaeological questions, and its chronological position between the two themes mentioned above is clearly of some interest to the goal of investigating change among later prehistoric hunter–gatherers. But equally important is the goal of examining long-term human adaptation. This is normally undertaken by examining the chronological fortunes of an archaeological culture, such as the Iberomaurusian, or period, for instance the Late Stone Age in Africa. On the other hand, a climatic division can be examined, as with the late glacial in Europe (de Sonneville-Bordes 1979), or the long-term land use of an area, for example Kakadu National Park in northern Australia (Jones 1985). These valuable case-studies have one drawback, that is the difficulty of cross-cultural comparison. What else is strictly comparable to either the Iberomaurusian or Late Stone Age? The late glacial in Europe and Kakadu was so different in environmental terms as to make the direct comparison of adaptive strategies a difficult, if not irrelevant, exercise.

Some of the problems are overcome by selecting the LGM as the comparative focus – but this focus also brings to the fore other significant issues. Specifically, a comparison of chapters dealing with northern latitudes with those on the southern ones in these volumes shows that the significance of the LGM graded latitudinally, longitudinally, regionally, as well as temporally. This suggests that our very selection of this time-spike as pivotal is conditioned by our own research agendas and biases – an issue we address in detail below. As the chapters that follow demonstrate, there is considerable asynchrony in the timing of the glacial maximum and the associated climatic minimum between the areas we have covered. However, what the chapters are investigating is the proposition that over a longer time-range minimum conditions affecting adaptive strategies did occur within their regions. This may have been precisely at 18 000 BP and lasted for a very short period of time indeed. Alternatively, it may have continued for several millennia with fuzzy boundaries between climatic periods. In some cases there may be a very distinctive archaeological signature to the LGM, as Straus (Vol. 1, Ch. 5) and Zilhão (Vol. 1, Ch. 6) show in their discussions of the Iberian Solutrean. Elsewhere there is none, measured either by technology, settlement patterns, or subsistence data, as Deacon (Vol. 2, Ch. 7) concludes for the South African evidence.

Some of the variation in defining the chronological limits of the LGM and the units by which it is discussed in these volumes is the result of the history of research into Pleistocene hunter–gatherers. This is reflected here in the number of regional chapters from Europe, which also coincides with the editors' area of primary expertise. The chapters also reveal different traditions of prehistoric research into hunter–gatherers. These are most apparent between chapters from the northern and southern hemispheres, with the latter found exclusively in Volume 2. Broadly speaking, the division highlights how, in the southern hemisphere, environmental selection on behaviour is regarded as a powerful and dynamic explanation for changes in the archaeological record. In the northern hemisphere, several of the chapters still show that the environment is used instead as a chronological framework against which technology, technocomplexes, and culture groups are reviewed. Concentrating on the LGM brings out these different approaches, as well as providing an opportunity to test the effect of environmental selection on patterning in the archaeological record.

However, even these traditional divisions between culture process and culture history are agreed that the LGM provides an opportunity, irrespective of approach, to speak of minimum conditions in critical resources and to document highly variable patterns of regional survival. All the chapters concur that it is possible to comment on longer-term adaptation by examining the bottom line in regional settlement requirements. It is not surprising that this is highly varied between regions, but shows why the choice of the LGM at 18 000 BP serves as a genuine meeting ground for very diverse case-studies drawn from such mixed traditions of research.

Review of the LGM volumes as a project framework

The purpose of the CLIMAP project was to generate data both to test models of climatic change and to serve as a benchmark for gathering and interpreting continental data. These took the form of periglacial features, pollen profiles, lake–levels, beetle assemblages, geomorphology, and so forth. The results have been impressive (Imbrie & Imbrie 1979). They have led to further regional projects such as CLIMANZ (1983), period reviews such as COHMAP (1988), and the current INQUA Commission to produce a Paleogeographic atlas of the Quaternary in which palaeogeographers and archaeologists are jointly involved (Madeyska, Vol. 2, Ch 1; Velichko & Kurenkova, Vol. 1, Ch. 13).

The results of these group ventures carry the following major implications for the framework of the LGM project:

(a)   the lessons to be learnt about project-based international research;
(b)   defining the LGM for archaeological purposes;
(c)   questions of temporal and spatial scale; and
(d)   the link between the creation of such data sets and the models which they serve.

International research projects

These are reviewed by van Andel (Vol. 1, Ch. 1) and need little elaboration except to comment that the CLIMAP project which, with hindsight, seems so 'obvious' (mapping ocean temperature and climatic conditions) did not appear so at the outset. Moreover, the process by which agreement was reached among the CLIMAP members over how and what to standardize in the oceanic record was long and not always easy. The article published in *Science* in 1976 sets out the steps that were eventually adopted. We have already mentioned that such a standardized approach was not followed in this project, although van Andel (Vol. 1, Ch. 1) does provide some pointers as to how this might be achieved.

The chapters in these volumes present their archaeological data in a variety of ways. Obviously, differences will exist between cave and open-site data and the level of research will, on occasion, make the calculation of regional density data very difficult. The survey of the Azraq Basin in the Jordanian desert (Byrd & Garrard, Vol. 2, Ch. 4, Tables 4.2–4.4) is an excellent example of a systematic, regional survey presented in the form of settlement sizes, densities, and dominant artefact and ecofact classes. Elsewhere, Bailey et al, (1983) have presented time-density data for cave and rockshelter sites in north-western Greece. Many of the chapters in these volumes, about a wide range of different environments, do show that these basic descriptions of the archaeological record are now becoming commonplace. It is to be hoped that qualitative terms, such as large and small site, dense and sparse occupation, will soon be replaced by international standards of the basic properties of the archaeological record as recovered from survey and excavation. However, as Jayaswal (Vol. 2, Ch. 12) comments, in many areas of India the full suite of environmental, chronometric, and archaeological data that make such estimates possible is still lacking.

These volumes do indeed show how international agreement on minimum recording standards would rapidly reap returns in terms of supplying us with much-needed quantified data for the purpose of elementary cross-cultural comparisons. It is interesting to note here that it is chapters from the arid and semiarid zones that show the greatest movement towards such compatibility in reporting.

Defining the LGM for archaeological purposes

The LGM is identified in stage 2 of the deep-sea isotope record at 18 000 BP. It is marked by the lowest isotopic values for ocean volume in the last full interglacial–glacial cycle. This date corresponds to the maximum extension of most of the continental ice sheets. Their position at 18 000 BP was the culmination of longer-term changes in insolation that led to massive continental glaciation in the northern hemisphere, and increased sea ice in the southern. At 18 000 BP the Earth's precession cycle of 23 000 years, which affects seasonality, and the 41 000-year tilt cycle, which governs the latitudinal distribution of solar radiation, were very similar to the present day. Climate at the LGM has therefore to be explained by changes in boundary conditions at 18 000 BP, and a recent review is provided by COHMAP project members (1988, Fig. 2). Pollen data available to this project were dominated by work in Europe and North America, while Africa provided valuable information on lake-levels. The reconstructions of the biosphere during the past 18 000 years follows a geographical division of these data into two sectors: (a) North American–Eurasian, and (b) monsoon sector and southern mid-latitudes (ibid.).

In the LGM project, the division has been drawn between northern latitudes above 37°N, Volume 1, while Volume 2 includes the low northern latitudes, the equatorial regions, and all southern latitudes. This division is partly determined by the profusion of archaeological data in the higher northern latitudes but also takes into account the very major climatic differences at the LGM between the two sectors, which broadly follow the same divisions used by COHMAP. Their summary of conditions at 18 000 BP shows that considerable asynchrony existed within the two sectors in respect of key resources such as lake-levels, moisture budgets, and vegetation. This has to be put into a longer perspective where, between 15 000 and 9000 BP, changes in the Earth's precession and tilt led to an increase in seasonality in the northern hemisphere such that by 9000 BP solar radiation was up by 8% in July yet down by 8% in January, from present values (COHMAP 1988, p. 1044). At the same time seasonality decreased in the southern hemisphere.

The complexity of climatic conditions at the LGM is best demonstrated in the evidence from a worldwide survey of lake status (Street-Perrott *et al.* 1985). This hydrological evidence shows a general lowering of levels during the period 21 000–12 000 BP. In Africa the LGM at 18 000 BP was arid, but from the hydrological evidence considerably less so than the period from 17 000 to 12 500 BP (Street-Perrott *et al.* 1985, p. 171) and where the peak of aridity was reached between 14 000 and 13 000 BP. In Central America the palaeohydrological data shows that between latitudes 35° and 25°N at 18 000 BP there was increased moisture but that south of 25°N conditions were drier than at present.

What emerges both from these data and the chapters in these volumes is a clear message that it is meaningless to consider a simple 'time-spike' for the purposes of studying past human behaviour – a hurdle which required a little extra effort for human populations to surmount. Rather, the LGM 'spike' was, as Weniger (Vol. 1, Ch. 9) describes it, a palimpsest of smaller-scale, independent climatic events. Their sum total added up to the LGM, which varied in impact and severity between and within regions. Secondly, the lake evidence points out the disparity at global, continental, and regional scales in the timing of the LGM as a minimum for critical resources, and partly explains why, in an original circular to authors, we asked them to consider the period between 22 000 and 14 000 BP. The lake-level data quoted above suggests a less arbitrary time-frame than 18 000 ± 4000 BP where, for example, falling water-levels and increasing aridity are not necessarily in step with the deep-sea chronology.

Analytical scales

Spatial and temporal scales are therefore of critical importance in building any framework for cross-cultural comparisons at the LGM. The Table (pp. 10–11) shows that the size and boundaries of the regions which are addressed by these chapters varies greatly. On a fine scale we have Edward's study of Wadi al-

Hammeh, which measures $12\,km^2$ (Vol. 2, Ch. 5, Fig. 5.1). Chen & Olsen, on the other hand, discuss the whole of China, while Velichko & Kurenkova work with a northern Eurasian area over $22\,000\,0000\,km^2$ in size. Between these scales are a whole range of regions determined by political and administrative boundaries (Weniger, Svoboda, Jayaswal, Walker, Mussi, Reynolds & Kaner) as well as palaeogeographic continents (Bellwood), environmental zones (Byrd & Garrard, Agrawal et al., Allen), topography (Schmider, Straus), and major subdivisions of continents (Deacon, Mitchell, Kozłowski, Otte). When these are combined (see the Table) with the time-ranges that each contribution covers and the number of sites sampled, then we begin to see the difficulties which face comparative studies.

Davis (1985) has pointed to the importance of determining the resolution of temporal scales. When combined with regional archaeological evidence this permits causal relationships to be drawn between climate and population. CLIMAP-style projects have produced data at two different time-scales, the spike and the cycle. The LGM at 18 000 BP, as defined within stage 2 of the oceanic isotope record, obviously fits the former (see CLIMANZ 1983, Maps 3a and 3b) but, as we have seen above, may not be archaeologically relevant. Examples of the latter are becoming increasingly common with the investigation of forcing effects on climate as predicted from astronomical calculations and observed through the oceanic record (e.g. Ruddiman et al. 1986).

A further reason for asking authors to look at the period between 22 000 and 14 000 BP took into account that strict adherence to material dated to 18 000 BP would produce a tiny set of data in most areas and, more importantly, would miss the opportunity to examine longer-term responses to the climatic minimum. Not surprisingly, the chapters show a wide interpretation of this arbitrary time-range (see the Table). Several in the southern hemisphere include evidence from the Holocene, although few increase the starting date by any great amount. It is more common to find the start date increased in northern hemisphere chapters, and especially those from Europe where the earliest upper Palaeolithic, at 40 000 BP, is taken as the chronological baseline. Indeed, the date ranges in the Table show that in the northern hemisphere the 18 000 BP spike is occasionally linked instead to earlier periods, but never with the Holocene. We discuss below why this might be, only noting here that within the framework provided by the LGM spike we have very different interpretations of the appropriate time-scale for discussing human adaptations, and these are not determined solely by the abundance of archaeological data.

The question of determining chronological limits for a project framework is shared with the palaeogeographers. Peterson et al. (1979), in their review of continental data, compiled 320 sites with 18 000 BP data. Of these only 65 were well dated to the bracket 23 000–13 000 BP, and 100 were considered undated or poorly dated. Increased precision would aid palaeogeographic reconstructions and, if the same could be achieved with archaeological data, would open up the possibility for compiling census data.

Climatic cycles have been investigated by Deacon & Thackeray (1984, Figs 2

Table Summary of the regional chapters in *The world at 18 000 BP*

	Region	Type	Time Range (kyr BP)	Orientation			Region (approx. km²)	Numbers of sites discussed	Source
				>18 000 BP	18–10 000 BP	<10 000 BP			
Volume 1: High latitudes									
Schmider	Paris Basin	topographic/political division	22.5–17		*		160 000	24	Figs 2.1, 2.3, 2.5
Otte	northwestern European Plain	topographic/sub-continental	40–12	*			500 000	33	Fig. 3.2
Rigaud & Simek	southwestern France	topographic/political division	24–14		*		420 000	71	Figs. 4.1, 4.3
Straus	northern Spain	topographic/political division	20.5–17		*		15 200	38	Fig. 5.1
Zilhão	Portuguese Estremadura	topographic/political division	18		*		12 000	18	Fig. 6.1
Mussi	Italy	modern state	20–16		*		350 000	31	Fig. 7.2
Bailey & Gamble	Balkans	topographic/political division	30–10	*	*		850 000	17	Figs 8.1, 8.2
Weniger	Germany	modern state	27–12		*		250 000	137	Text
Svoboda	Moravia	political division	24–15		*		22 500	7	Fig. 10.1
Kozlowski	North Central Europe	topographic/sub-continental	30/25–14	*			700 000	32	Figs 11.4, 11.5
Soffer	Russian Plain	topographic	20–18	*			1 250 000	9	Fig. 12.1
Velichko & Kurenkova	northern Eurasia	continental	30–12	*			22 000 000	40	Fig. 13.2
Davis	Central Asia	political division	22–14	*			2 400 000	0	Text
Chen & Olsen	China	modern state	18		*		9 600 000	21	Fig 15.1
Reynolds & Kaner	Japan and Korea	modern state/island	24–11		*		500 000	16	Figs 16.1, 16.2
Frison & Walker	New World	continental	?200–9	*	*	*	9 360 000	14	Fig. 17.1

Table cont.

	Region	Type	Time Range (kyr BP)	>18 000 BP	18–10 000 BP	<10 000 BP	Region (approx. km²)	Numbers of sites discussed	Source
Volume 2:									
Low latitudes									
Madeyska	Northern Hemisphere Old World	extra tropical latitudes	24–15		*		50 000 000	161	Fig. 1.1
Close & Wendorf	North Africa	environmental/arid	18		*		1 575 000	11	Fig. 2.1
Bar-Yosef	Mediterranean Levant	environmental/arid	20–9.5		*		375 000	15	Figs 3.1, 3.2
Byrd & Garrard	Jordanian Desert	environmental/arid	>24–11		*		12 000	17	Table 4.2
Edwards	Wadi al-Hammeh	environmental/arid	19.5–16.5		*		12	5	Table 5.1
Brooks & Robertshaw	Tropical Africa	sub-continental	22–12		*		18 453 000	61	Fig. 6.4
Deacon	South Africa	modern state	30–12	*	*		1 200 000	39	Fig. 7.1
Mitchell	southern Africa	sub-continental	25–12		*		1 000 000	33	Figs 8.1, 8.2
Walker	Zimbabwe	modern state	20–5			*	390 000	68	Table 9.1
Parkington	southern Africa	sub-continental	22–8		*	*	1 200 000	24	Fig. 10.1
Agrawal, Dodia & Seth	northern India	environmental/arid	20–16		*		1 120 000	na	
Jayaswal	Uttar-Pradesh	political division	22–14		*		70	43	Fig. 12.1
Bellwood	Sunda	palaeo–continent	20–5		*	*	2 000 000	8	Fig. 13.1
Jones	Kakadu/Tasmania	regional	38–6	*	*		32 000	32	Figs 14.2, 14.3
Allen	south eastern Australia	environmental/semi-arid	22–15		*		6 000	13	Fig. 15.3

& 3) for the last glaciation in southern Africa, while Allen's chapter (Vol. 2, Ch. 15) on the Willandra lakes is especially informative. These studies stress the importance in many southern hemisphere environments of changes in precipitation and variation in regional biomass that occur as the result of regular periodicities in climate. These fluctuations can be linked to cyclical changes in archaeological visibility within regions.

The definition of temporal units by climatic spikes and cycles will require new terms for comparative analysis. Measures of amplitude, perturbation, periodicity, frequency, and wavelength will need to be defined and agreed upon (Foley 1984, Fig. 1.2). Butzer (1982, Table 2.2) provides a useful discussion of the varying scales of climatic variation and the wavelengths which may have significance for adaptation and change. For example, Parkington's description of the archaeological sequence at Elands Bay Cave as a pulse (Vol. 2, Ch. 10; see also Jones, Vol. 2, Ch. 14) is a pointer to such new terminology for the discussion of key sequences for the investigation of long-term adaptation.

Butzer (1982) has also discussed some of the implications, if the study of recurrent cycles is adopted as a methodological device for studying long-term change:

> An important distinction should be drawn between material culture, on the one hand, and intangible adaptive strategies, on the other: It appears that tool kits were far less important for human adaptation in a changeable environment than were organisational devices. Yet standard archaeological procedures are almost exclusively focused on the artifactual residues and their patterning. Consequently, although the biophysical evidence leaves no doubt as to repeated environmental changes of different amplitudes and wavelengths, there is no archaeological case for causally related technological or behavioural readjustments. (1982, p. 301).

Human adaptations, at whatever wavelength of climatic cycle, need to be assessed in terms of organization rather than simply as a set of technological solutions. In many chapters in these volumes the conclusions reached are that local populations coped with the LGM cycle by organizational means reflected in settlement systems rather than through any technological shifts.

Data sets and model building

However, there is not much point in compiling spike or cycle data unless we want to test some models and theories. At one level this may be nothing more than an exercise in pattern recognition; finding where humans were at 18 000 BP and where they were not. This exercise in nominal data gathering necessarily raises interesting questions in need of resolution. Numerous contributors to these volumes clearly indicate that many regions in both northern and southern latitudes were apparently depopulated around the LGM (e.g. Bellwood, Mitchell, Brooks & Robertshaw, Davis, Kozłowski, Rigaud & Simek, Svoboda). Other regions, most notably southwestern France and Spain, pockets around the Mediterranean, and the Russian Plain in Europe served as refuges for hunter–gatherers (Gamble 1986b, Soffer 1987). This, together with the very equivocal data for human presence in the New World (Frison & Walker, Vol. 1, Ch. 17), indicates a very patchy distribution of humans in the glacial world and raises questions both about the cultural consequences and archaeological signatures of refugia and the implications of the recolonization process for the archaeological record. For example, Kozłowski (Vol. 1, Ch. 11) argues that groups occupying Central Europe were more mobile after the glacial maximum than before it, while Weniger (Vol. 1, Ch. 9) reaches a diametrically opposite conclusion for data from Germany. It is certainly possible that these interregional differences do indeed mirror cultural changes among the respective groups in question. On the other hand, a perspective which focuses on regional ebb and flow of populations suggests that we also need to consider the logistics of regional abandonment and recolonization. These processes may entail changes in the use of a region as a core area, to its exploitation as a periphery for logistically organized groups relocating elsewhere, while the reverse process may be involved when groups are colonizing a previously unutilized area. Furthermore, as Parkington (Vol. 2, Ch. 10) comments, the regions available for archaeological study in southern Africa may only have been central to settlement systems after the onset of the Holocene and a rise in sea-levels. These perspectives permit us to break with the practice of delimiting universal cultural practices at this or that point in time (e.g. the LGM) and consider instead the asynchronic changes in the use of the regions as core areas and peripheries.

At another level we could begin to use the data in order to establish rates of abandonment and colonization in different regional environments. An example would be the repopulation of the arid centres of northern and southern Africa, North America or northern Europe, post 18 000 BP.

The aims of monitoring long-term regional adaptation and cultural change suggest that the LGM project could be instrumental in testing theories of optimality, decision-making, and interaction between populations. Based on the preliminary evidence emerging from these volumes, it appears that the environmental consequences of the LGM may have been structurally very different in northern than in southern latitudes. Specifically, the latitudinal differences in the limiting factors (aridity in lower latitudes v. temperature in higher ones) themselves may have had diverse consequences for human adaptations. Given that the main limiting factor in arid areas, water, is by nature linear in its distribution and thus subject to less dramatic changes in its location or distribution, it may well be that refuging behaviour in arid areas during the LGM was far more similar to patterns of adaptations in wetter climates before and after this time. In northern latitudes, on the other hand, where the LGM brought far more dramatic environmental restructuring, successful coping strategies may have required greater changes in hunter–gatherer adaptations between climatically good and bad times.

Several chapters raise questions about the limiting factors on key resources such as precipitation (Mitchell, Vol. 2, Ch. 8) and snow cover (Davis, Vol. 1, Ch. 14, Frison & Walker, Vol. 1, Ch. 17) and how these might be expressed in terms of environmental diversity and seasonal bottlenecks in supply. Such considerations highlight research questions for palaeoecological inference which, when answered, would be of great assistance to archaeology.

We would also suggest several other areas where the acquisition of standard cross-cultural data could lead to significant developments. One of these areas clearly is in the general field of palaeoanthropology. Unfortunately these volumes contain no overview of physical anthropology at the LGM, and thus contributions which consider possible changes in the morphology of the hunter–gatherers themselves are needed. Too little attention has been paid to possible differences in anatomically modern humans between the time of their appearance in the world and the close of the Pleistocene. What studies exist focus on groups in northern latitudes and document morphological changes in post-LGM populations that make these groups more distinct from their pre-LGM predecessors than from their early Holocene successors (Frayer 1984, 1986, Jacobs 1985a, 1985b, Brennan 1987, 1988). Since we have suggested that groups in northern latitudes may have been far more profoundly affected by the LGM, we anticipate finding much greater morphological evidence of change among them and little, if any, among groups in lower latitudes.

Secondly, the refugia/colonization perspective calls for the development of models of gene flow and the impact of environmental change upon the expansion/contraction and admixture/isolation of human populations. Models dealing with genetically based change require the theoretical discussion of rates of change in genetic material as well as a better understanding of minimum conditions which human organizational systems require for continued regional survival. We predict particular future interest in rates of change linked to colonization and dispersal as groups expanded from their refugia after the LGM. Increasing chronological resolution allows us to measure accurately such range extensions and to develop a theory of long-term human colonization. However, we are not advocating a search for LGM refuges in the same manner as has been pursued for much earlier human 'cradles' or later 'hearths' of domestication. Discovering refuges should not be a research goal by itself but part of an investigation into the cross-cultural comparison of the long-term processes of adaptation and change.

Thirdly, more research is needed on transforming artefact and settlement data into demographic estimates (e.g. Attenbrow 1988). A consideration of where people were and were not also brings to the fore the little-investigated question about the spatial continuity of human settlement on a continental scale. Currently, this is an area of archaeological interpretation that remains woefully subjective (Gamble nd). We need to examine the differential distribution of human populations on a global basis and to model the effect of variation in density and interpopulation links towards long-term survival and population characters.

Finally, such a programme requires that archaeologists grasp the nettle of time in their theoretical studies (Bailey 1983, Davis 1985, Jones 1986) and investigate the possible casual relationships in climatic variation as set out by Butzer (see p. 12).

Some problems with the LGM framework

We believe that these volumes provide a positive answer to two questions facing a world prehistory: 'Can and do we want to compare archaeological records on a global scale?' This is not to belittle either the procedural problems that will face the project in the future or the discussion that we hope will come from any review of these chapters in assessing current models and frameworks. The contributions which follow provide ample material to form a judgement on the value of the LGM as an exercise in world prehistory. In this concluding section we want to touch on some associated problems in order to demonstrate the varied potential that this approach now affords.

We reiterate that the purpose of these two volumes is to examine the variability in hunter–gatherer adaptation during a specific and distinctive period of extreme climate. We are obviously some distance away from a comprehensive analysis and, as the reader will quickly appreciate, the question of a region at 18 000 BP is approached in disparate ways by our contributors. This is hardly surprising and reflects the different traditions of research within which prehistoric archaeology has operated for over 150 years. It also reflects the very great differences in the history of research questions asked and effort that has gone into the various regions. Research in some areas, admittedly small in size in global perspective, has been extensive enough to move beyond issues of chronology and culture history and to consider questions of past settlement systems. Good examples of this are Weniger's chapter (Vol. 1, Ch. 9) on southern Germany, as well as chapters by Deacon (Vol. 2, Ch. 7) and Parkington (Vol. 2, Ch. 10) on southern Africa. In other cases the sparseness of past research does not permit statements beyond simple documentation of sites occupied around the LGM. This disparity carries some dangers for synthetic works such as this one – dangers of utilizing patterns observed in one area as universals to be applied to archaeological records from other areas. Such extrapolations are less tempting when the regions in question are disparate in time or distant in space. As the contributions by Weniger (Vol. 1, Ch. 9) and Kozłowski (Vol. 1, Ch. 11) point out, closeness in time and space also does not guarantee universality in hunter–gatherer cultural practices. For these reasons we are still some way off a comprehensive analysis and these two volumes should, therefore, be seen as just establishing an agenda for Palaeolithic studies.

Northern agendas and southern latitudes

While we have considered the potential advantages to be gained by such an international collaborative effort as this one, it is also germane to question the global significance of our agenda. As we have noted previously, the LGM appears to have been an event of greater significance to humans in northern latitudes. Because of this an organization of research around it as a theme is, to some extent, an exercise in northern concerns writ large and superimposed on global data. We are aware of these covert biases and argue that they are best revealed through global cross-cultural comparisons, for it is only by considering a global sample on this scale that we can sort out the universals from the specifics.

One example of the insights that can be gained from the global data-gathering pertains to our understanding of those most visible and attention-getting Upper/Late Palaeolithic cultural paraphernalia generally considered as material remains of the ideological sphere and termed 'art', jewellery, musical instruments, and ritual objects and features. The appearance and proliferation of these is widely accepted as reflecting the development of sociopolitical complexity among Late Pleistocene hunter–gatherers and used as a collective 'index fossil' for cultural behaviour around the LGM.

A cursory look at the distribution of the portable paraphernalia indicates that, rather than being universal, their appearance and proliferation (with the exception of some lumps of ochre and ostrich eggshell beads) is restricted to northern latitudes. Their general absence from India, China, Japan, most of Africa, Australia, and the New World indicates their even greater regionalization. The division of the world into areas with and without these 'index fossils' can be and indeed too often has been, interpreted to mean that only some Late Pleistocene groups achieved more complex levels of cultural development. Such an explanation, however, can be satisfactory only for a very narrow time-frame because consideration of Eurasian material culture after 10 000 BP shows a disappearance of these paraphernalia for several millennia, and thus suggests not a continuity in complexity but rather its collapse in time. The reverse is the case in Australia, as excavations of Early Holocene inhumations with elaborate grave goods, as at Roonka flat (Pretty 1977), have shown. In southern Africa, Deacon (Vol. 2, Ch. 7) comments on the proliferation of ornamentation after 12 000 BP and how this contrasts with its previous paucity.

Wobst (in press, Vols 1 & 2, Afterword) has suggested recently that the relatively small number of sites with such items and their restriction to regions whose populations may have been most stressed by glacial environmental perturbations can be read as an example of aberrant behaviour. Thus at the LGM the north–south dichotomy in the distribution of non-utilitarian items of portable material culture may just be reflecting very regional and time-specific coping mechanisms of stressed populations, an example of 'arctic hysteria' rather than as metaphors for imminent complexity. They therefore provide an example of changes in cultural practices which ultimately had no impact on the evolution of cultural complexity whatsoever.

However, this north–south dichotomy with regard to portable art is not as clear-cut as it first seems. In this context the evidence of much earlier dated traditions of painted slabs, stencilling and rock engraving reported here for parts of southern Africa (Deacon, Vol. 2, Ch. 7; Mitchell, Vol. 2, Ch. 8) and Australia (Jones, Vol. 2, Ch. 14), dated at Karolta by cation ratios to the LGM and older (Dorn et al. 1988), raise further questions about the inferences to be drawn from such data. The painted and engraved sites most probably formed a focus for the all-important rituals associated with long-term alliances which guarded against 'feast and famine' particularly in arid environments. These ritual centres form the core, or estate, for landholding local groups throughout Australia (Gamble 1986b, p. 34, Peterson with Long 1986) and would now appear from archaeological evidence to be of primary importance in the long-term, and perhaps even initial, use of the diverse range of environments within the continent. The implication from the LGM data is that additional methods of risk avoidance, including in southern Africa hxaro with extensive exchange between partners of beads and other non-food items (Wiessner 1982), developed much later and for other reasons, as Mazel (1988, see also Deacon, Vol. 2, Ch. 7) has argued recently.

In the northern latitudes of Eurasia a different sequence can be discerned. Painting and engraving on cave walls and small stone plaques only assumed importance in some regions during the late glacial following the LGM. Portable objects were, however, abundant and widespread in burials and settlement sites throughout the Upper Palaeolithic. A comparison of north with south reveals the different development in each area from 40 000–10 000 BP of two major categories of non-utilitarian material culture that are often treated as completely interlinked and reinforcing since they fall under the rubric of art (Bahn & Vertut 1988).

Finally, a third pattern can be traced in those areas from Japan to North Africa where neither side of the LGM is there presently any substantial evidence for either painting/engraving or ornamentation/display during the Pleistocene

Since changes in cultural behaviour in northern latitudes around the LGM apparently had no long-term patterned directionality and were probably not examples of stabilization, it is pertinent to question the ultimate value of these fluctuations by briefly examining the role of change in the evolutionary process. Slobodkin (1977) pointed out over a decade ago that change is neither positive nor negative but instead a costly response to perturbation which, at best, may just permit the entity to survive. This Darwinian insight indicates that it is least costly and ultimately most adaptive to change as little as possible. It may well be that this is precisely what the archaeological record around the LGM is showing us – that the most dramatic cultural changes in northern latitudes were a high-cost response to stave off evolutionary failure in the short term, while in lower latitudes it was possible to successfully maintain long-term, but culturally conservative, adaptations. Such a perspective is obviously of interest when we turn to the next level of cultural complexity – namely a profound change in the relationship of people to nature entailed in food production – and ask why it developed in those lower latitudes where, as already noted, art of all forms is rare or absent, and whether this geographical correlation is significant. This confirms our earlier point that the environmental component of human adaptations must first be assessed before proceeding to an analysis of agency in socioeconomic change. The LGM project prepares the ground for an appreciation of what was involved in this long-term process. This is achieved through the regional case-studies, which show that many of the 'innovations' of food production were deep-rooted in much earlier patterns of hunter–gatherer organization; for example the appearance of reaping equipment soon after 16 000 BP in the Near East (Edwards, Vol. 2, Ch. 5). Moreover, the global distribution of permanent art (painted or engraved) and regional exchange systems that used material tokens indicate different relationships towards land and resources, as Davidson (nd, p. 10) has perceptively argued in this challenging hypothesis:

> The history of the study of Upper Palaeolithic art demonstrates, if nothing else, that art is emotionally linked to ideology. I suggest, here, that we might interpret the art as expressing the ideology of the collective appropriation of nature, and that this ideology may have been absent in South West Asia. Social control in Western Europe insured that this ideology continued throughout the period in which the crucial experiments which led to agriculture were taking place in South West Asia.

We suggest that it is no coincidence that the appearance of agriculture and domestic animals occurs first in those areas where territorial systems, inferred here from the distribution of parietal art, were perhaps weakest and that novel resources and patterns of exploitation had to be introduced into more southerly and northerly latitudes where painting and ornamentation were common. These examples suggest that the initial appearance of food production was not a watershed in prehistory but instead a continuous intensification in some regions of an existing suite of socioeconomic practices, enabled by existing ideology and social structure. At the LGM these are reflected in much larger geographical patterns which reveal contrasted human responses to climatic cycles (Gamble 1986c) and thereby open the possibility for the study of separate historical trajectories of change.

Missing continents and terra incognitae

Another problem which the reader will quickly discover in these two volumes is the sparsity or even complete absence of coverage for huge areas of the Pleistocene world. For example, although Volume 2 offers a number of contributions dealing with northern, eastern and southern Africa, the western part of the continent is dismissed with a few lines. As Brooks & Robertshaw (Vol. 2, Ch. 6) point out, the dearth of past research is the reason for such cavalier coverage. Their discussion of environmental changes which occurred in the forested areas of central and east Africa around the LGM suggest that a similar significant reduction of forest cover may have occurred in the western part of the continent as well. It is likely that these new non-arboreal environments may have been attractive for West African hunter–gatherers just as they were to groups to the east. Similar problems are faced by Bellwood (Vol. 2, Ch. 13) for Southeast Asia. He concludes, however, that initial expansion into the tropical rain forest areas occurred after 10 000 BP. The difficulties of archaeological research in such forested environments may contribute to such a picture, but in this context recent success in locating LGM occupation in the caves of the southwest Tasmanian temperate rain forest (Jones, Vol. 2, Ch. 14) must be remembered.

The archaeological record of the New World around the LGM is clearly the most problematic of all in these volumes. This record is also distinguished by being the most controversial for the longest period of time. While Frison & Walker (Vol. 1, Ch. 17) discuss the serious differences of opinion that exist on the question of human presence in North America around the LGM, these volumes have no contributions devoted to data from South America. We have decided not to deal with the issue of human presence on this continent at present because although such sites as Monte Verde (Dillehay 1986) and the recently reported painted caves and rockshelters in Brazil are most interesting and merit serious attention, at present they are known from very preliminary announcements and we chose to reserve judgement until they receive full publication.

Researcher pedigrees and chronological rubicons

Finally, we want to consider briefly perceptual differences which are embedded in these two volumes and which also seem to pattern along a latitudinal gradient. In the Table (pp. 10–11) we note a strong tendency of contributors writing about the archaeological record of northern latitudes (Vol. 1) to terminate their discussions at around 10 000 BP, the accepted Palaeolithic/Mesolithic and Pleistocene/Holocene boundary. These contributions also tend to refer to the generators of the archaeological records as Late/Upper Palaeolithic groups – terms which inherently stress disjunction and discontinuity in time between these people and their European or Asian descendents. Chapters dealing with southern latitudes, on the other hand, are far more likely to cross the 10 000 BP rubicon, use the term Pleistocene hunter–gatherers and, in doing so, stress the continuity of the record through time.

It could be argued that such differences in treatment follow naturally the patterning of the data – that southern latitudes, being less affected by the LGM, show more Pleistocene/Holocene continuity, while northern ones show more disjunction. Since, however, we do not find uniform treatment of the Pleistocene/Holocene boundary in all contributions on northern regions, this explanation is not sufficient. The terminological and chronological handling of the archaeological record of North America, a continent as profoundly affected by the LGM as was Eurasia, is a case in point. The contribution of Frison & Walker (Vol. 1, Ch. 17) shows that our North American colleagues treat their record more like Old World scholars working in southern latitudes than those dealing with Eurasia.

We find these paradigmatic differences in the perception and treatment of past hunter–gatherers – stressing continuity v. disjunction – clearly illustrate the reality that the past, however remote, is not a neutral construct but one which also serves as a backdrop for playing out our own political dramas. We suggest that archaeologists working in those parts of the world where hunter–gatherer groups still exist today, or have in the ethnographic past, and where their identity and integrity is of contemporary concern, are more likely to present terminal Pleistocene adaptations as examples of historic or pre-historic continuity. By accenting continuity v. disjunction, be it just in the use of terminology or in bypassing the geochronological rubicons, we contextua-lize present-day hunter–gatherers in history and in deep time. While this is clearly a laudable endeavour, it is also one beset by its own contradictions. We see its potential negative side as the use of the historically contextualized 'other' to justify and perpetuate our positions as *their* definers and legitimizers. We do not dwell on these issues here because they deserve a more comprehensive treatment that can be achieved in an introductory chapter on the world at 18 000 BP. We mention them in order to raise a broader question. 'What is World Prehistory?' – a simple narrative justifying the present condition, or a metaphor to reflect upon our universal humanity? At present it seems that it is both. We hope that demystifying the context of our research paradigms will help us to approach the second goal more closely in the future. Even with all of the above caveats and reflecsors in mind, we are optimistic that new understanding can be gained of such Pleistocene polyphony by considering a worldwide sample of hunter–gatherer data at a particular beat of Late Pleistocene time.

References

Allen, H. 1972. Where the crow flies backwards. Unpublished PhD thesis, Australian National University.
Attenbrow, V. 1988. The Upper Mangrove Creek catchment: a study of quantitative changes in the archaeological record. Unpublished PhD thesis, University of Sydney.

Bahn, P. G. & J. Vertut 1988. *Images of the ice age*. Leicester: Windward.
Bailey, G. N. 1983. Concepts of time in quaternary prehistory. *Annual Review of Anthropology* **12**, 165–92.
Bailey, G. N., P. L. Carter, C. S. Gamble & H. P. Higgs 1983. Epirus revisited:

seasonality and inter-site variation in the upper palaeolithic of north-west Greece. In *Hunter–Gatherer economy in prehistory*. G. N. Bailey (ed.), 64–78. Cambridge: Cambridge University Press.

Bender, B. 1985. Prehistoric developments in the American midcontinent and Brittany, northwest France. In *Prehistoric hunter–gatherers*, T. D. Price & J. A. Brown (eds), 21–57. Orlando: Academic Press.

Brennan, M. U. 1987. Nonspecific indicators of stress in the Upper Paleolithic. Paper presented at the 86th Annual Meeting of the American Anthropological Association, November, Chicago.

Brennan, M. U. 1988. Harris lines and dental hypoplasia in the French Paleolithic. *American Journal of Physical Anthropology* **75**, 190

Butzer, K. W. 1982. *Archaeology as human ecology*. Cambridge: Cambridge University Press.

Clark, J. G. D. 1977. *World prehistory in new perspective*, 3rd edn. Cambridge: Cambridge University Press.

CLIMANZ project members 1983. *A symposium of results and discussions concerned with late quaternary climatic history of Australia, New Zealand and surrounding seas*. Canberra: Australian National University, Research School of Pacific Studies.

CLIMAP project members 1976. The surface of the ice age earth. *Science* **191**, 1131–7.

CLIMAP project members 1981. *Seasonal reconstructions of the Earth's surface at the last glacial maximum*. Geological Society of America Map and Chart Series no. MC–36.

COHMAP project members 1988. Climatic changes of the last 18 000 years: observations and model simulations. *Science* **241**, 1043–52.

Davidson, I. nd. Art and agriculture: intensification of social relations and intensification of production. Precirculated paper for the IV International Conference on Hunting and Gathering Societies, 1986, London.

Davis, R. S. 1985. Upper pleistocene climatic fluctuations and palaeolithic settlement distributions in Soviet Central Asia and surrounding territories. In *Proceedings of the international workshop on the late cenozoic palaeoclimatic oscillations in Kashmir and Central Asia*, D. P. Agrawal (ed.), 215–21. New Delhi: Today and Tomorrow's Printers and Publishers.

Deacon, H. J. & J. F. Thackeray 1984. Late pleistocene environmental changes and implications for the archaeological record in southern Africa. In *Late cainozoic palaeoclimates of the southern hemisphere*, J. C. Vogel (ed.), 375–90. Rotterdam, A. A. Balkema.

Dillehay, T. D. 1986. The cultural relationships of Monte Verde: a Late Pleistocene Settlement Site in the sub-Antarctic forest of south-central Chile. In *New Evidence for the Pleistocene peopling of the Americas*, A. L. Bryan (ed.), 319–37. Orono, Maine: Center for the Study of Early Man.

Dorn R. I., M. Nobbs & T. A. Cahill 1988. Cation-ratio dating of rock engravings from the Olary province of arid South Australia. *Antiquity* **62**, 681–9.

Foley, R. 1984. Putting people into perspective. In *Hominid evolution and community ecology*, R. Foley (ed.), 1–24. London: Academic Press.

Frayer, D. F. 1984. Biological and cultural change in the European Late Pleistocene and Early Holocene. In *The origins of modern humans*. F. Smith & F. Spencer (eds), 221–50. New York: Alan R. Liss.

Frayer, D. F. 1986. Cranial variation of Mladec and the relationship between Mousterian and Upper Paleolithic hominids. In *Fossil man: New facts—new ideas*, V. V. Novotny & A. Mizerova (eds), 243–56. Brno: Anthropos Institute, Moravian Museum.

Gamble, C. S. 1986a. Hunter–gatherers and the origin of states. In *States in history*, J. A. Hall (ed.), 22–47. Oxford: Blackwells.

Gamble, C. S. 1986b. *The palaeolithic settlement of Europe*. Cambridge: Cambridge University Press.

Gamble, C. S. 1986c. The mesolithic sandwich: ecological approaches to the archaeological record of the early post-glacial. In *Hunters in transition*, M. Zvelebil (ed.), 33–42. Cambridge: Cambridge University Press.

Gamble, C. S. nd. Continents of hunters and gatherers: world models and a comparison of Europe with Australia. Precirculated paper for the IV International Conference on Hunting and Gathering Societies 1986, London.

Gates, W. L. 1976. Modeling the ice-age climate. *Science* **191**, 1138–44.

Gould, R. A. 1980. *Living archaeology*. Cambridge: Cambridge University Press.

Imbrie, J. & K. P. Imbrie 1979. *Ice ages: solving the mystery*. Short Hills, New Jersey: Enslow.

Jacobs, K. 1985a. Climate and the hominid postcranial skeleton in Würm and Early Holocene Europe. *Current Anthropology* **26**, 512–14.

Jacobs, K. 1985b. Evolution in the postcranial skeleton of Late Glacial and Postglacial European hominids. *Zeitschrift für Morphologie und Anthropologie* **75**, 307–26.

Jones, R. (ed.) 1985. *Archaeological research in Kakadu National Park*. Canberra: Australian National University, Australian National Parks and Wildlife Service Special Publication 13.

Jones, R. 1986. Palaeolithic time scales and rates of cultural change: evidence from Arnhem land and Tasmania. Final Papers, Vol. 1. Southampton: World Archaeological Congress.

Lourandos, H. 1987. Pleistocene Australia: peopling a continent. In *The Pleistocene Old World: regional perspectives*, O. Soffer (ed.), 147–66. New York: Plenum.

Mazel, A. D. 1988. People making history: the last ten thousand years of hunter–gatherer communities in the Thukela Basin. Unpublished PhD thesis, University of Cape Town.

Mellars, P. A., & C. B. Stringer (eds) 1989. *The human revolution*, Vol. 1. Edinburgh and Princeton: Edinburgh University Press and Princeton University Press.

Peterson, G. M., T. Webb, J. E. Kutzbach, T. van der Hammen, T. A. Wijmstra & F. A. Street 1979. The continental record of environmental conditions at 18 000 yr BP: an initial evaluation. *Quaternary Research* **12**, 47–82.

Peterson, N. with J. Long 1986. *Australian territorial organisation*. Oceania Monograph 30. Sydney: University of Sydney.

Pretty, G. L. 1977. The cultural chronology of the Roonka Flat. In *Stone tools as cultural markers*, R. V. S. Wright (ed.), 288–331. Canberra: Australian Institute of Aboriginal Studies.

Price, T. D. & J. A. Brown (eds) 1985. *Prehistoric hunter–gatherers*. Orlando: Academic Press.

Ruddiman, W. F., M. Raymo & A. McIntyre 1986. Matuyama, 41,000-year cycles: north atlantic ocean and northern hemisphere ice sheets. *Earth Planetary Science Letters* **80**, 117–29.

Sherratt, A. (ed.) 1980. *The Cambridge encyclopedia of archaeology*. Cambridge: Cambridge University Press.

Slobodkin, L. B. 1977. Evolution is no help. *World Archaeology* **8**, 332–43.

Smith, M. A. 1988. The pattern of timing of prehistoric settlement in Central Australia. unpublished PhD thesis, University of New England, Armadale.

Soffer, O. (ed.) 1987. *The Pleistocene Old World: regional perspectives*. New York: Plenum.

Soffer, O. 1989. The Middle to Upper Paleolithic transition on the Russian plain. In *The human revolution*, Vol. 1, P. Mellars & C. Stringer (eds), 713–41. Edinburgh and Princeton: Edinburgh University Press and Princeton University Press.

Sonneville-Bordes, D. de (ed.) 1979. *La fin des temps glaciaires en Europe: chronostratigraphies et écologie des cultures du paléolithique final*. Paris: CNRS.

Street-Perrott, F. A., N. Roberts & S. Metcalfe 1985. Geomorphic implications of late quaternary hydrological and climatic changes in the northern hemisphere tropics. In *Environmental change and tropical geomorphology*, I. Douglas & T. Spencer (eds), 165–84. London: Allen & Unwin.

Wenke, R. J. 1980. *Patterns in prehistory*. Oxford: Oxford University Press.

Wiessner, P. 1982. Beyond willow smoke and dogs' tails: a comment on Binford's analysis of hunter–gatherer settlement systems. *American Antiquity* **47**, 171–7.

Wobst, H. M. in press. Discussants comments. In *The human revolution*, Vol. 2, P. Mellars, & C. Stringer (eds). Edinburgh and Princeton: Edinburgh University Press and Princeton University Press.

Wolf, E. S. 1982. *Europe and the people without history*. Berkeley: University of California Press.

Wolpoff, M. H. & A. Nkini 1985. Early and early middle pleistocene hominids from Asia and Africa. In *Ancestors: the hard evidence*, E. Delson (ed.), 202–5. New York: Liss.

Zvelebil, M. (ed.) 1986. *Hunters in transition*. Cambridge: Cambridge University Press.

1 The distribution of human settlement in the extra-tropical Old World 24 000–15 000 BP

TERESA MADEYSKA

Introduction

In 1982 the INQUA commission with responsibility for compiling a Palaeo-geographical Atlas of the Quaternary decided to produce a series of maps at the scale of 1 : 30 000 000 for the extra-tropical regions of the northern hemisphere during the Last Glacial Maximum (LGM) 20 000–18 000 BP. Several maps are currently being prepared on glaciation (J. Mojski), vegetation (B. Frenzel & V. R. Grichuk), zoogeography (A. K. Markova), loess (M. Pécsi), palaeoclimates (A. Hecht & A. A. Velichko) and geomorphology (I. Spasskaya). In this chapter I present some preliminary conclusions based on my work on the map showing the distribution of human settlement at the LGM.

For the purposes of this chapter I have presented in Figure 1.1 a selection of important sites within four time-slices. Before discussing the significance of these distributions we must address some of the difficulties that are inherent in producing maps of this nature.

In the first place, correlating sites from such different palaeogeographical regions as western Europe, the Nile valley, Siberia and Japan is only possible where absolute dates are available, even though in the case of ^{14}C there may be as yet unknown problems of calibration. Where possible, local chronostrati-graphic schemes based mainly on a suite of climatic data were used as a control for interregional correlations. However, at an interregional scale these controls are less useful due to the diachronism of the extent of the maximum ice advance as well as regional variations in temperature and fluctuations in humidity.

Secondly, the map reflects the imbalance of research effort between regions as well as the ease of literature accessibility. It comes as no surprise that for these reasons the environment, chronology and cultural history of the period 24 000–15 000 BP is best understood in Europe. In this chapter I have therefore chosen to discuss the evidence outside this well-researched area and to include the European sites on the map only to provide a broader comparison. Detailed discussions of the European evidence can be found in Volume 1.

Settlement distributions

In broad terms human settlement in the higher latitudes was limited at the LGM by low temperatures and proximity to the margins of ice sheets. This also resulted in the southward shift of habitats.

In the lower latitudes – North Africa, the Near East and Central Asia – aridity was the main climatic factor affecting the distribution of settlement. Fluctuations in humidity were the result of modifications to the jet stream as well as many local changes in circulation patterns. These factors were also combined with changes in global temperature connected to variation in solar radiation. This resulted in considerable differences in humidity both areally and temporally (Rognon 1976, Rognon & Williams 1977).

These humidity variations are clearly reflected in both sediment sequences and pollen spectra from North Africa and the Near East. However, it is difficult to obtain any comparable data on temperature fluctuations and so establish any connection with climatic fluctuations in the higher latitudes.

Sahara

Rognon (1976) discovered that along the temperate borders of the Sahara during the period 40 000–20 000 BP temperatures were lower and precipitation higher than today. The tropical borders were, however, characterized by high lake-levels, while in the Saharan highlands the humid phase lasted for a much longer time. By 20 000 BP the lakes had become dry or very shallow, while north of the Sahara evidence for increased aridity has been found (Brunnacker 1969).

The youngest Aterian assemblages in the Sahara are dated to about 40 000 BP (Alimen 1955, Clark 1970, 1980, Camps 1974a). Following this date, and including the hyperarid period between 20 000 and 12 000 BP, the Sahara was unoccupied. This long arid phase has been established at several Aterian localities in the Sahara, e.g. Ténéré (Clark 1979), and in southern Egypt at Bir Tarfawi (Wendorf and Schild 1980), where the evidence includes the deflation of archaeological horizons as well as the wind polishing of artefacts.

Mediterranean

During this arid phase human settlement was concentrated along the Atlantic and Mediterranean coasts as well as in the Nile Valley. It is also highly likely that settlement extended onto the coastal plains that emerged as a result of lower sea-levels at the LGM [estimates of the extent of sea-level lowering range between 130 m (CLIMAP 1976) and 80 m (Said 1981)].

Along the Mediterranean coast the Iberomaurusian assemblages at the cave of Taforalt in Morocco are dated to 23 000–13 000 BP, while in Algeria the

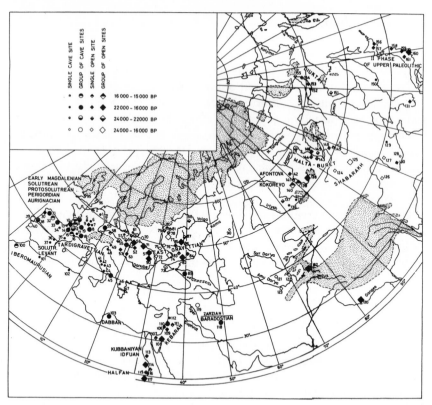

Figure 1.1   Major sites in the extra-tropical Old World 24 000–15 000 BP

Key

1, Spy; 2, Hallines; 3, Abri Fritsch, Montgaudier, Laraux; 4, Abri Foy, Roc aux Sorciers, Esclausure, La Marche; 5, Grotte du Renne; 6, Les Vignes; 7, Grotte Grappin; 8, La Colombière, La Crose, Grotte des Romains; 9, Solutre; 10, Abri Pataud, Laugerie Haute, Flageolet, Lascaux, La Mude; 11, Grotte de la Bergerie, Abri de la Chaire à Calvin, Grotte de Ste Eulalie, Lacave; 12, Abri du Facteur, La Ferrasie, Hermitage; 13, Grotte de Duruthy; 14, St Jean de Vergès, Grotte Pégourie; 15, Canecaude, Grotte Tournal; 16, Grotte de Gazel; 17, La Salpétrière; 18, Grotte Oullins, La Tête de Lion, Grotte Chabot, Peyrehaute; 19, Grotte de Cottier, Abri du Blot, Le Rond du Barry; 30, Budiño; 31, La Riera, Las Caldas; 32, Altamira, Rascaño, Ekain, Chufin, Juyo; 33, Lezetxiki, Cueva Morin, Urtiaga, Aitzbitarte; 34, Cueva Reclau; 36, Les Mallaetes; 37, Parpalló; 38, Caldeirão, Ourão; 39, Olival do Arneiro, Vale Almoinha; 40, Salemas, Ponte La Lage, Casa da Moura, Lapa da Suão; 41, Grotta La Punta; 42, Maurizio Riparo; 43, Grotta Paglicci; 44, Grotta de la Cala; 45, Taurisano, Cipolliane; 46, Kastritsa; 47, Franchthi; 48, Šandalia; 49, Ovča Jama; 50, Lespezi, Bistricioara-Lutarie; 51, Stanca Ripiceni, Crasnaleuca, Mitoc, Malul Galben; 52, Arca, Balla; 53, Ságvar; 54, Nitra Čermán; 55, Aggsbach; 56, Cejkov, Kašov; 57, Moravany; 58, Shussenquele; 59, Geissenklösterle, Höhler Felsen, Bockstein-Törle, Langmannersdorf, Brillenhöhle; 60, Kraków – Spadzista; 61, Maszycka cave; 62, Pilismarot, Remete; 63, Madaras; 64, Kůlna; 70, Lipa; 71, Molodova, Korman; 72, Bolshaya Akkarzha; 73, Syuren; 74, Kaistrovaya Balka; 75, Mezhirich; 76, Dobranichevka; 77, Bugorok, Mezin, Pushkari; 78, Khotylevo; 79, Berdyzh; 80, Eliseevichi; 81, Timonovka; 82, Muralovka, Kamennaya Balka; 83, Amvrosievka; 84, Zolotovka; 85, Avdeevo; 86, Kostenki, Borshevo; 87, Gagarino; 88, Sungir; 89, Akhshtyrskaya, Navalisheskaya, Apiancha; 90; Kapovaya – Shul gan-Tash; 95, Paviland cave; 96, Constantine Road; 100, Tamara, Dar es Soltan; 101, Taforalt; 102, Tamar Hat; 103, Haua Fteah, Hagfet et Dabba; 106, Nahal Oren; 107, Mushati; 108, Ein Aquev, Ein Avdat; 109, Wadi Hammeh; 110, Rakafet, Kebara, Sefunim; 111, Ein Ger; 112, Ksar Akil; 113, sites near Luxor; 114, sites near Isna, Idfu, El Kilh; 115, Wadi Kubbaniya; 116, Gebel material from Tamar Hat is of similar age (Biberson 1963, Camps 1974b, Delibrias & Roche 1976, Roche 1976, Clark 1980, Delibrias *et al.* 1982). The Iberomaurusian from Tamara on the Atlantic coast of Morocco is slightly younger (Roche 1976). Further east in Cyrenaïca the Levallois–Mousterian was replaced at *c.* 40 000 BP by the Dabban, which continued until *c.* 12 000 BP (McBurney & Hey 1955, McBurney 1960, Hey 1963, Clark 1970), or was replaced by the Eastern Iberomaurusian at 18 000 BP (Close & Wendorf, Vol. 2, Ch. 2)

Nile Valley

In the period of extreme aridity the Nile Valley acted as a refugium for human groups from the surrounding deserts, and later, as the climatic conditions ameliorated, provided the reservoir for the repopulation of these areas. This is shown archaeologically by the variety of contemporary industries, indicating at least several different groups within the valley region.

In lower Nubia, Butzer (1979) has established three aggradation formations, which are pre-dated by wadi floor conglomerate and separated by erosion episodes. The oldest, the Korosko formation, is a 50 m series of clastic wadi sediments and floodplain deposits from the Nile, having a minimum ^{14}C age of 27 250 BP. The second, Masmas, formation is also 50 m in thickness and consists of flood deposits, clayey silts and sands with carbonates that are similar to recent summer flood residues. This formation is dated to 25 000–18 000 BP. The Late Palaeolithic sites coincide with the youngest part of this formation when, in Egypt, violent floods occurred during a phase of arid climate. These floods were the result of increased summer precipitation along the eastern coasts of central Africa, in turn associated with the shift in monsoonal patterns during the last glaciation (Gates 1976).

The third formation, Gebel Silsila, consists of a differentiated sequence of silts, sands and gravels formed during three phases of Nilotic aggradation and separated from each other by episodes of downcutting. This formation started during the late Pleistocene and Early Holocene and is associated with the Terminal Palaeolithic cultures, Dabarosa, Quadan and Sebilian.

In Sudanese Nubia there is the Dibeira Jer formation (de Heinzelin & Paepe 1965) which, according to Butzer (1979) and Said (1981), is identical with the

Silsilan; 117, Wadi Halfa, Khor Musa, Dibeira; 118, Yafteh cave, Gar Arjeneh, Pa Sangar; 119, Zarzi, Hazar Merd; 120, sites in the Belan and Son river valleys; 121, Samarkanda; 122, Shugnou; 123, Ak Kupruk; 124, Moiltyn am; 125, Otson Maint, Shabarakh-usu, Tögrög-Shireet, Tagt; 126, Shuitungkou; 127, Tchziui; 128, Xiaonanhai; 129, Zhoukoudian – Upper Cave; 130, Xiachuan; 131, Sokchang-ni; 132, Olchibag, Sombur; 135, Ust Kanskaya; 136, Strashnaya Cave; 137, Bobkovo; 138, Golubaya, Oznachennoye; 139, Tashtyk; 140, Kokorevo; 141, Cheremushka; 142, Afontova Gora; 143, Malta, 144, Sosnovyi Bor; 145, Buret; 146, Krasnyi Yar; 147, Ust Kova; 148, Sannyi Mys; 149, Tolbaga; 150, Geographical Society Cave; 151, Filimoshky; 152, Diuktai Cave; 153, Ust Mil, 154, Verkhne Troitzkoye; 155, Ikhimie; 156, Shimaki; 157, Shukubai; 158, Odaino; 159, Hoshito; 160, sites by Tokyo; 161, Nojiri-ko.

Masmas formation. Wendorf & Schild (1980) consider it to be older. In the Wadi Halfa region this formation contains Aterian, Khormusan and Halfan assemblages. The latter developed at the same time as the younger Khormusan and lasted considerably longer (Chmielewski 1968, Marks 1968a, b, Wendorf 1968, Wendorf et al. 1970, Wendorf & Schild 1976, Hassan 1979). These cultures existed during the hyperarid period when the Aterian disappeared from the desert.

In the Nile Valley between Luxor and Idfu the Masmas formation is well developed as flood silts with aeolian sands and even, in the top part, with intercallated dunes known as Ballana. This intercallation of typical desert dunes with Nile silts confirms the correlation of the Masmas formation with the period of hyperarid conditions in the desert, and at Luxor the formation is called Masmas–Ballana. Within a small geographical area between Luxor and Aswan three different archaeological complexes are found, the Idfuan, Fakhurian and the Kubbaniyan (Wendorf & Schild 1976, Close & Wendorf, Vol. 2, Ch. 2).

Several ^{14}C dates exist between 25 000 and 15 000 BP for some of these industries. Unfortunately, the presence of younger carbonates casts doubt on the accuracy of some of them. However, it is still abundantly clear that human settlement in the Nile Valley continued during the whole period corresponding to the LGM in Europe (see Close & Wendorf, Vol. 2, Ch. 2).

Near East

The climatic history of the Near East during the Upper Pleistocene has been studied mainly through palynology. Since there are important differences between the vegetation along the Mediterranean coast and in the Syrian desert it is difficult to establish any general climatic trends. The pollen record shows the alternate expansion of steppe and forest, which can be explained by fluctuations in humidity due to changes either in temperature or precipitation (Bottema & van Zeist 1981, van Zeist & Bottema 1982). The main factor limiting tree growth was dryness.

Palynologists have correlated the period from 50 000 BP to between 16 000 and 14 000 BP with the European Pleniglacial. This is followed by two other periods regarded as the Late Glacial and Postglacial. During the first period temperatures were lower than today. Some fluctuations occurred in the proportions of arboreal pollen, as shown by diagrams from Turkey and Syria. Similar fluctuations also occurred in the Jordan Valley but are not contemporary. By contrast, throughout the period in the Zagros, tree pollen was absent and conditions were uniformly dry.

Apart from the desert, the environments of the Near East during this period were generally favourable for human settlement (Farrand 1979, 1981). On a local scale, environmental differences provided an impetus for some relocation; for example from mountains to lowlands and from open settlement in lake basins to cave occupation.

The Upper Palaeolithic of the Near East is believed to have originated from the local Mousterian via a number of transitional steps. The term 'Levantine Aurignacian' is generally applied to Upper Palaeolithic assemblages, although local variants are known, as with Ksar Akil in Lebanon, Kebara/Qafzeh or Hayonim/Sefunim in Israel (see Garrod 1962, Marks 1976, Ronen 1976, Bar-Yosef, Vol. 2, Ch. 3, Edwards, Vol. 2, Ch. 5). The Aurignacian techno-complex lasted from 40 000 to 20 000 BP, when it was replaced by the Kebaran, which in turn graded into the Geometric Kebaran by 16 000 BP (Bar-Yosef 1976). In the Zagros mountains an almost continuous regional occupation for the Upper Palaeolithic has been documented, with settlement confirmed at the LGM when, at 20 000 BP, the Baradostian was replaced by the Zarzian (Hole & Flannery 1967, Solecki 1971).

Central and southern Asia

The plains area between the Caspian and Aral seas and Lake Balkhash was probably devoid of human settlement during the LGM. Sites known from this area can be dated either earlier or later than this period. In the plateaus of Central Asia human settlement between 20 000 and 15 000 BP is known from several localities, including the multilevel site of Samarkanda (Ranov 1976, Ranov & Davis 1979, Niesmejanov 1980; see also Davis Vol. 1, Ch. 14). The archaeological assemblages show marked continuity from the local Mousterian to Upper Palaeolithic. Cultural similarities can be demonstrated with inventories from the Altai region (Dzurakulov et al. 1980).

The development of Upper Palaeolithic settlement in Kashmir is associated with a phase of climatic amelioration dated to 21 000–16 000 BP (Agrawal et al., Vol. 2, Ch. 11). Continuous occupation in Central India is documented from 24 000 to 10 000 BP in the Belan and Son river valleys (Pal 1986, Jayaswal, Vol. 2, Ch. 12).

Some sites from Mongolia are contemporary with the Siberian Karga interstadial and with the following complex phases of the Sartan glaciation (see below). Of these the Shabarakh industrial complex, the origins of which can be traced back to traditions using the Levallois technique, has been dated to between 20 000 and 10 000 BP (Kozłowski 1971, Aigner 1980, Laritchev 1980, Okladnikov 1981, Shackley 1984).

This evidence shows that although traces of human occupation in Central Asia are rare and sparsely scattered over an enormous area, within several regions settlement was continuous from the Middle Pleistocene to the Holocene.

Far East

In Japan the settlement evidence is much richer and the chronology is based on a combination of fission-track and radiocarbon dating. Relative dating through typological analysis of artefact assemblages is also used (Ikawa–Smith 1978, Akazawa *et al.* 1980, Recent Progress 1981, Ono *et al.* 1986, Reynolds & Kaner, Vol. 1, Ch. 16). However, ecological and chronostratigraphic data are poor, due to the rarity of organic materials.

The Upper Palaeolithic on Honshu is dated between 30 000 and 12 000 BP, while the oldest known settlement on Hokkaido is 17 000 years old. Sea-level changes have had a considerable effect on the Palaeolithic settlement of Japan. The earliest populations crossed on dry land when the islands formed part of continental Asia. At subsequent times of low sea-levels migration occurred in the opposite direction, as shown by cultural connections between the lithic industries of Japan, Korea and the Far East (Derevianko 1984, Reynolds & Barnes 1984). Evidence for the Upper Palaeolithic in China, Korea and other regions of the Far East is currently sparse (Kyung Rin Yang 1972, Aigner 1978a, b, 1980, Quaternary Geology 1982).

Some sites in China are probably dated to this period but the only securely dated example comes from the Upper Cave at Zhoukoudian (Quarternary Geology 1982, see also Chen & Olsen Vol. 1, Ch. 15).

Northern Asia

The evidence from Siberia is more abundant. Kind (1974) has distinguished two glacial periods in the Upper Pleistocene of Siberia. These are the Zyrianka and Sartan, separated by the Karga interstadial, which is regarded by some as possibly an interglacial. According to Kind (1974) the Karga ended at about 22 000 BP, although Tzeitlin (1979) puts it earlier, at 25 000 BP. They divide the Sartan glaciation as follows:

Gydanian cold stadial	25 000/22 000–16 000 BP
brief interstadial	16 000–15 500 BP
Niapan stadial	15 500–12 750 BP
Kokorevo interstadial	12 750–12 250 BP
stadial	12 250–12 000 BP
Tajmyr interstadial	12 000–10 800 BP
Norylsk stadial	10 800–10 300 BP

Recent archaeological investigations in Siberia have produced a differentiated picture of industries and inventories in the Upper Palaeolithic. The oldest occupation dates to the Kazantsevo interglacial, but only during the Karga interstadial was the Upper Palaeolithic industry widely distributed (Okladnikov & Abramova 1974, Okladnikov & Vasilevskij 1980). Mochanov (1977) has distinguished two main cultural traditions. The first is the 'unifacial' tradition, or Malta–Buret, which stems from the Middle Palaeolithic of Central Asia and occupies the region west of the Lena River. The second 'bifacial' tradition, or Diuktai, originated from the Acheuleo-Mousterian industries, which provide the first evidence of human colonization of the huge territory from the Urals through Kazakhstan and Mongolia to the Ordos plateau. The Diuktai occupied the Lena Valley and the regions to the east of it and lasted from 35 000 to 10 500 BP, and is therefore associated with both interstadial, Karga, and glacial, Sartan, climates.

An alternative cultural history has been proposed by Okladnikov & Abramova (1974, Abramova 1979). They date the Malta–Buret culture to the end of the Karga interstadial, while the Afontova culture developed in the Gydanian stadial of the Sartan glaciation – equivalent, in broad terms, to the LGM. Finally, the Kokorevo culture emerged during the older 'brief' interstadial then developed during the interstadial of the same name and lasted until the Norylsk stadial. During the Sartan glaciation, Upper Palaeolithic assemblages using the Levallois technique are found in southern Siberia, the Altai region and Transbaikal.

The chronology of the Upper Palaeolithic of northern Asia has been the focus of considerable research (Gerasimov 1958, Rudenko 1960, Okladnikov et al. 1968, 1973, Okladnikov & Abramova 1974, Mochanov 1977, Tzeitlin 1979, Astakhov 1983, Drozdov & Laukin 1983, Boriskovskij 1984), as has the Upper Pleistocene stratigraphy of Siberia (Zubakov 1972, Kind 1974). It has been based primarily on the investigation of river terraces where the majority of archaeological sites are found.

These recent geological observations have confirmed Shantzer's (1951) model that during interglacials and interstadials terraces were first incised and then followed the deposition of standard alluvial sediments in the valley bottoms, while at the same time soil development took place on higher terraces and outside the valleys. During the glacial periods the series of so-called periglacial alluvia accumulated in the valleys above the standard alluvial sediments. These periglacial deposits are composed of slightly laminated silty sands interspersed with lenses of gravels and rock debris and cut by cryogenic structures. At the same time, outside the river valleys solifluction deposits were formed, while the end of these cold phases is marked by the weathering of deposits and soil development.

During the Karga interstadial a series of standard alluvial deposits originated on the second terrace above the floodplains of the large Siberian rivers and was followed by the deposition of periglacial alluvial sediments associated with the Sartan glaciation. Amongst these periglacial alluvia Tzeitlin (1979) has distinguished several cryogenic horizons. These consist of solifluction on the surface of the Karga interstadial sediments (25 000–19 000 BP), frost wedges characteristic of the extreme conditions of the LGM (19 000–17 000 BP) and an ice-wedge horizon (16 000–13 000 BP). Within the later deposits he distinguished solifluction warping of the Late Sartan fossil soils between c. 12 000 and 10 800 BP. The final cryogenic horizon, consisting of polygonal fissures crossing both fossil soils, was dated to 10 500 BP. The stratigraphical sequence found on the second terrace is characteristic of many of the large Siberian rivers. However, in regions with tectonically induced subsidence, for example the Angara, the terraces do not follow this pattern.

When archaeological horizons are found within such sedimentary sequences their stratigraphic position is unambiguous. Sites from the higher terraces are dated on the basis of typological similarity.

In some cases additional stratigraphic information is provided by faunal remains. In southern Siberia the differences between the Sartan and Karga faunas is not very significant, but this picture changes for the transition zone between the taiga and the forest steppe. During the Karga interstadial the fauna for this zone included mammoth (late form), woolly rhinoceros, horse, bison, aurochs, reindeer, elk and red deer. The faunas of the Sartan glaciation lacked elk and red deer but included lemmings and arctic fox. The Gydanian stadial is characterized by the presence of woolly rhinoceros, which thereafter became extinct. Mammoth is found until the end of the Sartan, although gradually diminishing in numbers.

This 'cold' fauna is found throughout the Siberian periglacial zone, which extended southward during the phases of continental glaciation (Velichko 1973). The maximum extension of this periglacial zone (also referred to as the criotic zone) was up to 2000 km during the Sartan glaciation. In the northern part of this zone (Vangengaim & Ravskij 1965) the vegetation was dominated by tundra and steppe–tundra with an arctic fauna of mammoth and musk ox. In the southern part xerophilic vegetation, typical of periglacial steppe, and animals such as onager, indicative of dry, even semidesert conditions, have been found.

In Figure 1.1 the sites from this region are divided into three time-periods.

(1)   24 000–22 000 BP. Sites older than the maximum of the Sartan glaciation and dated to the youngest phase of the Karga interstadial or Lipovo–Novoselovsk amelioration as defined by Kind (1974). These sites are found either in the alluvial channel sediments or in the flood series of the second terrace. They are also associated with the cover sediments and fossil soils on the third terrace. The following fauna has been found: mammoth, woolly rhinoceros, horse, bison, aurochs, reindeer, elk, red deer and onager.

(2)   22 000–16 000 BP. Sites dated to the Gydanian stadial of the Sartan. Tzeitlin (1979) has divided this stadial into two phases: an older, relatively humid phase of increasing coldness that lasted until 19 000 BP; and a younger phase marked by extremely severe arid conditions, which terminated at 16 000 BP. Most sites are associated with the first phase, while the cultural layer from the Geographical Society Cave dates to the second. The faunal remains are dominated by mammoth and woolly rhinoceros, while the species from the earlier period (1) are also found, with the exception of elk and red deer and the addition of lemming and arctic fox. During this time human settlement was sedentary with permanent structures.

(3)   16 000–12 750 BP. These sites are younger than the Gydanian stadial but

older than the Kokorevo interstadial. On the second terrace on the Yenisey River archaeological materials are found under the late Sartan soils in the uppermost part of the periglacial–alluvial series. Along the Aldan River they occur in flood sediments of the second terrace, and under sand dunes on the surface of the third terrace of the Angara. During this period the woolly rhinoceros is no longer found in southern Siberia but only in Transbaikal and in the vicinity of the Aldan River.

Conclusion

During the time of the advance of the main Vistulian ice sheet in Europe the northern limit of ecological zones shifted further south than in the previous Middle Vistulian. The nearest sites to the margins of the ice sheets were between 400 and 600 km away.

A different picture emerges in dry climatic regions, such as North Africa, the Near East and Central Asia. In the first place, settlement associated with the Middle Palaeolithic is more abundant than for the Upper Palaeolithic. This is due to the development of more humid conditions in North Africa and the Near East, and also probably in Central Asia. Throughout this area the older part of the last cold period – known regionally as the Early and Middle Vistulian, the Zyrianka glaciation and Karga interstadial – was consistently more humid than the main phase of the LGM (Sartan glaciation). During the LGM increasing aridity in North Africa resulted in settlement concentration along sea coasts and the Nile Valley. A comparable shift in settlement northwards along the main Siberian rivers also occurred.

During the Sartan glaciation the continental climate of Siberia produced a vast steppe-tundra zone, which provided rich pasture for grazing animals. This was the resource base which permitted settlement north of latitude 60°N during phases of the Sartan glaciation, interspersed with short-lived displacements of settlement southwards during the coldest Gydanian stadial at the LGM.

References

Abramova, Z. A. 1979. *The palaeolithic of the Yenisey*. Novosibirsk: Nauka. (In Russian).

Aigner, J. S. 1978a. Important archaeological remains from North China in *Early palaeolithic in south and east Asia*, F. Ikawa-Smith (ed.), 163–262. The Hague: Mouton.

Aigner, J. S. 1978b. The palaeolithic of China. In *Early Man in America from a circum-Pacific perspective*, A. L. Bryan (ed.), 25–41. Edmonton: University of Alberta Press.

Aigner, J. S. 1980. Biocultural evolution of the China palaeolithic. In *The Palaeolithic of middle and East Asia*, 96–120. Novosibirsk: Nauka. (In Russian).

Akazawa, T., S. Oda & I. Yamanaka 1980. *The Japanese palaeolithic: a techno-typological study*. Tokyo: Rippu Shobo.

Alimen, H. 1955. *Préhistoire de l'Afrique*. Paris: N. Boubée.
Astakhov, S. N. 1983. *Palaeolithic in the western Sayans*. XI INQUA Congress Abstracts III, Moscow.

Bar-Yosef, O. 1976. *A note on the geometric Kebaran A*. IX Congrès UISPP Colloque III, 78–105. Nice.
Biberson, P. 1963. Human evolution in Morocco in the framework of the palaeoclimatic variation of the Atlantic pleistocene. In *African ecology and human evolution*, F. C. Howell & F. Bourlière (eds), 417–47. London: Methuen.
Boriskovskij, P. J. (ed.) 1984. *The Palaeolithic of the USSR*. Moscow: Nauka. (In Russian).
Bottema, S. & W. van Zeist 1981. *Palynological evidence for the climatic history of the Near East 50 000–6000 BP*. Colloquium Internationale CNRS N.598 – Préhistoire du Levant, 111–32. Paris.
Brunnacker, K. 1969. Affleurement de loess dans les régions méditerranéennes. *Revue Géographie Physique at Géologie Dynamique* **11**(3), 325–34.
Butzer, K. W. 1979. Pleistocene history of the Nile Valley in Egypt and Lower Nubia. In *The Sahara and the Nile*, M. A. J. Williams & H. Faure (eds), 248–76. Rotterdam: A. Balkema.

Camps, G. 1974a. *Les civilisations préhistoriques de l'Afrique du Nord et du Sahara*. Paris: Doin.
Camps, G. 1974b. Tableau chronologique de la préhistoire récente du Nord de l'Afrique. *Bulletin de la Société Préhistorique Française* **71**, 261–78.
Chmielewski, W. 1968. Early and middle palaeolithic sites near Arkin, Sudan. In *The Prehistory of Nubia*, F. Wendorf (ed.), 110–47. Dallas: Southern Methodist University Press.
Clark, J. D. 1970. *The prehistory of Africa*. London: Thames and Hudson.
Clark, J. D. 1980. Human populations and cultural adaptations in the Sahara and Nile during prehistoric times. In *The Sahara and the Nile*, M. A. J. Williams & H. Faure (eds), 527–82. Rotterdam: A. Balkema.
CLIMAP Project Members 1976. The surface of the Ice Age earth. *Science* **191**, 1131–7.

Delibrias, G. & J. Roche 1976. Datations absolues de l'epipaléolithique marocain. *Bulletin d'Archaeologie Marocains* **10**, 11–26.
Delibrias, G., M. T. Guillier & J. Labeyrie 1982. Gif natural radiocarbon measurements IX. *Radiocarbon* **24**(5), 291–343.
Derevianko, A. P. 1984. *The palaeolithic of Japan*. Novosibirsk: Nauka. (In Russian).
Drozdov, N. I. & S. A. Laukhin 1983. *The palaeolithic Ust-Kova site on the Angara river*. XI INQUA Congress, Abstracts III, Moscow.
Dzurakulov, M. D., J. P. Kholushkin, W. A. Kholushkina & B. X. Batyrov 1980. In *The palaeolithic of middle and east Asia*. Novosibirsk: Nauka.

Farrand, W. R. 1979. Chronology and palaeoenvironment of Levantine prehistoric sites as seen from sediment studies. *Journal of Archaeological Science* **6**, 369–92.
Farrand, W. R. 1981. Pluvial climates and frost action during the last glacial cycle in the eastern Mediterranean – evidence from archaeological sites. In *Quaternary palaeoclimates*, W. C. Mahaney (ed.), 393–410. Norwich: Geo Books.

Garrod, D. A. E. 1962. An outline of pleistocene prehistory in Palestine, Lebanon, Syria. *Quaternaria* **6**.
Gates, W. L. 1976. Modelling the ice-age climate, *Science* **191**, 1138–44.
Gerasimov, M. M. 1958. The palaeolithic site of Malta. *Soviet Ethnography* **3**. (In Russian).

Hassan, F. A. 1979. Prehistoric settlements along the main Nile. In *The Sahara and the Nile*, M. A. J. Williams & H. Faure (eds), 421–50. Rotterdam: A. Balkema.

Heinzelin, J. de & R. Paepe 1965. The geological history of the Nile valley in Sudanese Nubia: preliminary results. In *The Prehistory of Nubia*, F. Wendorf (ed.), 29–56. Dallas: Southern Methodist University Press.

Hey, R. W. 1963. Pleistocene screes in Cyrenaica (Lybia). *Eiszeitalter und Gegenwart* **14**, 77–84.

Hole, F. & K. V. Flannery 1967. The prehistory of southwestern Iran: a preliminary report. *Proceedings of the Prehistoric Society* **33**, 147–206.

Ikawa-Smith, F. 1978. Lithic assemblages from the early and middle upper pleistocene formation in Japan. In *Early Man in America from a circum-Pacific perspective*, A. L. Bryan (ed.), 42–53. Edmonton: University of Alberta Press.

Kind, N. W. 1974. Geochronology of the late anthropogene based on isotopic data. *Tr. GIN AN SSSR* **257**. (In Russian).

Kozłowski, J. K. 1971. The problem of the so called Ordos culture in the light of the palaeolithic finds from northern China and southern Mongolia. *Folia Quaternaria* **39**, 63–99. Kraków.

Kyung Rin Yang 1972. Atomic energy research institute of Korea radiocarbon measurements II. *Radiocarbon* **14**(2), 273–9.

Laritchev, W. E. 1980. The upper palaeolithic of the loessic area of middle and east Asia. In *The palaeolithic of middle and east asia*, 121–64. Novisibirsk: Nauka. (In Russian).

McBurney, C. B. M. 1960. *The stone age of northern Africa*. Harmondsworth: Penguin Books.

McBurney, C. B. M. & R. W. Hey 1955. *Prehistory and pleistocene geology in Cyrenaican Libya*. Cambridge: Cambridge University Press.

Marks, A. E. 1968a. The Khormusan: an upper pleistocene industry in sudanese Nubia. In *The Prehistory of Nubia*, F. Wendorf (ed.), 315–91. Dallas: Southern Methodist University Press.

Marks, A. E. 1968b. The Halfan industry. In *The Prehistory of Nubia*, F. Wendorf (ed.), 392–460. Dallas: Southern Methodist University Press.

Marks, A. E. 1976. Terminology and chronology of the Levantine upper palaeolithic as seen from the central Negev, Israel. IX Congrès UISPP Colloque III, 49–73. Nice.

Mochanov, Y. A. 1977. *The oldest stages of man's invasion of north eastern Asia*. Novosibirsk: Nauka. (In Russian).

Niesmejanov, S. A. 1980. Geology of the Samarkanda upper palaeolithic site. In *The palaeolithic of middle and east Asia*. 30–46. Novosibirsk: Nauka. (In Russian).

Okladnikov, A. P. 1981. *The palaeolithic of central Asia. Moity nam (Mongolia)*. Novosibirsk: Nauka. (In Russian).

Okladnikov, A. P., & Z. A. Abramova 1974. The oldest palaeolithic settlement of Siberia and the far east. In *Early man and the environment*. Moscow: Nauka. (In Russian).

Okladnikov, A. P. & R. S. Vasilevskij 1980. *North Asia at the beginning of history*. Novosibirsk: Nauka. (In Russian).

Okladnikov, A. P., N. K. Vereshchagin & N. D. Ovodov 1968. The discovery of the cave palaeolithic in Primorie. *Vestnik AN USSR* **10**. (In Russian).

Okladnikov, A. P., V. M. Muratov, N. D. Ovodov & E. O. Fridenberg 1973.

Strashnaya cave – a new site of the Altai palaeolithic. In *Materials of Siberian and Far East archaeology*, Vol. II. Novosibirsk: Nauka. (In Russian).

Ono, A. & Nojiri-ko excavation research group 1986. Bone technology in the late palaeolithic of east Asia: a Nojiri-ko case study. *The pleistocene perspective*, Southampton World Archaeological Congress, Vol. 1.

Quaternary geology and environment of China 1982. *Quaternary Research Association of China*. Beijing: China Ocean Press.

Ranov, V. A. 1976. *The palaeolithic industries of central Asia: a revision*. IX Congrès UISPP, Colloque VII, 91–130. Nice.

Ranov, V. A. & R. S. Davis 1979. Toward a new outline of the soviet central Asian palaeolithic. *Current Anthropology* **20**, 249–70.

Recent progress of quaternary research in Japan 1981. In *Recent progress of natural sciences in Japan*, Vol. 6. Tokyo: Science Council of Japan.

Reynolds, T. E. G. & G. L. Barnes 1984. The Japanese palaeolithic: a review. *Proceedings of the Prehistoric Society* **50**, 49–62.

Roche, J. 1976. *Cadre chronologique de l'epipaléolithique marocain*. IX Congrès UISPP, Colloque II, 153–67. Nice.

Rognon, P. 1976. Essai d'interprétation des variations climatique au Sahara depuis 40 000 ans. *Révue Géographique Physique et Géologie Dynamique* **18** (2–3), 251–82.

Rognon, P. & M. A. J. Williams, 1977. Late quaternary climatic changes in Australia and North Africa: a preliminary interpretation. *Palaeogeography, Palaeoclimatology, Palaeoecology* **21**(4), 285–327.

Ronen, A. 1976. *The upper palaeolithic in northern Israel: Mt Carmel and Galilee*. IX Congrès UISPP, Colloque III, 153–86, Nice.

Rudenko, C. V. 1960. Ust-Kanskaya palaeolithic cave site. In *Palaeolithic and Neolithic of the USSR*, Vol. 4. Moscow–Leningrad: Nauka. (In Russian).

Said, R. 1981. *The geological evolution of the river Nile*. Berlin: Springer Verlag.

Shackley, M. 1984. Palaeolithic archaeology in the Mongolian People's Republic, a report on the state of the art. *Proceedings of the Prehistoric Society* **50**, 23–34.

Shantzer, E. W. 1951. Alluvia of lowland rivers in the temperate zone. *Tr. IG. AN SSSR* **135**. (In Russian).

Solecki, R. 1971. *Shanidar: the first flower people*. New York: A. Knopf.

Tzeitlin, S. M. 1979. *The palaeolithic geology of north Asia*. Moscow: Nauka. (In Russian).

Vangengaim, E. A. & E. I. Ravskij 1965. On the continental type of the natural zonality in Eurasia during the quaternary. In *Problems of Cenozoic stratigraphy*. Moscow: Nauka. (In Russian).

Velichko, A. A. 1973. *The natural process in the pleistocene*. Moscow: Nauka. (In Russian).

Wendorf, F. (ed.) 1968. *The prehistory of Nubia*, 2 volumes. Dallas: Southern Methodist University Press.

Wendorf, F. & R. Schild 1976. *Prehistory of the Nile valley*. New York: Academic Press.

Wendorf, F. & R. Schild 1980. *Prehistory of the eastern Sahara*. New York: Academic Press.

Wendorf, F., R. Said & R. Schild 1970. Problems of dating the late palaeolithic age in Egypt. In *Radiocarbon variations and absolute chronology*, I. U. Olsson (ed.), 57–79. Stockholm: Almquist & Wiksell.

Zeist W., van & S. Bottema 1982. Vegetational history of the eastern Mediterranean and the Near East during the last 20 000 years. In *Paleoclimates, palaeoenvironment and human communities in the eastern mediterranean region in later prehistory*, J. L. Bintliff & W. van Zeist (eds), 277–321. Oxford: British Archaeological Reports International Series 133.

Zubakov, W. A. 1972. Young deposits of the west Siberian lowlands. *Tr. WSEGEI* **184** (In Russian).

NORTH AFRICA
AND
THE MIDDLE EAST

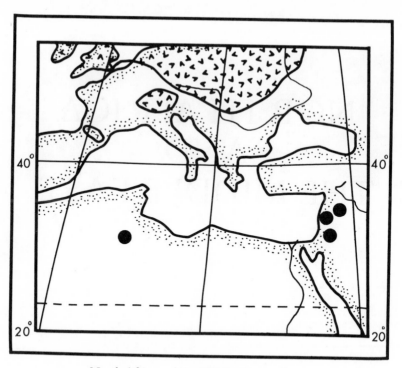

North Africa and the Middle East: study areas

2 North Africa at 18 000 BP

ANGELA E. CLOSE & FRED WENDORF

Introduction

Eighteen thousand years ago saw the first florescence of the Late Palaeolithic backed-bladelet industries across the northern and eastern margins of North Africa; these industries lasted down to the Holocene. However, 18 000 BP also corresponds to the maximum of the Last Glaciation, which was a special period, climatically different from what went before and what came afterwards. In the following survey, we confine ourselves rather strictly to that part of the archaeological record dated to 18 000 BP. This minimalist approach means that much that is of interest in the North African Late Palaeolithic has been omitted. Fortunately, some of the finest North African data are precisely from 18 000 BP.

Palaeoenvironment

On the broad scale, the most important fact in all periods of North African prehistory has been the great Sahara Desert. Saharan aridity has varied considerably during the two million years or so of human existence in Africa, but 18 000 years ago it was at least as extreme as it is today, and probably more so. Much of the desert was devoid of all life, and all of it was devoid of human life. Sufficient rainfall to support life existed along the Mediterranean coast of North Africa. This was probably brought by seasonal winter rains, as it is today, and may have been rather less than the modern rainfall, although the evidence is not conclusive (Couvert 1972). Today, the best-watered and most lush areas of Mediterranean North Africa are the northern coast of the Maghreb and the coast of Cyrenaïca. The remaining coastal areas of Tunisia, Libya, and Egypt are comparatively desertic, except for a small area around Tripoli (Higgs 1967, Fig. II.3).

In the Nile Valley, rainfall was as unknown as it is today, except in the extreme north, but water was provided by the River Nile. It is likely that the Nile in Lower Egypt was downcutting to the lowered base-level of the Mediterranean, which can be estimated at about 100 m below modern sea-level. In this case, the river would have been confined within a deep channel, with a very limited floodplain and correspondingly limited ability to support plant and animal life. In Upper Egypt and Nubia, on the other hand, this was a period of Nilotic alluviation. Lower temperatures and reduced, but still intense, summer rainfall in the headwaters of the Nile resulted in lower stream-competence but a greater sediment-load. The Nile was a much smaller river which flowed in several braided channels across a floodplain that was rising continuously as more and more sediment was deposited (Schild 1987, Schild & Wendorf 1989, Wendorf et al. in press b). This valley-filling was not affected by the level of the Mediterranean. The river may have carried only 10–20% of the modern annual flow and, during the dry season, water may have been limited to pools in the deeper channels, like the Atbara today. However, the summer floods, although absolutely less than those of today, were probably much larger relative to the flow during the low-water season. (The ratio on the main Nile today is 16 : 1, but was probably > 50 : 1 at 18 000 BP). This, combined with the river's higher base-level, meant that the floodplain was much higher and, topography permitting, usually wider than it is today.

The lowered temperatures at the Last Glacial Maximum constrained human occupation in North Africa much less than did the availability of water. The extreme west of the Maghreb was actually glaciated, and therefore uninhabitable, but summer temperatures in northeastern Algeria and northern Tunisia are estimated to have been only 3–4°C below modern ones (Gates 1976, Fig. 7). A corresponding lowering of the vegetation zones is indicated by the presence at Tamar Hat of carbonized remains of *Pinus nigra* (Couvert 1972, p. 48), which is now found at 1500–1700 m asl (Camps 1974, p. 90), and of the pollen of cedar, which does not now occur below 1400 m asl, at Grotte Rassel (Brahimi 1970, p. 79); Tamar Hat is today at sea-level and the massif behind Grotte Rassel reaches only 900 m asl. Oxygen-isotope analysis of shells from the Haua Fteah suggests that ocean temperatures were 7° or 8°C below modern averages (McBurney 1967, pp. 54–9), which accords well with the CLIMAP estimates of 8–9°C (Gates 1976). Summer temperatures in Upper Egypt and Nubia are estimated to have been 6–7°C below modern (Gates 1976). This is reflected in the occurrence in Late Palaeolithic sites of *Unio abyssinicus*, a freshwater mollusc which today is found only in the cooler waters of Lake Tana in Ethiopia (Martin 1968, p. 76).

Human occupation of the Maghreb

Forerunners

The occupants of the Maghreb 18 000 years ago were the makers of an industry called Iberomaurusian. The origins of the Iberomaurusian are obscure. It is known in eastern Morocco, at Taforalt, by 22 000 BP (Roche 1976) and in eastern Algeria, at Tamar Hat, before 20 000 BP (Saxon et al. 1974). However, there is no preceding Upper Palaeolithic known from the entire region, with the possible exception of the small collection of Upper Palaeolithic-like artefacts from the uppermost layer (L) of the long Middle Palaeolithic sequence at El Guettar in Tunisia (Gruet 1958–59, pp. 105–6). The industry preceding the Iberomaurusian throughout the Maghreb is the Middle Palaeo-lithic Aterian, which often directly underlies Iberomaurusian in the cave-sequences, although the two are usually separated by a significant unconfor-mity. Radiocarbon dates have been claimed for the Aterian almost down to 20 000 BP (Hassko et al. 1974, Roche 1976, Delibrias et al. 1982), but none of the more recent dates is beyond question (Close 1980, 1984) and it seems more likely, in light of the dating of the Middle Palaeolithic farther to the east (McBurney 1967, Wendorf et al. 1987, in press a, in press c), that the entire Aterian lies beyond the range of radiocarbon dating. This suggests that the Maghreb was essentially unoccupied for perhaps 20 000 years before the maximum of the Last Glaciation. It is difficult to accept such a long hiatus in occupation, but less so than so late a survival of the Middle Palaeolithic.

Site distribution

The Iberomaurusian came to florescence in what had been a more or less empty Maghreb, presumably with some stimulus from the east. (To the south lay the hyperarid and impassable Sahara; to the west lay the Atlantic; to the north lay southern Europe, where the people of this period differed both culturally and in physical type; to the east are found similarities in both of these features.) Not much recent work has been devoted to the Iberomaurusian as a whole, so our understanding of it is incomplete. Our knowledge of the Iberomaurusian at 18 000 BP is even more restricted. Only two sites were definitely occupied at that time (Fig. 2.1): Tamar Hat (Saxon et al. 1974, Close 1980–81) and Taforalt (Roche 1976), and only the radiocarbon dates are published concerning the 18 000 BP levels of Taforalt. There is a date of 22 630 BP ± 500 years (Gif-2576) for Iberomaurusian at Grotte des Contrebandiers, on the Atlantic coast of Morocco, but the same sample of marine shells gave a uranium–thorium date of 137 000 ± 17 000 years. They presumably date the terrace in which the cave occurs, rather than the Iberomaurusian occupa-tion (Delibrias et al. 1982).

Tamar Hat and Taforalt were certainly not the only sites occupied at this period, but all other dated sites are later. Like most Iberomaurusian sites (Camps 1974, Fig. 16), Tamar Hat and Taforalt are in the northern Maghreb, Tamar Hat actually on the coast and Taforalt some 25 km up the Wadi Moulouya at an altitude of 750 m asl (Roche 1963, p. 43). Iberomaurusian, or claimed Iberomaurusian, sites occur as far inland as the northern fringes of the Sahara, but all such occurrences that have been dated are very late [Columnata (Brahimi 1972); El Hamel (Tixier 1954); El Haouita (Estorges et al. 1969); El Onçor (Heddouche 1977); Es Sayar (Amara 1977)], suggesting that the early Iberomaurusian was essentially a coastal phenomenon.

The Atlantic coast of Morocco is more problematic. Iberomaurusian sites are numerous, but dates are rare. The 23rd millennium BP date from Grotte des Contrebandiers was noted above; a very similar date on bone from the same site (Gif-2582) was referred to the Aterian (Roche 1976) but may indicate

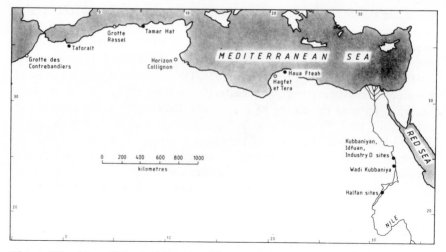

Figure 2.1 Map of North Africa (modern coastline), showing sites known to have been occupied at 18 000 BP (closed circles) and sites likely to have been occupied at 18 000 BP (open circles).

the presence of early Iberomaurusian. On the other hand, the mountain glaciers and the lack of northward-moving warm ocean currents at 18 000 BP (CLIMAP 1976, p. 1135) may have made northwestern Morocco unacceptably cold to the early Iberomaurusians.

There are no definite Iberomaurusian sites at all along the eastern coast of Tunisia. This accords well with the hypothesized strictly coastal orientation of early sites farther west: the eastern coastal plain of Tunisia is very shallow and gently sloping, so that the actual coastline at the glacial maximum was many kilometres out in the Gulf of Sirte. In considering the early Late Palaeolithic of Tunisia, some mention must be made of the Horizon Collignon at Sidi Mansour near Gafsa. This is a backed-bladelet horizon, possibly reworked, near the top of the high terrace of the Wadi Baiech. It is widely regarded as 'early' (Castany & Gobert 1954, pp. 17–21, McBurney 1967, p. 216, Camps 1974, p. 38), although it can really only be dated as post-Middle Palaeolithic and pre-Capsian (i.e. pre-Holocene). An early date for it is, however, supported by its typological similarities to the 'Eastern Oranian' of the Haua Fteah.

In summary, while occupation of southern Tunisia and Atlantic Morocco at 18 000 BP is possible, it is not well documented, and occupation of the interior of the Maghreb seems very unlikely. Populations seem, instead, to have confined themselves rather strictly to the Mediterranean coast from eastern Morocco to Tunisia, and to the immediate hinterland.

Physical type

The only human physical type indisputably found associated with the Iberomaurusian in the Maghreb is the Mechta-Afalou one (Camps 1974,

p. 81), a very robust and distinctive form closely related to contemporaneous populations in the Nile Valley (see below). A more gracile form was found in the shell-midden of Rachgoun, but the associated assemblage is very atypical for Iberomaurusian (Camps 1966). Several hundred Iberomaurusian skeletons have been found, often in large cemeteries, including almost 200 individuals from the later layers of Taforalt (Ferembach *et al.* 1962). Some 50 individuals were excavated from the ossuary of Afalou bou Rhummel (Arambourg *et al.* 1934), which is less than 2 km from Tamar Hat, is very similar in artefacts and could well be of the same age. There are some similarities between the rare Aterian skeletal remains and the Mechta-Afalou type and attempts have been made to derive the one from the other (Ferembach 1985); these must remain tenuous so long as the two are separated, archaeologically and anthropologically, by a gap of 20 000 years or more. The very existence of such similarities, however, suggests that the Mechta-Afalou form is African in origin.

Perhaps the most noteworthy aspect of the Iberomaurusian Mechtoids is not their distinctive physiognomy, but their systematic practice of removing the upper incisors, usually at about puberty (on the basis of the Afalou evidence). The practice was apparently universal and most commonly involved the two first upper incisors. One incisor found in a lower level of Tamar Hat may have been forcibly removed. (Saxon *et al.* 1974, p. 58), indicating that the practice was already in existence before 18 000 BP.

This can be interpreted as a rite of passage, but the possible significance of its universality should also be noted. Removal of the upper incisors is an obvious and unmistakable mutilation, which would serve to mark the individual as 'one of us'. It would then follow that all (known) Maghrebi Iberomaurusians regarded themselves, at some level, as members of the same self-conscious social group, implying a continuity all across the Maghreb for perhaps 10 000 years. An aspect of that broad continuity is also reflected in the stylistic evidence that Tamar Hat was reoccupied by the same, diachronic social group for almost 5000 years (Close 1977, 1978).

Way of life

The only sure evidence we have of the Iberomaurusian way of life at 18 000 BP is from Tamar Hat. Fortunately, this is also the only Iberomaurusian site for which there are quite complete descriptions of the organic remains (Saxon *et al.* 1974). Some complementary data are available from other sites, which are likely to be old, such as Grotte Rassel, which has a date of 14 270 BP ± 600 years (ALG-3) (Brahimi 1970, p. 77).

Tamar Hat was reoccupied many times, apparently by the same, diachronic, social group. This suggests not only an astonishing longevity and stability in the maintenance of group territories, but also a very successful pattern of adaptation. Oxygen–isotope analysis of marine mollusc shells indicates that the site was definitely occupied in winter (Saxon *et al.* 1974, pp. 69–70), but occupation in summer cannot be excluded. However, very few of the 100 +

identified plant remains are of edible plants, suggesting either a winter
occupation, when plant foods were not readily available, or that plant foods
were not part of the diet. The latter seems, a priori, unlikely, so the site may
not have been much used in summer. Its use in winter may have been related to
the rigours of the glacial winter on the exposed coastal plain. Even inside the
Tamar Hat rockshelter, it was necessary to build windbreaks around the
hearths (Saxon *et al.* 1974, Fig. 6), and there are no known open-air sites with
indications of any substantial structures. The Aymé site, for example, at
Courbet-Marine apparently consisted of the dug-out floor of a 'hut', but there
were no postholes to indicate more than the flimsiest of walls (Brahimi 1970,
p. 113–15).

On the basis of the organic remains, the winter occupants of Tamar Hat
supported themselves primarily by hunting the Barbary sheep, *Ammotragus
lervia*, whose bones make up more than 94% of the ungulate remains.
Although *Ammotragus* prefers hilly terrain and was doubtless common in the
massif behind Tamar Hat, this overwhelming, and long-lasting, predominance suggests specialization. It has been hypothesized that the *Ammotragus* might have been herded rather than hunted, on the basis of osteometric
data indicating the killing of young males and older females, and the
elusiveness of *Ammotragus* as a prey of modern hunters (Saxon *et al.* 1974,
pp. 76–82). However, the sex determinations are open to doubt (Lubell 1984,
pp. 48–9) and, if very young epiphyses have been differentially destroyed, as
happens in stratified sites, then the age profile may originally have been the
same as that of a normal living *Ammotragus* population (Klein & Scott 1986,
p. 535). In that case, *Ammotragus* could have been hunted by trapping or
driving over cliffs. The difficulties that modern hunters experience in taking
Ammotragus reflect primarily the self-imposed handicap of 'sportsmanship' that
accompanies high-powered rifles and telescopic sights; Iberomaurusian
hunters probably did not have the same compunctions.

While occupation of Tamar Hat was associated with the specialized hunting
of *Ammotragus*, as was probably also the case at Afalou bou Rhummel, this was
not necessarily true of other Iberomaurusian sites. Unfortunately, since faunal
reports are non-existent or consist of lists of species present, few comparative
data are available. However, *Ammotragus* is not among the faunas listed for
several Iberomaurusian sites; more specifically, hartebeest is said to be the
predominant species in caves around Algiers (F.-E. Roubet, reported by Saxon
et al. 1974, p. 76), while zebra is more common in the later, inland sites (Camps
1974).

In fact, absolutely the most numerous animal in the faunal remains from
Tamar Hat at 18 000 BP is the snail, *Helix aspersa*. These first appear in quantity
at about 18 700 BP and remain numerous thereafter, sometimes even forming
small shell-middens as they do also at Grotte Rassel (Brahimi 1970, p. 40), at
Abri Alain (or Carrières d'Eckmühl), near Oran, where the upper layer was
essentially a shell-midden 3 m thick (Vaufrey 1955, pp. 273–4), and at the
Khenzira caves, in Atlantic Morocco, with real shell-middens 0.75 and 1.25 m

thick (Vaufrey 1955, p. 285). The caloric value of a snail is obviously much less than that of a Barbary sheep, but the intensive collection of snails by Iberomaurusians has frequently been overlooked. The collection of *Helix* suggests occupation in autumn or spring. They hibernate in winter, often aestivate in summer and, consequently, can be gathered easily and in quantity only in spring and autumn (Lubell *et al.* 1975, pp. 73–4).

Marine molluscs also become more frequent after about 18 700 BP, but they are never numerous and most of them are the very small, pink *Homalopoma* shells, which were probably used for ornaments. However, their presence, as well as that of a few bones of sea-fish, indicates the people still went down to the seashore from Tamar Hat, but not often or to much purpose. The same is apparently true of Grotte Rassel, where marine molluscs were rare and fish absent (Brahimi 1970, pp. 80–1). Presumably, the sea and the coast were exploited in the warmer months, from sites now lying beneath the Mediterranean. At that season, one supposes that both fish and plant foods were more important parts of the diet than during the winter.

Human occupation of Cyrenaïca

Forerunners

The only site known to have been occupied 18 000 years ago in Cyrenaïca is the coastal site of the Haua Fteah (McBurney 1967), but there is some confusion as to what occupation that was. Until recently, Cyrenaïca was the only part of North Africa to have yielded a classic blade-and-burin Upper Palaeolithic. This is the Dabban, of which there is a long sequence in the Haua, probably beginning before 40 000 BP. It is directly overlain by the 'Eastern Oranian', or Eastern Iberomaurusian, which McBurney believed to have begun at about 14 000 BP. The oldest radiocarbon date he assigned to it was one of 12 750 BP ± 170 years (NPL-43), from the next-to-earliest Iberomaurusian layer; at that time, the oldest Iberomaurusian date he knew of from the Maghreb was about 12 000 BP at Taforalt (McBurney 1967, p. 215). However, it now seems more likely that two other dates, 16 070 BP ± 100 years (GrN-2586) and 18 620 BP ± 150 years (GrN-2585), may refer to the beginning of the Eastern Iberomaurusian, rather than to the underlying Dabban. The samples were taken from the Eastern Iberomaurusian–Dabban interface and were attributed to the Dabban primarily because they fell so far outside the known range of Iberomaurusian dates. However, since comparable backed-bladelet industries are now known both in the Maghreb and in the Nile Valley by 20 000 BP, it seems more likely that the dates do indeed refer to the Eastern Iberomaurusian, and the makers of the bladelets would thus be the occupants of the Haua Fteah at 18 000 BP.

The Eastern Iberomaurusian is so different from the underlying Dabban, and the change between them so abrupt, that McBurney suggested a change of population (1967, p. 327). While this may now appear rather extreme, some external stimulus would seem to be indicated. For the sake of economy, it seems best to attribute the development of the Eastern Iberomaurusian in Cyrenaïca to the same force as led to the development of the Iberomaurusian itself in the Maghreb. In this respect, we may recall that there are some very specific and detailed typological similarities between the Eastern Iberomaurusian and the Horizon Collignon in Tunisia (Close 1986, p. 176). Unfortunately, there are no Late Palaeolithic sites known between Cyrenaïca and southern Tunisia, which might be used to test this hypothesis. One can only suppose that occupation was closer to the 18 000 BP coastline and that the sites are now drowned. However, the location near Gafsa of the Horizon Collignon itself shows that there were some incursions into the hinterland.

Site distribution

The Haua Fteah lies about 1 km from the modern coast at 60 m asl, at the edge of the massif of the Gebel el Akhdar (Fig. 2.1). Its situation is thus comparable to that of the Maghrebi sites. A second Eastern Iberomaurusian site, the Hagfet et Tera, is southwest of the Haua, about 10 km inland from Benghazi and at the edge of the desert (McBurney & Hey 1955, pp. 176–90). There is, however, no positive indication of occupation at 18 000 BP.

Physical type

No human remains of this period are known from Cyrenaïca. However, since both the Lower Nile Valley and the Maghreb were occupied by Mechtoid populations, it would be surprising if the same were not true of the area between.

Way of life

There are no indications of strictly seasonal occupation of the Haua Fteah, but it was probably not permanent. The site was reoccupied many times and stylistic analyses again indicate reoccupation by a single, diachronic, social group (Close 1977, 1978). In this case, the stylistic continuity embraces the entire Eastern Iberomaurusian as well as the succeeding, and typologically different, Libyco-Capsian; that is, from 18 000 BP or before to about 8500 BP.

The faunal remains show that *Ammotragus* was again the most important game-animal, although its predominance is less overwhelming than at Tamar Hat: some 81% of the identified ungulate bones in the early Iberomaurusian are *Ammotragus* (Klein & Scott 1986, Table 2). Age and sex profiles of the *Ammotragus* are comparable to those of living populations (Klein & Scott 1986, pp. 532–4), which suggests hunting, perhaps by trapping or driving over cliffs, rather than the herding which Saxon hypothesized (Saxon *et al.* 1974, p. 79). That *Ammotragus* was the dominant faunal element throughout the prehistoric sequence at the Haua, from the Lower Palaeolithic to the Neolithic, suggests that its availability in the Gebel et Akhdar was a more important factor than were nuances of man–animal relationships. The same factor would explain the predominance of gazelle at the more desertic Hagfet et Tera (Higgs 1967, p. 33, Klein & Scott 1986, p. 537).

There is no evidence that the Haua Fteah was used as a base from which to exploit the sea and the coast at 18 000 BP. There are no fish-remains at all from the Eastern Iberomaurusian and very few marine molluscs in the earliest layer. If the sea was used, it was from other sites. Marine molluscs became numerous only above Layer XIII (Klein & Scott 1986, p. 520), which dates to about 12 000 BP (Close 1977, p. 62), presumably reflecting the approach of the coastline closer to the cave. Some land-snails are present in the earliest Iberomaurusian, but they were not collected intensively until some time after 18 000 BP. Almost all of them are of the large, edible species (Hey 1967).

It is particularly unfortunate that no floral remains were recovered from the Haua, since a limestone mortar was found in one of the earlier Eastern Iberomaurusian layers. It is difficult to imagine that a settlement system so successful as to persist for ten millennia was not based in part upon plant foods.

Human occupation of the Lower Nile Valley

Forerunners

True Upper Palaeolithic industries are known from the Lower Nile Valley before 30 000 BP at Nazlet Khater-4, near Qena (Vermeersch et al. 1982) and between 25 000 and 21 000 BP at Shuwikhat near Qena (Paulissen et al. 1985) and at E71K9 near Isna (Wendorf & Schild 1976, pp. 82–6). These are different from the succeeding bladelet industries in both artefacts and, in all probability, economy, but the difference is not so absolute as in Cyrenaïca. Some of the bladelet industries, such as the Idfuan, have a large blade component (Wendorf & Schild 1976, pp. 244–52), and continuity between the Upper and Late Palaeolithic seems likely. However, understanding of the processes of change between the two is hampered by the rarity of sites dating just before 21 000 BP.

Site distribution

The Late Palaeolithic bladelet industries of the Nile Valley begin to appear at about 21 000 BP and are known from at least the Second Cataract to the Qena Bend (Fig. 2.1). Three or four different industries can be dated to about 18 000 BP: the Halfan in Nubia, the Kubbaniyan (which is essentially an Upper Egyptian variant of the same industry), the Idfuan and the informally named 'Industry D', both from Upper Egypt.

The Halfan is known from ten sites in Nubia, between the Second Cataract and Ballana (Irwin et al. 1968, Marks 1968, Wendorf 1968a) and the most consistent radiocarbon dates indicate a span for the Halfan of about 19 500 to 17 500 BP. The Kubbaniyan is best known from Wadi Kubbaniya, on the west bank just north of Aswan, where it is firmly dated between 19 500 or 19 000 BP and about 17 000 BP (Wendorf et al. 1980, 1989a, b). The undated Site E71K13, near Isna, is identical to the Wadi Kubbaniya Kubbaniyan precisely at 18 000 BP and is most probably of that age (Phillips 1973). Kubbaniyan is also dated to 18 000 BP at Site E71P1, Areas C and D, near Idfu (Wendorf & Schild 1976, pp. 244–52).

The Idfuan is known from sites near Idfu and near Isna, most of them undated. However, a series of dates on *Unio* shell from E71P1, Areas A and B, would probably fall at about 18 000 BP if corrected for fractionation. (The uncorrected dates are 17 600–17 000 BP; Wendorf & Schild 1976, p. 32).

Site E71K12, near Isna (Phillips 1973), is not dated directly, but, stratigraphically, is only slightly later than the adjacent Site E71K13 and may therefore be regarded as about 18 000 years old. The assemblage from it is unique in the Nile Valley and has no formal name; it has been called informally 'Industry D'.

The Fakhurian industry from Isna is not included in this survey, although its age has previously been estimated as about 18 000 years (Lubell 1974, p. 3, Wendorf & Schild 1976, p. 252). However, the earlier radiocarbon dates (I-3415 and I-3416) are now regarded as too young because of inadequate pretreatment, and a thoroughly pretreated sample has given a date of 19 670 BP ± 180 years (SMU-1816; Wendorf et al. in press b). Similarly, Fakhurian-related sites at Wadi Kubbaniya date between > 21 000 and 19 500 BP (Wendorf et al. 1989b).

All of these sites are associated with the greatly expanded floodplain of the Nile at 18 000 BP; the hyperaridity of that period meant that no life could be supported beyond the reach of the river. Most of the sites are near the edge of the floodplain, sometimes well inside wadi mouths and several kilometres from the modern channel, as at Wadi Kubbaniya and the Khor Musa. Some of the sites at Kubbaniya are on higher gound (ancient dunes) within the floodplain. The only known sites that were close to the contemporaneous Nile channels are those on bedrock hillocks near Idfu (E71P1, P2, P7). All low-lying sites close to the channels are now destroyed or deeply buried.

Physical type

All human skeletal finds from the Nilotic Late Palaeolithic, both before and after 18 000 BP, are regarded as Mechtoids. Physically, they are closely related to the Mechta-Afalou Iberomaurusians of the Maghreb, but they differ from them in two important cultural aspects.

First, the removal of the first upper incisors, which was universal in the Maghreb, was unknown in the Nile. Secondly, there is considerable evidence of violence in the Nile Valley, but none at all in the Maghreb. The earliest Nilotic Late Palaeolithic skeleton (> 21 000 BP in Wadi Kubbaniya) is presumed to have been killed by the bladelets found in his abdomen; he had also been wounded on at least two previous occasions (Wendorf *et al.* 1986). In the cemetery at Jebel Sahaba, there is direct evidence that 40% of the individuals buried there died violently, regardless of age or sex, and the actual percentage to have died in this way was probably much higher (Wendorf 1968b). Violence on this scale is undocumented elsewhere at this period. It is tempting to suggest that it indicates intergroup conflict, or warfare, for the limited resources of a less than luxuriant Nile Valley that was surrounded by an utterly inhospitable desert.

Way of life

The principal factor governing ways of life in the Nile Valley 18 000 years ago was the annual Nile flood. Today, the flood begins slowly in early July, then rises rapidly to its peak level, 7 m or more above low-water, in mid-August and early September. It drops quickly and the season of lowest water is from February to June. The evidence indicates a similar regimen at 18 000 BP (Wendorf *et al.* 1989a).

Our best data for reconstructing the Late Palaeolithic way of life come from the Kubbaniyan sites of Wadi Kubbaniya, which have yielded large collections of organic remains. The faunal remains include a few shells of *Unio abyssinicus*; numerous bird bones, many of them of species that now winter in Egypt; bones of large mammals (essentially gazelle, hartebeest, and wild cattle); and enormous quantities of fish-bones, mostly adult catfish. These last probably reflect massive harvesting of catfish during the spawn that begins as the water starts to rise (July) and ends as soon as it begins to fall in early September (Gautier & Van Neer 1989). Apart from wood charcoal (all tamarisk), the identified plant remains are dominated by purple nut-grass tubers, which grow wild in the wetlands by the Nile. Other identified remains of native edible plants (some from human coprolites) include club-rush tubers, chamomile seeds, and dom-palm fruit (Hillman *et al.* 1989).

On the basis of the organic remains, as well as microstratigraphical and topographical data, we may reconstruct the Kubbaniyan way of life as follows. The intensive harvest of catfish spawning at the edge of the flood began in early- to mid-July as the water began to rise. So many fish were taken – one site yielded > 130 000 fish-bones – that some may have been dried or smoked for later consumption. At the peak of the flood all the known sites were under water, but the people returned as the waters receded and probably continued fishing in the cut-off ponds on the floodplain. Plant foods became important after the flood: chamomile seeds were available in October and the nut grass and club-rush tubers a little later. The young tubers may simply be rubbed and roasted before eating. However, tubers are most nutritious at maturity in December and January, when they must also be processed to remove the volatile toxins and to make the fibres more digestible. Grinding before cooking can accomplish both of these purposes, and the abundance of grinding-stones in some of the Kubbaniyan sites suggests that tubers were an important food-stuff. It is possible that a surplus could have been collected and processed; dried tubers retain their food-value for several months (Hillman *et al.* 1989). Water-birds were also taken during the winter months. Some occupation of the known sites later in the cycle is shown by the dom-palm fruits, which mature in February and March, and the *Unio* shells, which were probably gathered only during the lowest water (February–June). We do not know what sites were occupied during the season of lowest water, but the evidence for low-water, intensive exploitation of *Unio* by Kubbaniyans near Idfu makes it seem likely that occupation was usually inside the valley, close to the deepest channels, at sites now lost to us.

The large mammals could have been hunted throughout the year, but at Kubbaniya they were much less important in the diet than fish. It remains possible that the major hunting sites have not been found; if so, then hunting took place either predominantly in the highest- or lowest-water seasons, or from specialized sites away from the main sites known, for which there is evidence of some use during most periods of the year.

Evidence from elsewhere in the Nile Valley is complementary to that from Kubbaniya. Some sites of the closely related Halfan appear to have specialized as much in catfish as did the Kubbaniyans, but the Halfan sites near the Second Cataract (Sites 443, 1018 and 1020; Gautier 1968, Table 6) saw primarily the hunting of cattle and hartebeest and very little fishing. Unfortunately, there are no supplementary indications of why these sites were particularly suited for hunting, but the absence of grinding-stones from them may suggest that these were not winter occupations.

The Kubbaniyan sites at E71P1 (Areas C and D), near Idfu, yielded numerous catfish, large mammals and, most interestingly, small middens of *Unio* shells. These sites were on bedrock hillocks near the Nile channels; slightly lower areas of bedrock nearby would have been ideal habitats for *Unio* and would have been easily accessible during the lowest-water season. Since the sites would have been under water during the main part of the flood, the hunting and fishing must also have been practised during relatively low water, although we cannot determine if it was exactly the same season as the shellfish-collecting.

Some light may be cast on this by the neighbouring Idfuan sites of E71P1 (Areas A and B) and E71P2, which have similar geomorphological settings. The faunas from Areas A and B are like those from the Kubbaniyan areas. However, most of the animals from E71P2 were cattle and hartebeest, indicating that, at least sometimes, hunting was carried out separately from fishing and shell-fishing.

The 18 000-year-old sites near Isna are not informative about subsistence, but the Kubbaniyan site of E71K13 tells us something about the range of movement, or contacts, of groups along the Nile Valley at the time. It is identical in technology and typology to one of the sites at Wadi Kubbaniya, and stylistic studies show them to be very closely linked. (Close 1989). The only difference between them is the almost exclusive use of Egyptian flint at

E71K13 and its comparative rarity at Kubbaniya. Since the Isna area was a source of Egyptian flint within the Nile Valley, it is very possible that Kubbaniyan groups travelled there from Wadi Kubbaniya – a distance of about 150 km – to obtain this prized raw material.

Conclusion

Hyperaridity made most of North Africa uninhabitable 18 000 years ago. Human occupation was confined to the Lower Nile Valley, Cyrenaïca, the Mediterranean coast of the Maghreb and, possibly, the Atlantic coast of the Maghreb. However, we have no definite sites dated to 18 000 BP below the Qena Bend, only one in Cyrenaïca and only two on the northern Maghrebi coast. All the occupants of these sites were of the distinctive North African population called Mechtoids. In the Maghreb and Cyrenaïca, they maintained very stable and successful systems of adaptation that included considerable hunting of Barbary sheep in the coastal massifs. Land-snails were collected, but the sites from which marine resources were exploited are now drowned beneath the sea and we have no data on the use of plant foods.

In the Nile Valley, the business of making a living was apparently so hazardous that competition for resources resulted in warfare. In this limited and very constrained environment, people developed a complex, broad-based system of exploiting seasonally abundant resources. Two of these, the catfish in summer and the wetland tubers in winter, may have been deliberately harvested beyond immediate needs, and the surplus stored in anticipation of the lean periods in late spring and early summer. If so, this practice would represent an important innovation in Palaeolithic economies, and it seems significant that it should have appeared at the maximum of the last glaciation. It may also be observed that large mammals were a minor component of the diet, which was based primarily upon 'r-selected' species (Pianka 1970) in a fashion usually thought typical of the Holocene.

Acknowledgements

The research at Wadi Kubbaniya discussed in this chapter was carried out by the Combined Prehistoric Expedition, which is jointly sponsored by the Polish Academy of Sciences, the Geological Survey of Egypt and Southern Methodist University. The work was carried out with the help of grants to the second author from the National Science Foundation (Grants BNS-7680012 A01, BNS-7823943, and BNS-8023411) and from the Foreign Currency Program of the Smithsonian Institution (Grants FR5-46240, FC-70174900, and FC-80185500). The reconstruction of the Nilotic subsistence system draws heavily upon palaeoeconomic data resulting from the work of Gautier & Van Neer (1989) and of Hillman et al. (1989). The final reports of the Wadi Kubbaniya project are now being published (Wendorf et al. 1986, 1989 a,b).

References

Amara, A. 1977. Le gisement Es-Sayar, Bou Saâda (Algérie). *Libyca* **25**, 59–71.
Arambourg, C., M. Boule, H. Vallois & R. Verneau 1934. *Les grottes paléolithiques des Béni-Segoual (Algérie)*. Archives de l'Institut de Paléontologie Humaine 13. Paris: Masson.

Brahimi, C. 1970. *L'Ibéromaurusien littoral de la région d'Alger*. Mémoires du Centre de Recherches Anthropologiques, Préhistoriques et Ethnographiques 13. Paris: Arts et Métiers Graphiques.
Brahimi, C. 1972. Deux campagnes de fouilles à Columnata, 1969–1971. Premiers résultats. *Libyca* **20**, 49–101.

Camps, G. 1966. Le gisement de Rachgoun (Oranie). *Libyca* **14**, 161–88.
Camps, G. 1974. *Les Civilisations préhistoriques de l'Afrique du Nord et du Sahara*. Paris: Doin.
Castany, G. & E. G. Gobert 1954. Morphologie quaternaire, paléothnologie et leurs relations à Gafsa. *Libyca* **2**, 9–37.
CLIMAP Project Members 1976. The surface of the ice-age earth. *Science* **191**, 1131–7.
Close, A. E. 1977. *The Identification of Style in Lithic Artefacts from North-East Africa*. Mémoires de l'Institut d'Egypte 61. Cairo: Institut d'Egypte.
Close, A. E. 1978. The identification of style in lithic artefacts. *World Archaeology* **10**, 223–37.
Close, A. E. 1980. Current research and recent radiocarbon dates from northern Africa. *Journal of African History* **21**, 145–67.
Close, A. E. 1980–81. The Iberomaurusian sequence at Tamar Hat. *Libyca* **28–29**, 69–104.
Close, A. E. 1984. Current research and recent radiocarbon dates from northern Africa, II. *Journal of African History* **25**, 1–24.
Close, A. E. 1986. The place of the Haua Fteah in the Late Palaeolithic of North Africa. In *Stone Age prehistory: studies in memory of Charles McBurney*, G. N. Bailey & P. Callow (eds), 169–80. Cambridge: Cambridge University Press.
Close, A. E. 1989. Stylistic analysis of the Late Paleolithic of Wadi Kubbaniya and the Lower Nile Valley. In *The prehistory of Wadi Kubbaniya*. Vol. 3: *The Late Paleolithic occupations*, F. Wendorf, R. Schild (assemblers) & A. E. Close (ed.) 752–67. Dallas: Southern Methodist University Press.
Couvert, M. 1972. Variations paléoclimatiques en Algérie. Traduction climatique des informations paléobotaniques fournies par les charbons des gisements préhistoriques. Note préliminaire. *Libyca* **20**, 45–8.

Delibrias, G., M-T. Guillier & J. Labeyrie 1982. Gif natural radiocarbon measurements, IX *Radiocarbon* **24**, 291–343.

Estorges, P., G. Aumassip & A. Dagorne 1969. El Haouita, un exemple de remblaiement fini-würmien. *Libyca* **17**, 53–91.

Ferembach, D. 1985. On the origin of the Iberomaurusians. A new hypothesis. *Journal of Human Evolution* **14**, 393–7.
Ferembach, D., J. Dastugue & M.-J. Poitrat-Targowla 1962. *La nécropole épipaléolithique de Taforalt (Maroc oriental). Etude des squélettes humains*. Paris: Centre National de la Recherche Scientifique.

Gates, W. L. 1976. Modeling the ice-age climate. *Science* **191**, 1138–44.
Gautier, A. 1968. Mammalian remains of the northern Sudan and Southern Egypt. In

The prehistory of Nubia, F. Wendorf (ed.), 80–99. Dallas: Fort Burgwin Research Center and Southern Methodist University Press.

Gautier, A. & W. Van Neer 1989. Animal remains from the Late Paleolithic sequence at Wadi Kubbaniya. In *The prehistory of Wadi Kubbaniya*. Vol. 2: *Paleoenvironmental and stratigraphic studies*, F. Wendorf, R. Schild (assemblers) & A. E. Close (ed.), 119–61. Dallas: Southern Methodist University Press.

Gruet, M. 1958–9. Le gisement d'El Guéttar et sa flore. *Libyca* **6–7**, 79–126.

Hassko, B., B. Guillet, R. Jaegy & R. Coppens 1974. Nancy natural radiocarbon measurements: III. *Radiocarbon* **16**, 118–30.

Heddouche, A. E. K. 1977. Le gisement épipaléolithique d'El-Onçor près Bou-Saâda (Algérie). *Libyca* **25**, 73–84.

Hey, R. W. 1967. Land-snails. In *The Haua Fteah (Cyrenaïca) and the Stone Age of the south-east Mediterranean*, C. B. M. McBurney (ed.), 358. Cambridge: Cambridge University Press.

Higgs, E. S. 1967. Environment and chronology – the evidence from mammalian fauna. In *The Haua Fteah (Cyrenaïca) and the Stone Age of the south-east Mediterranean*, C. B. M. McBurney (ed.), 16–44. Cambridge: Cambridge University Press.

Hillman, G., E. Madeyska & J. Hather 1989. Wild plant-foods and diet at Late Paleolithic Wadi Kubbaniya: the evidence from charred remains. In *The prehistory of Wadi Kubbaniya*. Vol. 2: *Paleoenvironmental and Stratigraphic Studies*, F. Wendorf, R. Schild (assemblers) & A. E. Close (ed.), 162–242. Dallas: Southern Methodist University Press, in press.

Irwin, H. T., J. B. Wheat & L. G. Irwin 1968. *University of Colorado investigations of Paleolithic and Epipaleolithic sites in the Sudan, Africa*. University of Utah Papers in Anthropology 90. Salt Lake City: University of Utah Press.

Klein, R. G. & K. Scott 1986. Re-analysis of faunal assemblages from the Haua Fteah and other Late Quaternary archaeological sites in Cyrenaïcan Libya. *Journal of Archaeological Science* **13**, 515–42.

Lubell, D. 1974. *The Fakhurian: A Late Paleolithic industry from Upper Egypt*. Papers of the Geological Survey of Egypt 58. Cairo: Geological Survey of Egypt.

Lubell, D. 1984. Paleoenvironments and Epi-Paleolithic economies in the Maghreb (ca. 20,000 to 5000 B.P.). In *From hunters to farmers. The causes and consequences of food production in Africa*, J. D. Clark & S. A. Brandt (eds), 41–56, Berkeley: University of California Press.

Lubell, D. J.-L. Ballais, A. Gautier, F. A. Hassan, A. E Close, C. Chippindale, J. Elmendorf & G. Aumassip 1975. The prehistoric cultural ecology of Capsian *escargotières*. Preliminary results of an interdisciplinary investigation in the Chéria-Télidjène region (1972–1973). *Libyca* **23**, 43–121.

McBurney, C. B. M. 1967. *The Haua Fteah (Cyrenaïca) and the Stone Age of the south-east Mediterranean*. Cambridge: Cambridge University Press.

McBurney, C. B. M. & R. W. Hey 1955. *Prehistory and Pleistocene geology in Cyrenaïcan Libya*. Cambridge: Cambridge University Press.

Marks. A. E. 1968. The Halfan industry. In *The prehistory of Nubia*, F. Wendorf (ed.), 392–460. Dallas: Fort Burgwin Research Center and Southern Methodist University Press.

Martin, F. 1968. Pleistocene mollusks from Sudanese Nubia. In *The prehistory of Nubia*, F. Wendorf (ed.), 56–79. Dallas: Fort Burgwin Research Center and Southern Methodist University Press.

Paulissen, E., P. M. Vermeersch & W. Van Neer 1985. Progress report on the Late Paleolithic Shuwikhat sites (Qena, Upper Egypt). *Nyame Akuma* **26**, 7–14.

Phillips, J. L. 1973. *Two Final Paleolithic sites in the Nile Valley and their external Relations*. Papers of the Geological Survey of Egypt 57. Cairo: Geological Survey of Egypt.

Pianka, E. R. 1970. On *r* and *K* selection or *b* and *d* selection? *American Naturalist* **106**, 581–8.

Roche, J. 1963 *L'Epipaléolithique marocain*. Lisbon: Fondation Calouste Gulbenkian.

Roche, J. 1976. *Cadre chronologique de l'Epipaléolithique marocain*. Congrès de l'UISPP, Colloque II, Nice, 153–67.

Saxon, E. C., A. E. Close, C. Cluzel, V. Morse & N. J. Shackleton 1974. Results of recent investigations at Tamar Hat. *Libyca* **22**, 49–91.

Schild, R. 1987. Unchanging contrast? The Late Pleistocene Nile and Eastern Sahara. In *Prehistory of arid North Africa. Essays in honor of Fred Wendorf*, A. E. Close (ed.), 13–27. Dallas: Southern Methodist University Press.

Schild, R. & F. Wendorf 1989. The Late Pleistocene Nile in Wadi Kubbaniya. In *The prehistory of Wadi Kubbaniya*. Vol. 2: *Paleoenvironmental and stratigraphic studies*, F. Wendorf, R. Schild (assemblers) & A. E. Close (ed.), 15–100. Dallas: Southern Methodist University Press.

Tixier, J. 1954. Le gisement préhistorique d'El-Hamel. *Libyca* **2**, 78–120.

Vaufrey, R. 1955. *Préhistoire de l'Afrique. Tome I: Le Maghreb*. Publications de l'Institut des Hautes Etudes de Tunis 4. Paris: Masson.

Vermeersch, P. M., M. Otte, E. Gilot, E. Paulissen, G. Gijselings & D. Drappier 1982. Blade technology in the Egyptian Nile Valley: some new evidence. *Science* **216**, 626–8.

Wendorf, F. 1968a. Late Paleolithic sites in Egyptian Nubia. In *The prehistory of Nubia*, F. Wendorf (ed.), 791–953. Dallas: Fort Burgwin Research Center and Southern Methodist University Press.

Wendorf, F. 1968b. Site 117: a Nubian Final Paleolithic graveyard near Jebel Sahaba, Sudan. In *The prehistory of Nubia*, F. Wendorf (ed.), 954–95. Dallas: Fort Burgwin Research Center and Southern Methodist Press.

Wendorf, F. & R. Schild 1976. *Prehistory of the Nile Valley*. New York: Academic Press.

Wendorf, F., A. E. Close & R. Schild in press a. Africa during the period of *Homo sapiens neanderthalensis* and his contemporaries. In *History of the scientific and cultural development of mankind*, S. J. de Laet (ed.). Paris: Unesco.

Wendorf, F., R. Schild (assemblers) & A. E. Close (ed.) 1980 *Loaves and Fishes: The prehistory of Wadi Kubbaniya*. Dallas: Department of Anthropology, Institute for the Study of Earth and Man, Southern Methodist University.

Wendorf, F., R. Schild (assemblers) & A. E. Close (ed.) 1986. *The prehistory of Wadi Kubbaniya*. Vol. 1: *The Wadi Kubbaniya skeleton: A Late Paleolithic burial from southern Egypt*. Dallas: Southern Methodist University Press.

Wendorf, F., R. Schild & A. E. Close 1987. Recent work on the Middle Palaeolithic of the Eastern Sahara. *African Archaeological Review* **5**, 49–63.

Wendorf, F., R. Schild (assemblers) A. E. Close (ed.) 1989a. *The prehistory of Wadi Kubbaniya*. Vol. 2: *Paleoenvironmental and stratigraphic studies*. Dallas: Southern Methodist University Press.

Wendorf, F., R. Schild (assemblers) & A. E. Close (ed.) 1989b. *The prehistory of Wadi*

Kubbaniya. Vol. 3: *The Late Paleolithic occupations*. Dallas: Southern Methodist University Press.

Wendorf, F., A. E. Close, R. Schild, H. Wieckowska, A. Gautier, G. Hillman, W. Van Neer & E. Madeyska in press b. La vallée du Nil inférieure entre 21 000 et 17 000 B.P. *L'Anthropologie*.

Wendorf, F., A. E. Close, R. Schild, H. P. Schwarcz, G. H. Miller, K. Kowalski, H. Królik, D. Robins, A. Bluszcz & R. Grun in press c. La dernière interglaciale dans le Sahara de l'est. *L'Anthropologie*.

3 The Last Glacial Maximum in the Mediterranean Levant

OFER BAR-YOSEF

Introduction

The Mediterranean Levant is a small region located at the geographical crossroads between three continents. It is bordered by the Mediterranean Sea on the west, the Sinai desert in the south, the Syro-Arabian desert on the east, and the Taurus mountains (southern Turkey) in the north. The scale of its topographic variability, the proximity to the sea, and its location in relation to the patterns of global atmospheric circulation, created a high degree of ecological variability across short distances unparalleled within the Old World (Wigley & Farmer 1982, Bar-Yosef 1987a, see Fig. 3.1). This unique ecological mosaic greatly affected the socioeconomic developments during the closing millennia of the Pleistocene, which ultimately led to the emergence of sedentism and the subsequent adoption of agriculture.

These cultural changes took place in hunter–gatherer societies, which at first glance do not seem to differ from their contemporaries in most regions of the Old World during the Last Glacial Maximum (LGM). The basic assumption of this chapter is that cultural adaptations during the LGM had a definitive role in shaping the decision-making processes of Epi-Palaeolithic groups. The goal of this chapter is to determine what made the pre-agricultural history of Levantine hunter–gatherers unique. Specifically, how and why human adaptations following the LGM stimulated Levantine groups to drastically change their subsistence strategies.

Palaeoenvironments in the Levant

The most reliable sources for palaeoclimatic reconstructions are the ^{18}O fluctuations as recorded in deep-sea cores (Nesteroff et al. 1983, Patterne et al. 1986). Terrestrial events are reflected in palynological sequences obtained from cores drilled in several lakes in Turkey, Iran, Syria and Israel. Unfortunately, these records are in partial disagreement with each other, due either to insufficient radiocarbon dates or gaps in the sedimentary columns (van Zeist & Bottema 1982, Bottema 1987). Other sources, such as ^{18}O changes in land-snails and nodular carbonate horizons (Margaritz 1986, Goodfriend &

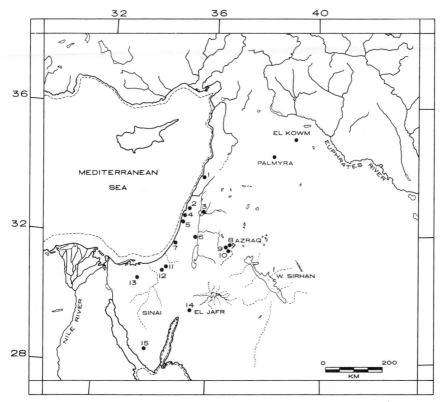

Figure 3.1   Location of the main sites mentioned in the text: 1, Jaita II; 2, Hayonim Cave; 3, Ein Gev I–IV; 4, Neveh David and Nahal Oren; 5, Kebara Cave; 6, the Fazael sites; 7, the Ashdonian sites (Kefar Darom 3, 8, etc.); 8, Uwaynid sites; 9, Kharaneh IV; 10, Wadi Jilat sites; 11, Shunera sites; 12, Azariq sites; 13, Gebel Maghara sites; 14, Gebel Qalkha sites; 15, Wadi Sayakh.

Margaritz 1988), fluctuations in animal sizes (Tchernov 1982), depositional and aggradational events in fluviatile terraces (Goldberg 1986), and strand levels of palaeolakes (Roberts 1982, Begin *et al.* 1985) provide supportive although rather patchy evidence.

Faunal and palynological spectra recovered from archaeological sites, in general, are of doubtful palaeoclimatic value. This is because a biased picture may result from varying hunting strategies and from taphonomic processes (e.g. selective preservation). Several specialists, however, report a good fit between their observations and palaeoclimatic conditions. This is the case with mammalian bone frequencies from the Levantine coastal ranges and with pollen spectra from the Jordan Valley sites (Davis 1982, Garrard 1982, Leroi-Gourhan & Darmon 1987).

The number of published deep-sea cores from the eastern Mediterranean is still rather small. Data on hand from the entire northern hemisphere, however, do demonstrate several good synchronic correlations between the major climatic fluctuations and their timing across the north Atlantic and the Mediterranean Sea. This is true for the LGM, Termination IA and Termination IB, the warming between them ('Bölling–Alleröd' in European terminology), and the last cold and dry event of the 'Younger Dryas' (Boyle & Keigwin, 1987, Margaritz & Goodfriend 1987).

In the Levant the LGM probably lasted from about 22 000 until 16 000 BP. Warm spells have been recognized around 16 000–15 000 BP, 13 500 BP, and 12 800 BP, becoming warmer around 11 900, with a cold period ('Younger Dryas') in the mid-11th millennium and continuous warming from 10 000 BP onwards (Nesteroff *et al.* 1983). While increases in mean annual temperature did influence the air humidity, it is the pattern of winter precipitation that is the prominent variable affecting vegetation growth in Levantine woodland and shrub desert environments (Shmida *et al.* 1986). This factor was responsible for the expansion or shrinkage of inland lakes such as Lake Lisan (Begin *et al.* 1985).

Palynological studies of the Levant provide a picture which was interpreted as reflecting rainfall fluctuations with considerable regional variability (van Zeist & Bottema 1982). Better dating eliminated apparent contradictions between the Lake Van and Lake Zeribar sequences (Bottema 1987). Similar results are expected from redating the important sequence of the Ghab, in northern Syria. The general correlation between the well-dated Hula sequence and the eastern Mediterranean deep-sea core data of van Zeist and Bottema (1982) indicates the following palaeoclimatic sequence for the Levant (Rognon 1987):

(1) *c.* 20 000–14 500/14 000 BP. Cold and dry over the entire region. The coastal ranges in Syria, Lebanon, and Israel received winter precipitation and were covered with forests, which became more open in the south. Lakes (such as Lake Lisan) were reduced in size. Only a narrow strip of open forest or a parkland stretched along the Transjordanian plateau. The steppic belt was reduced and the Saharo-Arabian belt expanded westward in Syria and Jordan and northward in the Sinai and Negev region.

(2) *c.* 14 500–13 000/12 800 BP. A wet period marked by an increase in precipitation, expansion of forests in the hilly areas and of steppic vegetation into the deserts, the appearance of temporary small lakes, and the restored size of larger lakes. The last recognizable palaeosol was formed during this period. Higher temperatures matched by rises in the sea-level were reducing the width of the relatively flat coastal plain. This process primarily affected the southern Levant and had less impact along the steeply shelving shores of Syria and Lebanon.

(3) *c.* 13 000/12 800–10 000 BP. A brief warm spell was followed by a warm and still somewhat wet period, which finally became dry and cold (*c.* 10 800—10 000 BP, known in Europe as the 'Younger Dryas'). Sometime around 10 000 BP conditions became wet and warm, although a

greater increase in precipitation is recorded in the subsequent millennium.

This climatic sequence also corresponds to fluctuations recorded in Lake
Ioannina and Phillipon Tenaghi in northern Greece (van Zeist & Bottema
1982). In higher altitudes in the Near East, such as the region around Lake
Zeribar in the Zagros mountains, arboreal vegetation is recorded only after
11 000 BP (van Zeist & Bottema 1982).

While chronological discrepancies exist between the studied cores, as well as
disagreements among the various scholars about the interpretation and
publication of uncritical compilations of palaeoclimatic observations (Bottema
1987), these problems do not obscure the fact that most of the known Kebaran
Complex sites (c. 19/18 000–14 500/14 000 BP) were occupied under relatively
dry and cold conditions, and that the Geometric Kebaran and its contemporaries (c. 14/14 000–12 800 BP) enjoyed wetter climatic conditions. The
generalization of 'cold and dry conditions' does not mean that the entire
Levant became a desert, but only that the Saharo-Arabian belt expanded while
the Irano-Turanian steppe and especially the Mediterranean park and
woodland habitats were considerably reduced. Under these conditions the
most productive foraging territories included the forested Levantine hilly
ranges and the Israeli coastal plain, the forests and parkland belt along the
Transjordanian plateau which stretched as a narrow 40–20 km wide strip, from
the Damascus Basin to southern Jordan, the desert oases mostly within the
steppic belt (e.g. El-Kowm, Palmyra, and Azraq), and the riverine habitats
along the Euphrates. The climatic improvement between about 14 000–13 000
BP caused a slight expansion of the Mediterranean woodland belt and, more
importantly, made vast additional steppic and previously desertic areas
accessible for human adaptation.

The definition of Epi-Palaeolithic entities

The Epi-Palaeolithic archaeological record is sizeable but fragmentary. Two
problems make it difficult to use this data base to answer questions about
cultural adaptations: (a) the limitations of the samples (including the degree of
bone and plant preservation), and (b) the existing mixture of taxonomic
approaches used to deal with the data base. Specifically:

(a)   There are only a few Kebaran sites in which the excavated areas are large
      enough to provide some clues about intrasite variability and the overall
      content of the sites. Geometric Kebaran and Mushabian sites are known
      from many excavated and surface-collected small sites within the main
      part of the central and northern hilly Levant; however, our information
      is derived from soundings of limited size. Moreover, while wood
      charcoal is often well preserved, bone preservation in the sandy desert

region is nil. On the other hand, in the forested and steppic belts bones are commonly well preserved while charcoal is very rarely found.

(b) For a variety of historical and political reasons, some portions of southwestern Asia are less well studied than others. Furthermore, there are a number of taxonomic ambiguities in this data base which reflect the diversified approaches of different 'schools of archaeology'. Nowhere in the world is there such a small region as the Levant where so many different schools, representing a large number of countries, are involved in field work. Thus professional differences mixed with various modes of archaeological training intermingle to create a jumble of cultural/industrial labels.

In contrast to the more common taxa 'Upper Palaeolithic', 'Late Palaeolithic', or 'Late Stone Age' used in other parts of the Old World, the term 'Epi-Palaeolithic' is currently used in the Levant to refer to cultural complexes between the LGM and the close of the Pleistocene. The term 'Epi-Palaeolithic' was introduced to the Levant by Perrot (1966) in his report on the excavation of the Natufian site of Mallaha (Eynan). Thus in the late 1960s the European taxon 'Mesolithic' seemed inappropriate for the description of lithic assemblages such as those of the Kebaran or the Natufian. The adoption of the term North African 'Epi-Palaeolithic' enabled the incorporation of archaeological entities, which were considered originally to be part of the Upper Palaeolithic sequence (Stage VI according to Neuville 1934, Garrod & Bate 1937), into an independent large time-unit that terminated in the Early Neolithic (Bar-Yosef 1970a, 1975, Besançon et al. 1975–77).

During the 1970s it became evident that high frequencies of microliths (various types of retouched and backed bladelets) pre-dated the Kebaran. For example, the Lagaman industry in northern Sinai, dated to around 32 000–30 000 BP, contained up to 40% retouched bladelets (Bar-Yosef & Belfer 1977), while various layers at Ksar Akil (beginning with level 12, c. 30 000 BP) (Tixier & Inzian 1981) contained up to 65% of this tool group. Therefore, it is not surprising that the suggested Upper Palaeolithic/Epi-Palaeolithic threshhold, estimated in the 1970s at around 18 000–19 000 BP, has recently been questioned (Bar-Yosef 1981, Gilead 1984).

Although there is a paucity of ^{14}C dates, the chronological framework of the different Levantine cultural complexes is known (Bar-Yosef 1987a, Bar-Yosef & Vogel 1987) (Fig. 3.2). The continuing need to use a relative chronology is solved in two ways depending on how the archaeological assemblages are ordered. The first is achieved by assigning the assemblages, layers and sites into time-units, such as Period 0, 1, 2, 3 ... (Aurenche et al. 1981), Epi-Palaeolithic 1, 2 (Moore 1985), or Early, Middle, and Late Epi-Palaeolithic (Garrard et al. 1988). The second is to define archaeological entities on the basis of the geographic and temporal distribution of certain typological features (Bar-Yosef 1981, Goring-Morris 1987, Henry 1983).

Clearly, each approach has its own advantages and deficiencies. When the

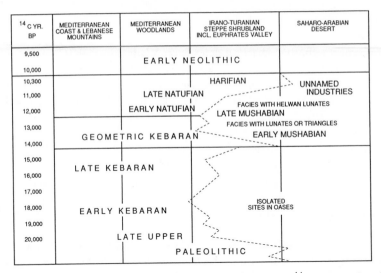

^{14}C YR. BP	MEDITERRANEAN COAST & LEBANESE MOUNTAINS	MEDITERRANEAN WOODLANDS	IRANO-TURANIAN STEPPE SHRUBLAND INCL. EUPHRATES VALLEY	SAHARO-ARABIAN DESERT

Figure 3.2 A chronological chart based on the available ^{14}C dates. The chart is organized in west–east geographic transects. Note that the Natufian sites are absent from the Lebanese mountains but the groups are known to have exploited the Levantine coast.

major changes in the non-perishable material culture are observed, however, whether we use the first or second approach, we face a major question: What caused the change? On the practical level, at the same time we have to decide whether the later assemblages should be given a new name. Unfortunately, in many cases researchers do not try to answer the first question and resort to giving new names which often commemorate their sites. This chapter uses separate labels only for the large cultural complexes (Fig. 3.2).

The Kebaran Complex

The term 'Kebaran' was originally coined to incorporate the microlithic-dominated assemblages of the Terminal Upper Palaeolithic. Intensive excavations which commenced during the 1960s at Ein Gev I and Jaita II (Bar-Yosef 1970a, Hours 1973, 1976), accompanied by the typological analysis of many surface collections, led to the subdivision between the Kebaran and the Geometric Kebaran (Bar-Yosef 1970a, 1975, 1976, Hours *et al.* 1973, Besançon *et al.* 1975–77; Hours 1976). ^{14}C dates support the few stratigraphies in which Geometric Kebaran assemblages follow the Kebaran.

It should be stressed that the Levantine Kebaran Complex is not solely defined on the basis of technotypological features of the assemblage of layer C at Kebara, from which its name was derived. Such a procedure of using one assemblage as the 'type-site' is unacceptable in view of the diverse processes responsible for the formation of an entire archaeological entity, which in its various assemblages represents the year-round activities of a hunter–gatherer group.

The recently published charcoal dates from Wadi Hammeh 27 (19 500 BP) and Wadi Hasa (Clark *et al.* 1988, Edwards *et al.* 1988) support the earlier bone dates from other sites and indicates that the Kebaran spanned from *c.* 20 000 to 14 500/14 000 BP. Moreover, the contention that late Upper Palaeolithic assemblages (classified on the basis of their microlithic tools) from oases can be contemporary with the Kebaran is given credence (Bar-Yosef & Vogel 1987). However, there is a great need for many more ^{14}C dates from this period before the various industries can be considered as well dated.

The procedure for including assemblages within each of the Epi-Palaeolithic entities is based on the shapes and the type of retouch of the microliths. The reasons for using this tool group are as follows:

(a)   Microliths are found in every type of site, regardless of its location, size, or inferred possible function. They are also found isolated on the surface, especially in regions with better visibility, such as the desert.

(b)   Microliths always form at least 40% of each assemblage and thus provide a large sample for detailed attribute analysis.

(c)   These artefacts, as demonstrated by microwear, edge damage, and hafting studies (Kukan 1978, Anderson-Gerfaud 1983, Tomenchuck 1983, Bar-Yosef 1987b) served as components of both hunting and cutting tools.

(d)   Contrary to the investment in producing the shafts of arrows or spears, which are time and energy consuming, microliths are easily shaped once the blanks are ready. While retooling, it is undoubtedly easier and quicker to make the same microlithic form that was damaged or fell off than to reshape the shaft.

(e)   The secondary trimming techniques, several of which are more elaborate than others, are interpreted as reflecting 'schools of knapping', and therefore convey social information.

(f)   Differences in the shapes of microliths result from hafting methods and stylistic variability. The mixture of both carries social information, although when hafted most of the attributes become invisible (Bar-Yosef 1981, Henry 1983, Goring-Morris 1987). It is therefore assumed that additional stylistic attributes were expressed in the visible parts of the perishable hunting tools (Bar-Yosef 1987b).

(g)   Seriation of frequencies of microlithic types based on stratified sites provide the means for tracing changes through time and space. Some of these morphological changes, such as from obliquely truncated backed bladelets to trapeze-rectangles, may reflect improvements in hafting techniques (Kukan 1978).

Using the quantitative and qualitative results of the detailed lithic studies, it seems that the Kebaran Complex, at least within the Mediterranean vege-

Table 3.1 Estimated totals of Kebaran and Geometric Kebaran assemblages

Sites	Excavated sample			Estimated totals		
	Excavated surface (m²)	Volume (m³)	Retouched pieces per m³	Site size (m²)	Volume (m³)	Total retouched pieces
Coastal plain						
Hefsibah	42	38	3100	700	560	1 736 000
Nahal Hadera V	10	8	3600	200	180	648 000
Kefar Darom 8	35	17	620	600	300	186 000
Sefunim Cave A2	10	0.5	70	—	—	
Azraq Basin, Jordan Valley						
Kharaneh IV/I	2	3	600	5600	5600	3 360 000
Fazael III/4	5	3	1150	80	40	46 000
Fazael III/6	1	0.5	430	50	10	4 300
Sinai–Negev Desert						
Shunera XVII	6	0.6–0.3	392	10		650
Azariq I	72	7.2–3.6	633	100		900
Mushabi I	170	17–8.5	3025	200		3 600
Mushabi XIV/1	28	2.8–1.4	520	50		1 500
Wadi Sayakh	28	14–7.0	745	50		1 350

All desert sites can be considered as deflated to varying degrees.
Volume estimates are problematic. The vertical distribution of artefacts is rarely greater than 5–10 cm in depth.

tational belt, has an overall unity that separates it from both the earlier Upper Palaeolithic assemblages and the later Geometric Kebaran and its contemporaries. Within a specific area which encompassed the region from Wadi Antelias (Lebanon) through Yabrud (Anti-Lebanon Mts), Azraq Basin, southern Jordan and the western Negev, the Late Kebaran is dominated by obliquely truncated backed bladelets (Kebara point). However, the earlier stage, or stages, of the Kebaran are characterized in each subregion by a dominance of various types of backed bladelets, most of which do not appear in high frequencies in pre-Kebaran times.

Regional lithic characteristics, such as microgravettes and Falita points, are ubiquitous north and east of the Jordan Rift mainly during the Late Kebaran. Sporadic occurrences of triangles (often accompanied by microburin technique) occur within the Kebaran sequence. They do not, however, herald the shift to trapeze-rectangles as they were probably hafted in the same way as were the Kebara points (Bar-Yosef 1987a). This facies is well developed in the Wadi Jilat 6, top level and in the Qalkhan of southern Jordan (Henry 1983, 1988, Garrard et al. 1986).

The quantities of flint artefacts in several of the Kebaran sites are impressive. Table 3.1 offers some examples.

Given the richness of the Kebaran lithic industry the number of bone objects is surprisingly small. They include a few points, some burnishers made of horn-cores, and a single bone point with an engraved zigzag pattern found at Jaita II (Lebanon).

Table 3.2 Presence or absence of marine shells in Kebaran, Geometric Kebaran, and Mushabian sites (after Bar-Yosef & Phillips 1977, Goring-Morris 1987, D. Bar-Yosef pers. comm.)

Species	Kebaran			Geometric Kebaran			Mushabian					
	1	2	3	1	2	3	1	2	3	4	5	6
Columbella rustica	+	−	+	+	+	−	−	−		−	−	−
Mitrella sp.	−	+	+	+	−	−	−	−		−	−	−
Nassarius gibbosulus	−	+	−	+	+	+	−	−	−	−	−	−
Conus	+	−	−	−	−	−	−	−		−	−	−
Anachis miser	−	−	−	−	−	−	−	+	−	−	−	+
Dentalium sp.	−	+	+	+	−	+	+	+	+	−	−	+
Others		+	+	−	+	−	−	+	−	−	−	+

Kebaran: 1, Ein Gev I; 2, Fazael III/4; 3, Urqan er-Rub III
Geometric Kebaran: 1, Hayonim Terrace; 2, Wadi Sayakh; 3, Kadesh Barnea 8.
Mushabian: 1, Ira 23; 2, Azariq IX; 3, Mushabi I; 4, Mushabi IV; 5, Mushabi XIV/1; 6, Shunera IV.

Ground stone objects include mortars, bowls, small 'cup-holes', pestles, and *manos*, found primarily at Ein Gev I with isolated items recorded at other sites. The identification of the sources of most of these items, which were made from basalt, is crucial for reconstructing possible exchange and/or mobility patterns. A few of these items found at the coastal sites could have come from distances of 20–100 km away. Marine shells, although rarely numerous, are mainly of Mediterranean origins (Table 3.2). The most distant were a Red Sea shell (*Nerita* sp.) found at Khareneh IV (Azraq Basin) and the Mediterranean shells in Wadi Sayakh (southern Sinai) found 300 km away from their sources.

Kebaran burials are few. At Ein Gev I a semiflexed burial of a female was excavated (Arensburg & Bar-Yosef 1973) and two burials were recovered from Kharaneh IV (Muheisin 1985).

All Kebaran sites are located at altitudes below 900 m above sea level. Given the lower level of the Mediterranean (about 130 m below the present-day shoreline) around the LGM, this means that higher altitudes were avoided by Kebaran groups.

Within the Mediterranean woodland Kebaran sites range in size between 15–25 m² and 400 m². The basis for calculating site size is derived from the site of Ein Gev I, where the remains of a clearly delineated hut were uncovered. (Bar-Yosef 1970a, Arensburg & Bar-Yosef 1973). Surface scatters, which on the coastal plain can reach a size of over 30 000 m² (such as Kefar Darom 8, see Bar-Yosef 1970b), are considered as resulting from penecontemporaneous erosion as well as post-depositional erosion, which possibly destroyed evidence of ephemeral structures. Larger surfaces of over 5000 and 20 000 m² are reported from Wadi Jilat and Wadi Kharaneh, respectively (Muheisin 1985, Garrard et al. 1986). In these cases, however, the excavations were rather limited in size and the possibility that these large surfaces represent successive reoccupations of a wadi bank, cannot be ruled out. The stratigraphy at Jilat 6 (Azraq Basin), for example, suggests that the reported typological variability in each of the three layers could have come from discontinuous successive reoccupations. The sterile deposits that separate each occupation could represent hiatuses of as much as several hundred years. Thus each industry could belong to either different groups of the same population, who kept changing their toolkits through time, or to three different groups.

Densities of artefacts per cubic meter (Table 3.1) indicate that the sites within the Mediterranean belt were occupied more often than those in the steppic region. Hypothetically, higher mobility in the more arid areas would lead to the dispersal of sites, to smaller densities, and thus to lower visibility. While these small ephemeral sites can be found in deserts (for examples see Bar-Yosef & Phillips 1977, Goring-Morris 1987), such occurrences are hardly preserved in the Mediterranean woodland region, which has undergone agricultural cultivation for the past 10 000 years. Here small ephemeral occupations are preserved in caves and rockshelters, such as at Sefunim (Mt Carmel) and Yabrud III (Anti-Lebanon mountains).

Large sites within the Mediterranean woodland and parkland are located near the wadi courses on the coastal plain and along the two flanks of the Jordan Rift Valley. Similar large and rich sites are also found near permanent water sources in oases such as Azraq and El-Kowm.

The reconstruction of prehistoric subsistence strategies depends on the recovery of plant and animal remains and their detailed analyses. Unfortunately, the state of our knowledge in this sphere is far from satisfactory. The amount of recovered plant remains from sites of this period (including the Geometric Kebaran and the Mushabian complexes) is scanty and gathering practices, therefore, can only be reconstructed from our knowledge of what fruits, seeds, and edible leaves could have been available (Zohary 1973). Such a hypothetical reconstruction, when taken together with the presence of a few mortars, stone bowls, pestles, and some grinding stones (mostly in the sites within the Mediterranean woodland or along the parkland/steppic ecotone), leads to the suggestion that acorns, legumes, and various fruits were collected during spring and autumn.

Bone preservation is fairly good in most places, except for the sandy region of the western Negev and northern Sinai. The game taken, as indicated by archaeozoological studies, seems to reflect the immediate environment (Table 3.3). This table only stresses the fact that our knowledge of the Kebaran lithics is much better than what we know about hunting practices from faunal remains. Moreover, it indicates that, on the average, an excavated cubic meter provides many times more stone artefacts than bones even when the preservation is fairly good. It probably means that most of the Kebaran diet was based on vegetal sources and that animal protein comprised only 10–20% of their calories.

Finally, large-scale excavations are urgently needed to uncover intrasite patterning at Kebaran sites. It is quite possible that the distribution of hearths,

Table 3.3 Frequencies and presence/absence of main faunal remains in Kebaran and Geometric Kebaran sites (*sources*:Bar–Yosef 1981, Garrard et al. 1986, 1987)

	Fallow deer	Red deer	Roe deer	Gazelle	Caprovines	Hartebeest	Cattle	Wild boar	Equids
Kebaran									
Hayonim	6	3	2	82	5		1	3	
Kebara	36	0.5	1	55			5		3
Nahal Oren	20		0.5	74	0.5	1	4	0.5	
Rakefet	14			77	1		1	6.5	
Nahal Hadera V	20		1	74		1	3.5	+	+
Jordan Valley									
Ein Gev I	26	6	1	46	16		4	1	
Fazael III/4	15		3	75	5		1	2	+
Geo. Kebaran									
Ein Gev III	17	10	3	21	10			38	
Ein Gev IV	8			91				2	
Nahal Oren	15	1	0.5	77			3.5	3	
Hefsibah	25	2		48		3	22		
Azraq Basin									
W. Uwaynid 18				+	+		+		+
W. Jilat 6				+			+	+	+

Frequencies were rounded and those less than 0.5% are marked with ' + '.
Only two sites from the Azraq Basin are given, for comparative purposes. For a fuller description see Byrd & Garrard (Vol. 2, Ch. 4).

and of bone and lithic debris at the sites, will reveal the activities that were responsible for their accumulation and will enable us to suggest some organizational reconstructions, similar to those suggested for the Magdalenian sites in the Paris Basin (Audouze in press).

The Geometric Kebaran Complex

The Geometric Kebaran overlies the Kebaran at a number of sites. This stratigraphic relationship is supported by an increasing number of radiometric dates (Bar-Yosef & Vogel 1987).

Overall, the Geometric Kebaran assemblages are considered as contemporary with the Mushabian ones on the basis of both ^{14}C dates and the stratigraphic evidence from Sinai. A reinterpretation of the radiocarbon dates, however, may indicate that the Geometric Kebaran was earlier than the Mushabian in the desert areas (Waterbolk 1987), but lasted longer in the central and northern part of the Levant. In the woodland region the Geometric Kebaran immediately underlies the Early Natufian and is considered by all scholars to be its forerunner.

Technotypological studies of Geometric Kebaran assemblages are available primarily from a few sites in the central and southern Levant (Bar-Yosef 1976, Simmons 1977, Fujimoto 1979, Garrard et al. 1986, 1987, Goring-Morris 1987). Here, production of bladelets and blades was often achieved by removals from single-platform cores. Bladelets, and at a later phase blades, were modified into trapeze-rectangles. A few late assemblages contain high frequencies of very large geometrics and asymmetric trapezes, which were often made from flakes. Uniformity among the microlithic tool group with overwhelming dominance of geometrics, characterizes the desert sites, while a wider range of variability is reported from sites in the woodland belt.

The incidental high occurrences of Krukowski microburins is a specific feature of the Geometric Kebaran. This resulted from the use of stone anvils for the production of the geometrics. Thus, Krukowski microburins as by-products of microlithic production are a common component of the debitage at some sites. Broken geometrics, on the other hand, resulted either from mishaps in the process of retouching or from use. Their numbers, therefore, are great at sites where retooling and secondary trimming took place.

Assemblages dominated by triangles (produced mostly by microburin technique) and containing some lunate microgravette points, were identified at several localities. In southern Jordan (the Late Hamran), they appear to precede lunate-dominated assemblages (Henry 1983, 1988). In other cases they are found at isolated sites, such as Ein Gev IV (Bar-Yosef 1970a), Wadi Jilat 6, upper layer (Garrard et al. 1986), and Hamifgash IV (Goring-Morris 1987). The distribution of these occurrences is rather patchy and their age debatable. In general, they can be assigned to about 13 000 BP.

Geometric Kebaran sites in the Mediterranean woodland belt (e.g. Neveh David and Hefsibah) contain pounding stones and some grinding tools. The lack of plant remains at these sites, however, precludes the reconstruction of vegetal dietary choices.

A few bone points have been found at some sites but these tools are not numerous and cannot be seen as heralding the later flourishing of the bone industry in the Natufian culture.

Two human burials were recently found at Neveh David, a large Geometric Kebaran base camp at the foot of Mt Carmel near Haifa (Kaufman 1986, Kaufman & Ronen 1987). One of these burials was covered with several broken mortars and bowls.

Known Geometric Kebaran sites vary in size. The smallest consist of a hearth with a few geometrics and some debitage products and debris – possibly representing a hunters' camp where retooling took place. Medium-sized sites are possibly represented by Ein Gev III, where the remains of a tent or brush shelter with a full range of artefacts were uncovered (Martin & Bar-Yosef 1979). Ein Gev III measured about 100 m^2 and is similar in size to Ein Gev I. Neveh David (Kaufman 1986) and perhaps Kharaneh IV (Muheisen 1985) represent much larger Geometric Kebaran sites.

The distribution of the sites indicates that the entire array of ecological zones were exploited by the Geometric Kebarans. Large sites, which indicate either a larger population or repeated occupations over long periods, are located in favourable habitats. This is the case with Neveh David at the foot of Mt Carmel and Ein Gev III at the foot of the Golan Heights near Lake Kinneret. These lowland sites represent favoured winter habitats, while the small ephemeral sites in the wooded highlands were occupied during summer months.

A different distribution of Geometric Kebaran sites is seen in the Negev and in northern Sinai. Here small sites (25–200 m^2) are found in the lowlands while a few larger ones are located in the highlands (for an updated site gazetteer see Goring-Morris 1987). This pattern has been interpreted as reflecting dispersed fissioned groups who, in winter months, occupied the lowlands as well as sheltered localities which were warmer and had better water sources (Bar-Yosef 1987a). These groups aggregated during the short summer season to exploit the highland resources (seeds, fruits, ibex, hare, and some gazelle).

In brief then, the original Geometric Kebaran Complex emerged from the Late Kebaran and expanded its territory into desert areas. Its geographic distribution stretched from El-Kowm in northeastern Syria through the Azraq Basin, southern Jordan, and as far south as Wadi Sayakh in southern Sinai (Cauvin et al. 1982, Bar-Yosef & Killebrew 1985). The distribution of this complex overlapped that of the Mushabian Complex as well as possibly other contemporary industries, such as the unnamed ones in the Azraq Basin (Garrard et al. 1987, 1988). If these two (or more) archaeological entities represent actual human groups, then continuous interaction between them probably stimulated mutual cultural changes, including changes in lithic technology. For example, late Geometric Kebaran assemblages, in addition to the trapeze-rectangles, also contain arched backed bladelets and La Mouillah points, and show the intensive use of the microburin technique, traits typical of the Mushabian Complex.

Finally, if our interpretations of site seasonality are correct, the Geometric Kebarans departed from the uniform Kebaran settlement pattern and developed different adaptations and settlement systems in the more steppic–desertic region. While the Kebarans aggregated during winter and early spring and dispersed during the summer, a pattern which seems to have been followed also by the Geometric Kebaran in the Mediterranean woodland and parkland region, their steppic–desertic equivalents apparently did almost the reverse.

The Mushabian Complex and its contemporaries

The term Mushabian takes its name from Wadi Mushabi in Gebel Maghara in northern Sinai where this complex was first identified (Phillips & Mintz 1977). Since then, Mushabian sites have been found in the Negev (Goring-Morris 1987) and possibly in Jordan (Henry 1988).

The Mushabian Complex is technologically characterized by the intensive use of microburin technique with which bladelets, often wider than in the Kebaran, were shaped into forms such as arched backed bladelets, obliquely truncated backed bladelets (also called Ramon points; Goring-Morris 1987) and La Mouillah points. Since there are numerous former or current labels given to various assemblages that all specialists agree represent the same lithic tradition (Goring-Morris 1987), this complex is currently subdivided into Early and Late Mushabian (Bar-Yosef 1987a).

The main typological shift within the Mushabian is from a dominance of arched backed bladelets in the Early phase to obliquely truncated backed bladelets in the Late phase. Several Late Mushabian assemblages contain Helwan lunates and are therefore, due to absence of radiocarbon dates, considered as contemporary with the Early Natufian. The Mushabian industry has no demonstrable technotypological origins in the Levantine coastal ranges and, given its southern distribution, is seen as affiliated with North African industries (Bar-Yosef & Phillips 1977).

The Mushabian sites occupy the semidesert region of the southern Levant. They are located in similar topographic and ecological zones as the Geometric Kebaran sites, and include two different sizes of sites: large ones (several hundred square metres) in the higher altitudes and small ones (25–150 m²) in the sandy lowlands. Despite the lack of bones or plant remains at these sites, it is assumed that they represent winter dispersals in the lowlands and late summer and autumn aggregations in the highlands. These aggregations could have been supported by the late harvest of wild barley, the ripening of pistachio nuts and other fruits, as well as by the availability of game and permanent water sources (Bar-Yosef 1987a, Goring-Morris 1987).

A much wider typological variability is now in evidence in the Azraq Basin and in southern Jordan (Muheisen 1985, Garrard et al. 1988, Henry 1988, Schyle & Uerpmann 1988, Byrd & Garrard, Vol. 2, Ch. 4). Even if the Mushabian Complex is partially represented, the region also contains many assemblages that were produced by groups who originated in the hilly and plateau areas that stretch southward and eastward from the Damascus Basin

Discussion

In the evaluation of the success of human groups adapting to the varied Levantine environments during the LGM, we are limited to the distribution of the sites and the fragmentary records of their contents. Ecological determinants operating in the Levant (i.e. the distribution, accessibility, reliability, and predictability of vegetal and animal resources) have favoured a semisedentary settlement pattern (Bar-Yosef & Belfer-Cohen 1989). The hazards of a seasonal exploition of steppe and desert belts would have increased considerably under conditions of environmental deterioration. Such a reconstruction, if correct, explains the lack of Kebaran sites in the open steppe belt and accounts for the ephemeral nature of Kebaran oasis occupations when compared to those in the continuous Mediterranean woodland belt. In band societies the loss of foraging territory among groups with semisedentary subsistence strategies often leads both to closed social systems and to increased risk of biological extinction. The social mechanisms employed to alleviate these pressures include the maintenance of large social networks. Unfortunately, the archaeological evidence, apart from a small collection of predominantly Mediterranean marine shells and a few basalt items, does not provide further evidence about the existence of such networks. We interpret this paucity in exotics as indicative that the Kebaran population was maintained within confined territorial boundaries, at a stable demographic level that was large enough to ensure biological survival.

To estimate the possible size of band territories during this period, we considered the distribution of edible vegetal resources (seeds, fruits, and leaves) as well as the ecology of gazelles, fallow deer, and roe deer (Bar-Yosef & Belfer-Cohen 1989). A cautious estimate indicates that 500–1000 km^2 could have provided sufficient food resources for an average band, despite annual fluctuations. These optimal conditions, however, existed only within the Mediterranean parkland belt, including the ecotone along the steppic Irano-Turanian belt. In the south and east such band territories would have been limited by the deserts, while along the Jordan Rift they would have been separated by the 250 km-long Lake Lisan.

The overall typological uniformity that commonly characterizes single large Kebaran sites (especially those with thick occupational deposits – e.g. Jaita II, Ein Gev I, Nahal Hadera) suggests semisedentary occupation. Changes in the lithic industry are interpreted as representing a time trajectory – an interpretation supported by stratified sites (e.g. Jaita II, Yabrud III, Fazael III).

No biological indicators, such as the presence of house mice found in the later Natufian sites, corroborate this presumed semisedentism. Microvertebrate assemblages, however, are often poor at open-air sites and a recovery of an adequate rodent sample would require a volume of excavated sediments much larger than that reported from most recent excavations.

The advent of the Geometric Kebaran reflects an important cultural change, not so much in lithic technology or in the dominant types of microliths, as in the expansion in the variety of ecozones exploited and in the introduction of an additional type of settlement pattern. During this time higher altitudes (above 1000 m) as well as desert areas became inhabited. This resulted from climatic amelioration and permitted more intensive and extensive foraging. These developments brought about the adoption of a new spatial organization in the newly occupied areas. While the Geometric Kebaran settlement pattern followed that of the Kebaran in the Mediterranean woodland, the steppe–desertic region featured a fissioning of large groups in wintertime and their aggregation in the summer and autumn when they exploited the resources of higher altitudes.

Lithic technotypological attributes of the Geometric Kebaran indicate that the human groups who occupied the steppe and desert regions were the direct descendents of the Mediterranean Kebarans. The expansion of these people into the previously unoccupied, more arid areas possibly led to the relaxation of population controls (Bar-Yosef & Belfer-Cohen in 1989).

The Mushabian colonization of the arid and semiarid region occurred at more or less the same time (the precision level of ^{14}C dates does not allow us to specify the exact prehistorical course of events). The variability among the industries recently recovered in the Azraq basin and in southern Jordan seems to reflect a more complex situation (Garrard et al. 1987, 1988, Henry 1988, Byrd & Garrard, Vol. 2, Ch. 4). In the Levant, the degree of typological variability in the microlithic assemblages around 13 000 BP is unmatched either in the preceding period or in the subsequent Natufian Complex. The environmental reconstructions suggest that the variety of ecological niches on hand at this time surpassed those available during the LGM. It is tempting to suggest that the ecological variability around 13 000 BP was responsible for the cultural diversity expressed in the lithic assemblages. It should be remembered, however, that this time was also favourable for long-distance mobility and for the renewal of contacts with neighbouring regions, such as northeastern Africa.

It is important to underscore that we also lack evidence for other components of hunter–gatherer subsistence systems. For example, there is no evidence for the presence of storage facilities. We can speculate that baskets may have been used for food collection and storage, but the earliest direct evidence for their use in the Levant comes from Neolithic sites dating to the 9th millennium BP. Storage pits are reported from Natufian sites, but none were recovered from the Kebaran or Geometric Kebaran ones. If these facilities were located outside the main habitation areas (as in Abu Madi I, an Early

Neolithic hunter–gatherer site in southern Sinai), then the failure to expose them is not surprising, given the limited areas excavated to date. If semisedentism did characterize Kebaran adaptations, then we can anticipate finding their storage facilities.

In conclusion, there were considerable differences in the intensity and nature of human occupation in the Levant between the LGM and the closing millennia of the Pleistocene. Long-term Kebaran adaptations together with the social mechanisms developed during the LGM enabled Kebaran descendents to successfully cope with the environmental changes during the Terminal Pleistocene.

References

Anderson-Gerfaud, P. 1983. A consideration of the uses of certain backed and "lustered" stone tools from late Mesolithic and Natufian levels of Abu Hureyra and Mureybet (Syria). In *Traces d'utilisation sur les outils néolithiques du Proche Orient*, M. C. Cauvin (ed). 77–106. Lyon: Publications de la Maison de l'Orient.

Arensburg, B. & O. Bar-Yosef 1973. Human remains from Ein Gev I. Jordan Valley, Israel. *Paleorient* **1**, 201–6.

Audouze, F. in press. Les activites de boucherie à Verberie (Oise). In *Étude technologiques*, J. Tixier (ed.). Paris: CNRS.

Aurenche, O., J. Cauvin, M. C. Cauvin, L. Copeland, F. Hours, P. Sanlaville 1981. Chronologie et organisation de l'espace dans le Proche Orient de 12 000 à 5600 av. J.C. (14 000 à 7600 BP). In *Préhistoire du Levant*, J. Cauvin & P. Sanlaville (eds), 571–601. Paris: CNRS.

Bar-Yosef, O. 1970a. The Epi-Palaeolithic Cultures of Palestine. Unpublished PhD thesis, Hebrew University, Jerusalem.

Bar-Yosef, O. 1970b. Gisements épipaléolithiques près d'Ashdod, Israel. *Bulletin de Societé Royal de Anthropologie Préhistorique* **81**, 5–27.

Bar-Yosef, O. 1975. The Epi-Palaeolithic in Palestine and Sinai. In *Problems in prehistory: North East Africa and the Levant*, F. Wendorf & A. E. Marks (eds), 363–78. Dallas: Southern Methodist University Press.

Bar-Yosef, O. 1976. *A note on the Geometric Kebaran A*. Proceedings of the IX UISPP Congress, Colloque III, 78–105. Nice.

Bar-Yosef, O. 1981. The Epipalaeolithic complexes of the Southern Levant. In *Préhistoire du Levant*, J. Cauvin & P. Sanlaville (eds), 389–408. Paris: CNRS.

Bar-Yosef, O. 1987a. The Late Pleistocene in the Levant. In *The Pleistocene Old World: regional perspectives*, O. Soffer (ed.), 219–36. New York: Plenum Press.

Bar-Yosef, O. 1987b. Direct and indirect evidence for hafting in the Epi-Palaeolithic and Neolithic of the Southern Levant. In *La main et l'outil: manches et emmanchements préhistoriques*, D. Stordeur (ed.), 155–64. Lyon: Maison de l'Orient.

Bar-Yosef, O. & A. Belfer 1977. The Lagaman industry. In *Prehistoric Investigations in the Gebel Maghara, Northern Sinai, Qedem 7*, O. Bar-Yosef & J. L. Phillips (eds), 115–48. Jerusalem: Institute of Archaeology, Hebrew University.

Bar-Yosef, O. & A. Belfer-Cohen 1989. The origins of sedentism and farming communities in the Levant. *Journal of World Prehistory*, in press.

Bar-Yosef, O. & A. Killebrew 1985. Wadi Sayakh – A geometric Kebaran site in the southern Sinai. *Paléorient* **10**(2), 95–102.

Bar-Yosef, O. & J. L. Phillips (eds) 1977. *Prehistoric Investigations in the Gebel Maghara, Northern Sinai, Qedem 7*. Jerusalem: Institute of Archaeology, Hebrew University.

Bar-Yosef, O. & J. C. Vogel 1987. Relative and absolute chronology of the Epi-Palaeolithic in the southern Levant. In *Chronologies in the Near East: relative chronologies and absolute chronology 16 000–4000 BP*, O. Aurenche, J. Evin & F. Hours (eds), 219–45. Oxford: BAR International Series 379.

Begin, B. Z., W. Broeker, B. Buchbinder, Y. Druckman, A. Kaufman, M. Margaritz, D. Neev 1985). *Dead Sea and Lisan Lake levels in the last 30 000 years, a preliminary report*. Jerusalem: Geological Survey of Israel.

Bensaçon, J., J. Copeland & F. Hours 1975–77. Tableaux de prehistoire libanese. *Paléorient* **3**, 5–46.

Bottema, S. 1987. Chronology and climatic phases in the Near East from 16 000 to 10 000 BP. In *Chronologies in the Near East: relative chronologies and absolute chronology 16 000–4000 BP*, O. Aurenche, J. Evin & F. Hours (eds), 295–310. Oxford: BAR International Series 379.

Boyle, E. A. & L. I. Keigwin 1987. North Atlantic thermohaline circulation during the past 20 000 years linked to high-latitude surface temperature. *Nature* **330**, 35–40.

Cauvin, M. C., E. Coqueugniot & A. Nierlé 1982. Rapport préliminaire sur la campagne 1980 d'El-Kowm 1, *Cahiers de l'Euphrate* **3**, 27–32.

Clark, G., A. Betts, B. Byrd, S. Colledge & C. Hunt 1988. Excavations at Middle, Upper and Epipalaeolithic sites in the Wadi Hasa, west-central Jordan. In *The prehistory of Jordan: the state of research in 1986*, A. N. Garrard & H. G. Gebel (eds), 209–85. Oxford: BAR International Series 396(i).

Davis, S. 1982. Climatic change and the advent of domestication of ruminant artiodactyls in the late Pleistocene–Holocene period in the Israel region. *Paléorient* **8**(2), 5–16.

Edwards, P. C., S. J. Bourke, S. M. Colledge, J. Head & P. G. Macumber 1988. Late Pleistocene prehistory in the Wadi al-Hammeh, Jordan Valley. In *The Prehistory of Jordan: the state of research in 1986*, A. N. Garrard & H. G. Gebel (eds), 525–65. Oxford: BAR International Series 396 (ii).

Fujimoti, T. 1979. The epi-palaeolithic assemblages of Douara Cave. *Bulletin of the University Museum, Tokyo* **16**, 47–75.

Garrard, A. 1982. The environmental implications of a reanalysis of the large mammal fauna from the Wadi el-Mughara Caves, Palestine. In *Palaeoclimates, palaeoenvironments and human communities in the eastern Mediterranean region in later prehistory*, J. L. Bintliff & W. van Zeist (eds), 165–87. Oxford: BAR International Series 133.

Garrard, A., A. Betts, B. Byrd, & C. Hunt 1987. Prehistoric environment and settlement in Azraq Basin: an interim report on the 1985 excavation season. *Levant* **19**, 5–25.

Garrard, A., B. Byrd, P. Harvey & F. Hivernel 1986. Prehistoric environment and settlement in the Azraq Basin: an interim report on the 1984 excavation season. *Levant* **18**, 1–20.

Garrard, A., A. Betts, B. Byrd, S. Colledge & C. Hunt 1988. Summary of the palaeoenvironmental and prehistoric investigations in the Azraq Basin. In *The prehistory of Jordan: the state of research in 1986*, A. N. Garrard & H. G. Gebel (eds), 311–87. Oxford: BAR International Series 396(ii).

Garrod, D. A. E. & D. M. Bate 1937. *The Stone Age of Mount Carmel*, Vol. 1, Oxford: Clarendon Press.

Gilead, I. 1984. Is the term "epi-palaeolithic" relevant to Levantine prehistory? *Current Anthropology* **25**, 227–9.

Goldberg, P. 1986. Late Quaternary geological history of the southern Levant: a geoarchaeological approach. *Geoarchaeology* **2**, 225–44.

Goodfriend, G. A. & M. Margaritz 1988. Palaeosols and late Pleistocene rainfall in the Negev Desert. *Nature* **332**, 144–6.

Goring-Morris, A. N. 1987. *At the edge: Terminal Pleistocene hunter–gatherers in the Negev and Sinai*. Oxford: BAR International Series 361.

Henry, D. O. 1983. Adaptive evolution within the epi-palaeolithic of the Near East. In *Advances in world archaeology*, F. Wendorf & A. E. Close (eds), Vol. 2, 99–160. New York: Academic Press.

Henry, D. O. 1988. Summary of prehistoric and palaeoenvironmental research in the northern Himsa. In *The prehistory of Jordan: the state of research in 1986*, A. N. Garrard & H. G. Gebel (eds), 7–37. Oxford: BAR International Series 396(i).

Hours, F. 1973. Le Kebarien au Liban: réflexions à partir des fouilles de Jiita en 1976. *Paléorient* **1**, 185–200.

Hours, F. 1976. *L'épipaléolithique au Liban: résultats acquis en 1975. Second Symposium on the Terminology of the Near East. IX UISPP Congress, Nice*.

Hours, F., L. Copeland & O. Aurenche 1973. Les industries paléolithiques du Proche Orient: essai de corrélation. *L'anthropologie* **77**, 229–80, 437–96.

Kaufman, D. 1986. A reconsideration of adaptive changes in the Levantine Epi-Palaeolithic. In *The end of the Palaeolithic in the Old World*, L. G. Straus (ed.), 117–28. Oxford: BAR International Series 284.

Kaufman, D. & A. Ronen 1987. La sépulture Kébarienne Géométrique de Néve David, Haifa, Israël. *L'anthropologie* **91**, 335–42.

Kaukan, G. 1978. A technological and stylistic study of microliths from certain Levantine epi-palaeolithic assemblages. Unpublished PhD thesis, University of Toronto.

Leroi-Gourhan, A. & F. Darmon. 1987. Analyses palynologiques de sites archéologiques du Pléistocene Final dans la Vallée du Jourdain. *Israel Journal of Earth Sciences* **36**, 65–72.

Margaritz, M. 1986. Environmental changes recorded in the Upper Pleistocene along the desert boundary, southern Israel. *Palaeogeography, Palaeoclimatology, Palaeoecology* **53**, 213–29.

Margaritz, M. & G. A. Goodfriend 1987. Movement of the desert boundary in the Levant from the latest Pleistocene to early Holocene. In *Abrupt climatic change*, W. H. Berger & L. D. Labeyrie (eds), 173–83. Dordrecht: Reidel.

Martin, G., & O. Bar-Yosef 1979. Ein Gev III, Israel (1978). *Paléorient* **5**, 219–20.

Moore, A. M. T. 1985. The development of neolithic societies in the Near East. In *Advances in world archaeology*, F. Wendorf & A. E. Close (eds) Vol. 4, 1–69. New York: Academic Press

el-Muheisen, M. 1985. L'Epipaléolithique dans le gisement de Kharaneh IV. *Paleorient* **11** , 149–60.

Nesteroff, W. D., C. Vergnaud-Grazzini, L. Blanc-Vernet, P. Olive, J. Rivault-Znaidi & M. Rossignol-Strick 1983. Evolution climatique de la Méditerranée orientale au cours de la dernière glaciation. In *Paleoclimatic research and models*, A. Ghazi (ed.), 81–94. Boston: D. Reidel.

Neuville, R. 1934. La Préhistoire de Palestine. *Revue Biblique* **43**, 237–59.

Patterne, M., F. Guichard, J. Labeyrie, P. Y. Gillot, J. C. Duplessy 1986. Tyrrhenian sea tephrochronology of the oxygen-isotope record for the past 60 000 years. *Marine Geology* **72**, 259–85.

Perrot, J. 1966. Le gisement natoufien de Mallaha (Eynan), Israël. *L'anthropologie* **70**, 437–84.

Phillips, J. L. & E. Mintz 1977. The Mushabian. In *Prehistoric investigations in the Northern Sinai, Qedem 7*, O. Bar-Yosef & J. L. Phillips (eds), 149–63. Jerusalem: Institute of Archaeology, Hebrew University.

Roberts, N. 1982. Lake levels as indicators of Near Eastern paleoclimates: a preliminary appraisal. In *Palaeoclimates, palaeoenvironments and human communities in the eastern Mediterranean region in later prehistory*, J. L. Bintliff & W. van Zeist (eds), 235–67. Oxford: BAR International Series 133.

Rogon, P. 1987. Relations entre phases climatiques et chronologiques au Moyen Orient de 16 000 à 10 000 BP. In *Chronologies in the Near East: relative chronologies and absolute chronology 16 000–4000 BP*, O. Aurenche, J. Evin & F. Hours (eds), 189–206. Oxford: BAR International Series 379.

Schyle, D. & H.-P. Uerpman 1988. Palaeolithic sites in the Petra area. In *The prehistory of Jordan: the state of research in 1986*, A. N. Garrard & H. G. Gebel (eds), 39–65. Oxford: BAR International Series 396(i).

Shmida, A., M. Evenari & I. Noy-Meier 1986. Hot desert ecosystems. In *Hot deserts and arid shrublands*, M. Evenari (ed.), 379–87. Amsterdam: Elsevier.

Simmons, A. H. 1977. The Geometric Kebaran "A" campsite of D101c. In *Prehistory and palaeoenvironments in the Central Negev, Israel*, A. E. Marks (ed.), Vol. 2, 119–31. Dallas: Southern Methodist University Press.

Tchernov, E. 1982. Faunal responses to environmental changes in the eastern mediterranean during the last 20 000 years. In *Palaeoclimates, palaeoenvironments and human communities in the Eastern Mediterranean region in later prehistory*, J. L. Bintliff & W. van Zeist (eds), 105–27. Oxford: BAR International Series 133.

Tixier, J. & M.-L. Inzian 1981. Ksar Aqil, stratigraphie et ensembles lithiques dans le paléolithique superieur, fouilles 1971–1975. In *Préhistoire du Levant*, J. Cauvin & P. Sanlaville (eds), 353–68. Paris: CNRS.

Tomenchuck, J. 1983. Predicting the past: examples from the use-wear study of selected chipped stone tools from two epi-palaeolithic occupations in Israel. In *Traces d'utilisation sur les outils néolithiques du Proche Orient*, M. C. Cauvin (ed.), 57–76. Lyon: CNRS.

Waterbolk, H. T. 1987. Working with radiocarbon dates in South-western Asia. In *Chronologies in the Near East*, O. Aurenche, J. Evin & F. Hours (eds), 39–60. Oxford: BAR International Series 379.

Wigley, T. M. L. & G. Farmer 1982. Climate of the Eastern Mediterranean and the Near East. In *Palaeoclimates, palaeoenvironments and human communities in the eastern Mediterranean in later prehistory*, J. L. Bintliff & W. van Zeist (eds), 3–37. BAR International Series 133(i).

Zeist, W. van & S. Bottema 1982. Palynological investigations in western Iran. *Paleohistoria* **19**, 19–95.

Zohary, M. 1973. *Geobotanical foundations of the Middle East*, 2 vols. Stuttgart-Amsterdam: Fischer.

4 The Last Glacial Maximum in the Jordanian desert

BRIAN F. BYRD & ANDREW N. GARRARD

Introduction

Southwest Asia is one of a number of areas worldwide in which there was an increase in the control and manipulation of plant and animal populations in the late Pleistocene, leading to full domestication of crops and livestock in the early Holocene. During the past 30 years a number of archaeological projects have examined this process and its environmental, demographic, and social background. Initially, most of these survey and excavation projects were undertaken in the present woodland and moist steppe vegetational zones that stretch in an arc from the Mediterranean coast to the Zagros range in western Iran (the 'Fertile Crescent'): this being the recent habitat of a number of the domesticates.

In the past few years, there has been increased interest in the present dry steppe and subdesert areas lying inside and to the south west of this arc (the Syrian–Arabian, Negev, and Sinai deserts). It is hoped that research in these presently marginal regions will give us a clearer understanding of the role that environmental change played in the Late Glacial and early Post Glacial subsistence changes. These areas have been less disturbed by agriculture, urban, and industrial developments than the Fertile Crescent, hence site survival is generally better and the opportunity for studying past settlement patterns and demography substantially greater. Given the ecological sensitivity of such regions, one can also argue that the palaeoenvironmental record provides a clearer indication of past climate than many other localities.

Recent surveys and excavations of late Pleistocene sites in these semiarid/arid regions have been undertaken in the Azraq Basin of east-central Jordan (Muheisen 1983, 1985, 1988, Garrard et al. 1988), the Black Desert of northeastern Jordan (Betts 1982, 1986, 1988), the Wadi el Hasa in west-central Jordan (McDonald et al. 1983, Byrd & Rollefson 1984, Clark et al. 1988), the Hisma of southern Jordan (Henry 1982, 1987, Jones 1985), the Palmyra region of Syria (Suzuki & Kobori 1970, Suzuki & Takai 1973, 1974, Hanihara & Sakaguchi 1978, Hanihara & Akazawa 1979, 1983), the El-Kowm Basin of Syria (J. Cauvin et al. 1979, M. C. Cauvin 1981, J. Cauvin 1982), northern Sinai (Bar-Yosef & Phillips 1977), and the Negev (Marks 1976, 1977, 1983, Goring-Morris 1987).

For the purposes of this discussion, we will focus on our research in the Azraq region. The basin has been an excellent 'natural' laboratory for studying changes in late Pleistocene environment, subsistence, and settlement. First, because it contains a large number of *in situ* archaeological sites with well-preserved faunal and macrobotanical remains. Secondly, recent ecological, hydrological, and soil studies have provided a modern environmental baseline. Finally, the basin is a self-contained geographical entity, which probably had a sufficient range of ecological variability to have provided for the year-round needs of nomadic hunter–gatherer groups.

Environmental setting

The Azraq Basin is a shallow depression that extends over $12\,000$ km^2 of the east Jordanian plateau (Fig. 4.1). It is structurally underlain by a graben that formed in the late Cretaceous (Bender 1974). The elevation at the centre of the basin is approximately 500 m, while along its northern perimeter it reaches 1800 m and along its other boundaries 600–900 m.

The northern portion of the basin is covered by basalts and tuffs that were mainly emitted from volcanoes and fissures between the Oligocence and Pliocene, although a localized discharge occurred as recently as $4\,000$ BP. (de Vries & Barendsen 1954, Bender 1974). Large portions of this area have been eroded down to a boulder field, making access very difficult. By contrast, the southern half of the basin is surfaced by Cretaceous and Tertiary chalks and marls with a canopy of flint gravel. Both flint and basalt are therefore available for chipped and ground-stone industries.

Modern climatic records show that the temperature regime at the centre of the basin varies between 45° and $-10°$ C annually (Nelson 1973). Rainfall averages 84 mm per year, ranging from just over 200 mm in the northwest to less than 50 mm in the southwest (UNDP 1966). Most of this precipitation falls in erratic, unevenly distributed storms between November and March. The minimum rainfall requirement for woodland vegetation is thought to be 300 mm, and 200 mm for reliable dry farming (Zohary 1973). Consequently, 'dry' cultivation is only practised on the northern and western fringes of the basin.

There are no perennial streams or permanent bodies of surface water except for the springs and pools in the centre of the basin at Azraq. After storms, water runs off in temporary stream channels and collects in *qas (playas)*, where it usually evaporates within a few months, leaving a deposit of salts and gypsums. The largest of these is the Azraq Qa, which can flood to a depth of 2 m and cover an area of 50 km^2 in wet winters. The extent and timing of these floods varies greatly between years. Less than 2% of the rainfall replenishes the groundwater in the underlying geological formations, and this flows slowly in a down–gradient direction until it is eventually discharged through springs and seeps in the freshwater pools at Azraq. The two largest springs have created marshlands of 5.6 and 1.8 km^2 respectively (UNDP 1966, Nelson 1973).

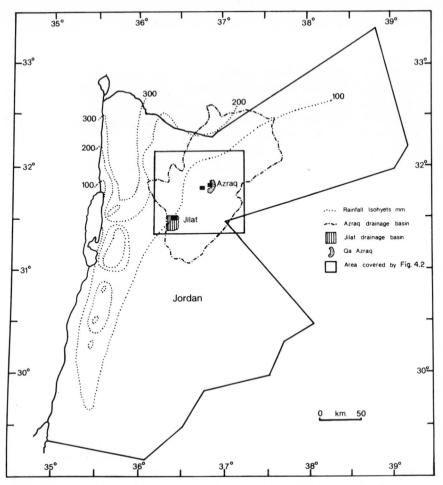

Figure 4.1 Rainfall map of Jordan (based on Agrar und Hydrotechnik 1977), showing the Azraq and Jilat drainage catchments and the position of survey areas.

With the exception of the northwestern moist steppic areas, permanent vegetation is generally limited to the wadis (dry river beds), to the silty area around the *playas* and to the wetlands at Azraq. There is, however, a spring bloom of annuals on the basalt and flint surfaces. The region produces a range of wild edible plant products, including the seeds of grasses, legumes, and chenopods, and the roots or stems of genera such as *Erodium, Orobranche, Ferula, Scorozonera, and Biebersteinia* (Hillman pers. comm).

Today, the large mammal, bird, and reptile fauna is much depleted, but earlier in the century gazelle, hare, bustard, partridge, tortoise, caracal, cat, hyena, wolf, jackal, and fox inhabited the basin. In addition, pig and a wide range of spring and autumn migrant birds, including large raptors, storks, herons, and cranes, were found in and around the Azraq wetlands (Nelson 1973).

Research design

In 1975 a preliminary reconnaissance was undertaken to assess the potential of the Azraq basin for a detailed study of late Pleistocene and early Holocene environment, settlement, and subsistence (Garrard & Price 1975–77). From the survey results it was clear that future work should involve several components. First, a geomorphological survey of the centre of the basin and its inflow wadis to reconstruct its hydrological and climatic history and to date the exposed land surfaces. Secondly, systematic survey in order to reconstruct regional settlement patterns. Thirdly, test excavations to obtain stratified chronological data on the sedimentary record, and human settlement and subsistence. Finally, large-scale excavations to gain a better understanding of site function and internal settlement plans.

Between 1982 and 1988 five seasons of survey and excavations have been undertaken (Garrard et al. 1985, 1986, 1987, 1988). Three locales within the basin have been selected for detailed study (Fig. 4.2). The first of these is the Wadi Jilat, a tributary of the Wadi Dhobai, situated 55 km to the southwest of the Azraq oases and the central playa into which it drains. It was selected for examination for several reasons. First, this was a locality in which an earlier project had identified a number of impressive Epi-Palaeolithic and Neolithic sites (Waechter et al. 1938). Secondly, it contains a gorge with a number of rock pools where standing water remains well after the end of the rainy season, providing a natural focus for settlement. Finally, it lies in the present transition zone between dry steppe and desert. The second study area is the Wadi Uwaynid, which runs along the southern margin of Jebel Uwaynid, a basalt outlier 10 km southwest of Azraq. This wadi carries much of the water from the west-central side of the basin. The third study area is the central basin adjacent to the southern springs, marshes and the playa. By sampling three locales in different environmental settings, we hoped to gain greater insight into shifting subsistence and settlement strategies.

Field methods

We undertook survey by two methods: by walking transects designed to cross-cut a range of the ecological/geomorphological units in a given region, and by area survey of selected units. In both cases, artefacts were collected by a stratified random sampling technique at the denser sites and by purposive sampling at the smaller more diffuse scatters. Differences between the frequencies of microliths from surface and excavated samples, led us to collect and fine sieve the top 2–3 cm of deposit when surface collecting.

Excavations have been undertaken at 19 sites ranging from late Acheulean to Chalcolithic. Nine late Pleistocene sites are included, and the area of excavation at each ranges from 4 to 12 m². This has allowed a preliminary appraisal of sedimentary history, chronology, material culture, and subsistence, but obvi-

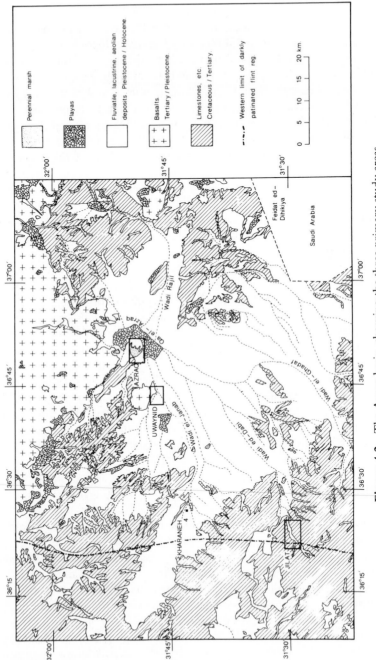

Figure 4.2 The Azraq basin, showing the three primary study areas.

Perennial marsh

Playas

Fluviatile, lacustrine, aeolian
deposits Pleistocene / Holocene

Basalts
Tertiary / Pleistocene

Limestones, etc.
Cretaceous / Tertiary.

Western limit of darkly
patinated flint reg

0   5   10   15   20 km

Table 4.1 Radiocarbon dates from late Pleistocene Azraq Basin sites (determined at the Radiocarbon Accelerator Unit, Oxford University★)

Late Upper Palaeolithic			
Uwaynid 18	wood charcoal	OxA– 867	23 200 ± 400
Jilat 9	burnt bone	OxA– 519	21 150 ± 400
Early Epi-Palaeolithic			
Uwaynid 18	wood charcoal	OxA– 864	19 800 ± 350
	wood charcoal	OxA– 868	19 500 ± 250
Uwaynid 14	wood charcoal	OxA– 866	18 400 ± 250
	wood charcoal	OxA– 865	18 900 ± 250
Late Epi-Palaeolithic			
Jilat 8	burnt bone	OxA– 636	10 540 ± 160
	wood charcoal	OxA– 521	13 310 ± 120
Jilat 10	wood charcoal	OxA– 520	14 790 ± 200
	wood charcoal	OxA–1000	13 120 ± 180
	wood charcoal	OxA– 918	12 700 ± 300

★ Other radiocarbon samples from the project that appear to be incorrect have not been included (see Garrard et al. 1988).

ously does not allow the analysis of intrasite variability. Sediments were coarse sieved through a 5 mm mesh and then washed by an earth flusher to collect macrobotanical remains. The heavy fraction was wet sieved through a 1.5 mm mesh. Although labour intensive, this allowed the adequate collection of microlithic tools, beads, small bone tools, and microfaunal and floral remains.

Preliminary results

For the purpose of this volume, we have divided the late Pleistocene into three episodes: late Upper Palaeolithic (>24 000–20 000 BP); Early Epi-Palaeolithic (20 000–15 000 BP); and Late Epi-Palaeolithic (15 000–11 000 BP). Each episode will be discussed separately and at the end there is a summary, outlining discernible environmental, cultural, and economic trends. It should be pointed out that the three-period subdivision is somewhat arbitrary and is based on initial radiocarbon dates and comparisons of industries. Field research and processing is still continuing and further radiocarbon samples have been submitted. Our final interpretations may be slightly different from those presented in this chapter.

Late Upper Palaeolithic (> 24 000–20 000 BP)

Surface Upper Palaeolithic occurrences are scarce in the areas that have been surveyed and of the three sites positively identified by excavation, two are heavily deflated and the third buried beneath a later occupation. These sites are located in the diverse settings of the surface levels of an alluvial terrace in Jilat at

Table 4.2 Site characteristics including deposit thickness, artefact density, and ratios of chipped stone artefact classes, by period, from the Azraq Basin*

	Site size	Thickness	Density	FBRatio	DCRatio	DTRatio	TCRatio	TDLENST	CDENST	MBI	N
Late Upper Palaeolithic											
Jilat 9	7 075	5d	15 342	0.63	53.7	9.8	5.5	1571.4	285.7	0	4 296
Azraq 17 Tr. 2	?	2d	15 171	0.86	88.1	15.0	5.9	1011.1	172.2	0	2 731
Uwaynid 18 Early Ph. (Upper)	?	4	233	—	—	—	—	—	—	—	28
Uwaynid 18 Early Ph. (Lower)	?	4	1 108	—	—	—	—	—	—	—	133
Mean		3.8	7 963	0.75	70.9	12.4	5.7	1291.2	228.9	0	
Early Epi-Palaeolithic											
Uwaynid 18 Tr. 2 Upper Ph. (Up.)	1 200	10	406	—	—	—	—	—	—	—	203
Uwaynid 18 Tr. 2 Upper Ph. (low.)	1 200	20	22 390	0.63	213.2	9.6	22.2	467.0	21.0	NIA	22 390
Uwaynid 18 Tr. 1 Upper Ph.	1 200	12	2 491	0.67	99.7	8.9	11.2	281.2	25.0	NIA	1 196
Uwaynid 14 Late Ph.	1 400	2	18 533	0.68	171.1	10.9	15.7	1700.0	108.3	39.3	2 224
Uwaynid 14 Middle Ph.	?	2	20 583	0.39	123.5	11.3	10.9	1816.7	166.7	20.8	2 470
Jilat 6 Lower Ph.	?	3	15 991	0.48	119.9	10.1	11.9	1591.7	133.3	54.9	1 919
Jilat 6 Middle Ph.	?	5	7 455	0.6	64.8	5.8	11.2	1285.0	115.0	24.3	1 491
Mean		7.7	12 549	0.58	132.0	9.3	13.8	1190.3	94.9	34.8	

	Site size	Thickness	Density	FBRatio	DCRatio	DTRatio	TCRatio	TLDENST	CDENST	MBI	N
Late Epi-Palaeolithic											
Jilat 6 Upper Ph.	18 200	45d	11 275	0.97	92.7	9.4	9.8	1196.1	121.7	55.7	20 294
Jilat 8	6 400	30d	3 577	0.63	53.7	9.8	5.5	366.7	66.7	38.2	4 293
Jilat 10	?	15d	14 061	0.76	86.9	77.4	1.1	181.7	161.7	0	8 437
Jilat 22 Upper Ph.	5 500	30d	13 546	1.03	68.6	15.4	4.4	877.5	197.5	NIA	16 256
Azraq 17 Tr. 1	?	10d	1 652	1.42	—	7.9	—	210.0	—	61.9	661
Azraq 18	2 200	30d	17 965	0.94	75.9	16.3	4.7	1102.5	236.7	5.1	21 559
Mean		26.6	10 346	0.96	75.6	22.7	5.1	655.8	156.9	40.2	

Site size, square metres of surface artefacts; Thickness, centimetres; d, deflated; Density, chipped stone artefacts per cubic metre (not including indeterminate debitage/chips and debris); FBRatio, flake/blade ratio; DCRatio, Debitage/Core ratio; DTRatio, debitage/tool ratio; TCRatio, tool/core ratio; TLDENST, tool density/cubic metre; CDENST, core density/cubic metre; MBI, adjusted microburin index; N, sample size of chipped stone artefacts (excluding indeterminate debitage/chips & debris); NIA, no information yet available.

★ This information reprents preliminary deposit and phase distinctions. Occupation horizons with a tool sample size of less than 300 are not included in chipped stone artefact ratios.

the present steppe/desert margins, buried within an aeolian silt close to a presently seasonal spring at Uwaynid, and deflated and partially cemented within calcretes adjacent to the perennial springs at the centre of the basin. Reliable radiocarbon dates have been obtained from two of these sites (Table 4.1). The site at Jilat is contained in a well-developed palaeosol, suggesting damper conditions than the present with continuous vegetation. There is also evidence of weak pedogenesis in the levels containing the Upper Palaeolithic occupation at Uwaynid 18. At the present time no pedogenesis is occurring in these areas of the basin.

It is not possible to estimate the area of the lower phase of occupation at Uwaynid 18 and Azraq 17, but the surface spread of artefacts at Jilat 9 covers 7075 m². This is unusually large for the time-period and is likely to result from the deflation of a series of smaller overlapping campsites. Sheetwash may also have been an agent in the dispersal of artefacts. The surviving occupation horizons tend to be fairly thin, averaging 3.8 cm in thickness (Table 4.2). The density of chipped stone artefacts is high, with a mean of 7963 artefacts per m³, but varies considerably between occupation horizons.

The chipped stone assemblages from these sites are based on a blade/bladelet technology (Table 4.2). Cores are generally single platform blade/bladelet cores, with 90° change of direction, and opposed blade/bladelet and flake cores less common. The utilization of core tablet removal to rejuvenate the platform angle on blade cores was customary.

The retouched tool assemblages are non-microlithic, with most of the tools being produced on blades and occasionally on bladelets. Flake tools are rare. A diverse range of tool types was recovered, with endscrapers, burins, re-touched blades, and finely retouched bladelets the predominant tool classes (Table 4.3). Backed bladelets, particularly fragments of non–geometrics, are present, while the associated microburin technique, used to segment bladelets prior to backing, is absent.

The diversity of non-lithic material culture at these occupation horizons is extremely low. No bone tools, groundstone objects, imported stone objects, or shell beads were recovered. This is in contrast to the later periods, where such items are more common. There were no structural features in the areas excavated, but a large hearth was found at Uwaynid 18, containing basalt pebbles that may have been used for heat storage during cooking.

Direct evidence of subsistence is limited, as animal bone collections are small and no botanical material survives. The faunal remains include wild ass, gazelle, hare and, in the case of Jilat 9, large quantities of tortoise carapace fragments (Table 4.4). The latter are not burnt and there is no evidence of working, but it is possible that the carapaces were used as containers.

Early Epi-Palaeolithic (20 000–15 000 BP)

The period of settlement that encompasses the LGM is represented at three excavated sites in the Jilat and Uwaynid study areas (Table 4.2). The

Table 4.3 Tool group percentages, by period, from the Azraq Basin

	Scrapers	Burins	N & D	Ret.	Trunc.	Geo.	Nongeo.	RtBlt	Var.	Sample size
Late Upper Palaeolithic										
Jilat 9	35.7	3.2	8.7	24.6	3.9	1.6	4.8	6.3	11.1	126
AZ 17 Tr. 2	19.8	7.1	0.6	11.0	2.2	0.0	20.9	34.6	3.9	182
Mean	27.8	5.2	4.7	17.8	3.0	0.8	12.8	20.4	7.5	
Early Epi-Palaeolithic										
Uwaynid 18 Tr. 2 Upper Ph. (Low)	1.7	0.9	0.0	3.8	1.3	0.0	89.0	0.0	3.4	472
Uwaynid 18 Tr. 1 Upper Ph.	2.7	0.0	0.0	0.0	4.8	0.0	87.1	0.0	5.4	147
Uwaynid 14 Upper Ph.	1.0	2.5	0.0	2.0	5.9	0.0	85.3	1.0	2.5	204
Uwaynid 14 Middle Ph.	0.9	0.9	0.0	1.4	1.4	0.0	94.5	0.5	0.5	218
Jilat 6 Lower Ph.	2.1	0.7	2.8	9.0	4.9	1.4	79.2	0.0	0.0	144
Jilat 6 Middle Ph.	1.9	2.7	10.5	7.0	2.3	1.6	73.0	0.0	1.2	257
Mean	1.7	1.3	2.2	3.9	3.4	0.5	84.7	0.2	2.2	
Late Epi-Palaeolithic										
Jilat 8	15.6	2.9	1.2	4.4	2.0	5.0	67.3	0.0	1.7	410
Jilat 10	16.1	18.3	2.1	32.3	12.9	0.0	11.8	5.4	1.1	93
Azraq 17 Tr. 1	1.2	2.4	1.2	8.3	2.4	45.6	36.5	0.0	2.4	84
Jilat 6 Upper Ph.	14.8	10.8	0.9	5.9	1.1	36.8	25.7	0.0	4.2	562
Azraq 18	2.1	0.4	0.9	4.7	4.3	66.0	17.9	0.0	3.9	235
Mean	10.0	7.0	1.3	11.1	4.5	30.7	31.8	1.1	2.7	

N & D, notches & denticulates; Ret., retouched pieces; Trunc., truncations; Geo., geometrics; Nongeo., nongeometrics; RtBlt, marginally retouched bladelets; Var., various.

Table 4.4 Proportional representation of animal species from Late Pleistocene Azraq Basin sites (based on total number of identifiable bones/teeth)

	WJ9	Upper Palaeolithic AZ17* Tr.2	Early Epi-Palaeolithic UW18	UW14*	WJ6 Lower	WJ8	WJ10	Late Epi-Palaeolithic AZ17* Tr.1	WJ6 Up.	AZ18
Mammals										
Bos primigenius	—	—	0.8	9.1	—	—	—	—	0.3	36.6
Equus hemionus/asinus	—	—	—	—	—	—	—	—	0.1	5.7
Equus hydruntinus	—	—	—	—	—	—	—	—	—	0.1
Equus sp.	10.7	—	12.0	9.1	25.7	2.2	58.2	—	7.1	30.5
Camelus dromedarius	—	—	0.2	—	—	—	—	—	—	—
Large herbivore	—	7.4	1.0	—	—	—	1.5	5.1	—	0.4
Sus scrofa	—	—	—	—	—	—	—	—	0.1	—
Ovis/Capra sp.	—	—	0.2	—	—	1.1	—	—	0.2	—
Gazella subgutturosa	—	1.0	—	—	—	—	—	—	—	—
Gazella sp.	2.9	92.6	69.7	54.6	37.1	79.4	—	94.9	73.2	23.6
Lepus capensis	1.0	—	0.8	18.2	1.4	1.1	—	—	2.0	0.4
Canis lupus	—	—	0.2	—	—	—	1.5	—	0.2	0.4
Vulpes sp.	—	—	—	—	—	—	—	—	0.6	0.4
Gerbillus/Meriones sp.	0.9	—	—	—	—	—	—	—	0.1	—
Microtus sp	—	—	0.2	—	—	—	—	—	—	—
Jaculus sp.	—	—	—	—	—	—	—	—	0.1	—

Birds										
Syrrhaptes paradoxus	—	—	—	—	—	—	—	—	0.4	—
Pterocles alchata	—	—	—	—	—	—	—	—	0.4	—
Pterocles orientalis	—	—	—	—	—	—	—	—	0.1	·
Pteroclidae	—	—	—	—	—	—	—	—	0.2	—
Phasianidae	—	—	—	—	—	—	—	—	0.1	—
Galerida cristata	—	—	—	—	—	—	—	—	0.1	—
Anas acuta	—	—	—	—	—	—	—	—	—	0.4
Anas querquedula	—	—	—	—	—	—	—	—	—	0.4
Anatinae	—	—	—	—	—	—	—	—	—	0.4
Rallus aquaticus	—	—	0.2	—	—	—	—	—	—	—
Reptiles										
Testudo graeca	84.5	—	14.6	9.1	35.7	16.3	38.8	—	14.9	—
Sample sizes	103	27	610	11	70	92	67	39	3155	246

* Small sample sizes

occupations at these sites are contained in aeolian silts, but in each case these have been modified quite strikingly by pedogenesis. This suggests vegetational cover and damper conditions than the present. This is not to say that the whole period under consideration was more humid than the present, but that there were episodes when conditions were more amenable. The site of Jilat 6 is situated on an alluvial fan in fairly close proximity to the main wadi, and the two sites at Uwaynid are located in a fluvially incised terrace adjacent to a present-day annual spring. Four reliable radiocarbon dates have been obtained from the Uwaynid sites (Table 4.1).

The areal extent of the lower phase of occupation at Jilat 6 cannot be calculated, but the upper phase occupations in the Uwaynid area appear to be in excess of 1000 m^2 (Table 4.2). Occupation thickness is twice that of the preceding period. There is, however, a bimodal distribution, represented by thin occupation horizons (less than 5 cm) and thicker ones (greater than 10 cm). The former probably represent single occupational events, whilst the latter indicate repeated use of the same locale. The average density of lithic artefacts, in excess of 12000 pieces per m^3, is greater than in the preceding period, but there is considerable variability between occupation horizons.

The chipped stone industry is characterized by the intensive production of blade/bladelets. The debitage/core ratio is twice that of the previous period. (Table 4.2). The flake/blade ratio is lowest during this episode with blade/bladelets being almost twice as abundant as flakes. Bladelets *sensu stricto* are more common than blades *sensu stricto*.

Single platform bladelet cores predominate, although opposed platform bladelet cores and flake cores also occur. Ninety degree opposed bladelet cores are rare. The presence of glossy red-brown flints suggest that the raw material may have been heat treated, but this has not been experimentally demonstrated. The core-tablet technique was seldom used to rejuvenate cores.

The tool assemblages are almost exclusively represented by non-geometric backed bladelets (Table 4.3). Very few non-microlithic tools, such as scrapers, burins, and retouched blades, occur. The microburin technique was extensively used to truncate bladelets prior to their backing (Table 4.2). The use of this technique in eastern Jordan by at least 20000 BP is considerably earlier than it has been dated in other parts of the Near East (see Henry 1974).

Change occurs in the predominate types of backed bladelets through this period. The earlier assemblages are dominated by small narrow microliths characterized by arched backed, curved pointed pieces. By contrast, the later assemblages are characterized by larger and thicker backed bladelets, such as robust La Mouillah points showing the negative scar of the micorburin or double-truncated backed bladelets.

There are a fair range of non-lithic artefacts at these sites, including basalt grinding stones, bone points, and pieces of ochre. *Dentalium* and other pierced marine shell beads are common. Their sources are the Mediterranean and Red Sea coasts, which lie 200 and 300 km away, respectively, indicating long-distance movement or regional exchange networks. There is no evidence of structures from our limited soundings, but hearths have been identified.

Faunal exploitation during the Early Epi-Palaeolithic was focused on gazelle, but wild ass remained an important supplement. Other species include wild cattle, hare, wolf, and tortoise (Table 4.4). The cattle were only found at the Uwaynid sites, which lie within 10 km of the Azraq marshes. It is likely that the inflow wadis at the centre of the Basin were fairly well vegetated. Unfortunately, in spite of flotation, we have not recovered any identifiable remains of food plants.

Late Epi-Palaeolithic (15 000–11 000 BP)

The third period, dating well after the LGM, is represented at six excavated occupation horizons in the Jilat and Azraq areas (Table 4.2). The Jilat sites are contained in aeolian silts in a valley-floor setting, while the Azraq sites are located beside the perennial springs at the centre of the basin. There is no evidence of pedogenesis in the sediments containing the Jilat sites and this suggests drier conditions then were witnessed in periods of the late Upper Palaeolithic and Early Epi-Palaeolithic. All the sites are partially deflated and the artefact scatters vary considerably – between 2200 and 18 200 m^2 (Table 4.2). The average thickness (26.6 cm) of deposits is greater than previous periods. The increased area and thickness of occupations suggests more frequent and extended use of the same locales. A sounding in the largest of these sites (Jilat 6) revealed a series of dwelling floors, two of which were coated with a red ochre pigment.

Chipped stone production is focused on blade/bladelets, although flakes are more common than in the previous period (Table 4.2). Cores are typically single platform blade/bladelet forms but opposed blade/bladelet and flake cores are also present. Ninety degree opposed blade/bladelet cores are uncommon. The blanks used for tool manufacture are generally blade–bladelets, but it is often difficult to determine blank form on extensively retouched microliths.

The diversity of chipped stone tool types is greater than in the preceding period (Table 4.3). Although the assemblages are generally microlithic, larger tools, such as scrapers, burins, and retouched blades are more abundant. There is, however, considerable variability between sites. Non-geometric microliths are more frequent in the earlier assemblages, but with different tool types than in the Early Epi-Palaeolithic. These include small La Mouillah points, arched backed pieces, and fragments of rectangles and trapezes. Later occupation horizons have higher frequencies of geometric microliths, some assemblages being dominated by triangles and others by lunates. At most sites, except the latest (Azraq 18) and a specialized encampment (Jilat 10), extensive use was made of the microburin technique in the manufacture of backed bladelets (Table 4.2).

Bone tools, basalt grinding stones, ochre, and shell beads occur at most of the sites. Basalt is locally available at Azraq but would have had to have been transported a minimum of 50 km to Jilat. The abundance of marine shell beads indicates continued long-distance procurement or trade networks.

The skeletons of a maximum of 11 individuals, including three definite females, two fairly certain males, one subadult and two young children were found as secondary burials in the occupation levels at Azraq 18. Their skeletal morphology was at the robust end of the range for the time period (Bourke pers. comm.).

Botanical remains recovered from Jilat 6 included the seeds of chenopods, crucifers, sedges, and grasses, as well as nutshell fragments and textured pieces of roots and bulbs. Partly as a result of the larger sample sizes, faunal remains are more diverse than from earlier periods (Table 4.4). Gazelle continued to predominate, followed by wild ass, cattle (at Azraq only), hare, wolf, fox, ostrich, game birds, and duck (at Azraq only).

Summary of Azraq Basin adaptations

In terms of palaeoclimatic reconstruction, the best local evidence we have is the sedimentary record at the various dated archaeological sites. Unfortunately, pollen is very poorly preserved in this calcareous environment, and macro-fauna is not a very sensitive indicator of the smaller-scale oscillations in climate. Although it would appear to contradict the traditional view of an arid glacial maximum in the near East (e.g. Bintliff & van Zeist 1982), we have evidence, at several widely separated radiometrically dated sites, of periods of pedogenesis at intervals between $c.$ 24 000 and 15 500 BP. This is in areas in which no pedogenesis is occurring at the present time, and it would suggest periodic vegetational cover and damper conditions than the present. There is no evidence of such events post $c.$ 15 500 BP.

Extreme caution is needed in the interpretation of settlement pattern data. A major problem is that the proportions and types of artefacts collected in surface survey very often do not reflect those found in the underlying occupation horizons. Obviously, microliths are a very important component of late Upper and Epi-Palaeolithic industries, but very often these were not visible in surface collections, having sunk into the upper sediments. A further major difficulty is that of determining the effects of erosional and aggradational factors on observed settlement patterns. Upper Palaeolithic and Early Epi-Palaeolithic sites appear to be scarcer than those of later periods, but most of those found were in buried rather than surface contexts. Because of burial, it is often difficult to estimate the full extent of many earlier sites.

In terms of thickness of cultural deposits, the Upper Palaeolithic and Early Epi-Palaeolithic occupation horizons fall into two classes. Thin occupation horizons probably represent relatively short-term encampments. The thicker occupation horizons are likely to result from multiple periods of occupation at the same locale. Artefact densities are often extremely high (a mean of 7963 artefacts per m^3 for the Upper Palaeolithic and 12 549 per m^3 for the Early

Epi-Palaeolithic), although there is considerable variability between occupation horizons.

During the Late Epi-Palaeolithic occupation, deposits are considerably thicker on average than previously, indicating more reoccupation of the same locale and perhaps longer stays. Site size also appears to be larger – with one exceptional site of 18 200 m^2. A similarly substantial Epi-Palaeolithic site, Kharaneh 4 (30 km north of Jilat), is presently being excavated by Muheisen (1988). These exceptionally large and deep sites must result from repeated occupation at the same locales and probably longer periods of residence, and both have produced evidence of structures. Secondary burials were found at the latest site sounded (Azraq 18).

During the Upper Palaeolithic the diversity of lithic tool classes suggest that a wide range of subsistence activities were being undertaken. In contrast, the chipped stone artefacts from Early Epi-Palaeolithic occupation horizons appear to represent a very narrow range of activities, primarily focused on the intensive production of hunting armatures. During the Late Epi-Palaeolithic the diversity of chipped stone tools increases again, suggesting that a considerable range of tasks were being undertaken.

Almost no non-lithic artefacts were found in the Upper Palaeolithic sites, but the range and density of these artefacts increases during the Epi-Palaeolithic. Non-lithic artefacts include a wide array of Mediterranean and Red Sea shell beads, which must have been exchanged or carried over a distance of at least 200–300 km. Basalt grinding stones appear in the Early Epi-Palaeolithic but were more common in the Late Epi-Palaeolithic. Basalt was locally available at Uwaynid and Azraq, but would have been carried over 50 km to Jilat. Ochre was also in common use in the later sites and may derive from sources in the Western Highlands, 70 km from Jilat and over 100 km from Azraq.

All sediments excavated from the Upper and Epi-Palaeolithic sites were floated, but unfortunately only the Late Epi-Palaeolithic levels at Jilat 6 yielded identifiable seed remains. These were all of genera that could inhabit the area under present conditions. It is possible that the chenopods, legumes, and grasses were collected as food resources. Faunal exploitation patterns were fairly similar throughout the time-period. A greater range of species has been found in the Late Epi-Palaeolithic sites, but this is probably related to the larger sample sizes. The predominant species throughout was gazelle, followed by wild ass, wild cattle (in the Azraq oasis area), hare, tortoise, fox, wolf, and various species of game bird.

There is obviously still a considerable amount of work to be done in the Azraq Basin before we can make detailed statements about the history and environment of human settlement and subsistence during the late Pleistocene. Nevertheless, it is apparent that occupation of the eastern desert of Jordan saw no major periods of abandonment during the period under discussion. In addition, the impressive size and sheer quantity of artefacts at many sites in the basin are a testimony to a successful and varied range of late Pleistocene subsistence adaptations.

Acknowledgements

We are grateful to Dr Adnan Hadidi, Director-General of the Department of Antiquities in Jordan for permission to undertake this research. The field project has been supported by the British Institute at Amman for Archaeology and History, the British Academy, the British Museum, the National Geographic Society, the Palestine Exploration Fund, and the Wainwright Fund. Analysis of the chipped stone artefact assemblages has been supported by the National Endowment for the Humanities and the Wenner-Gren Foundation.

References

Agrar und Hydrotechnik 1977. *National water master plan of Jordan.* Atlas. Main Report, Volume 2. German Agency for Technical Cooperation, Frankfurt.

Bar-Yosef, O. & J. L. Phillips 1977. *Prehistoric investigations in Gebal Maghara, Northern Sinai. Qedem 7.* Hebrew University, Jerusalem.
Bender, F. 1974. *Geology of Jordan.* Berlin: Borntraeger.
Betts, A. 1982. A Natufian Site in the Black Desert, Eastern Jordan. *Paléorient* **8** (2), 79–82.
Betts, A. 1986. The Prehistory of the Basalt Desert, Transjordan: an Analysis. Unpublished PhD Thesis, London University.
Betts, A. 1988. The Black Desert survey. Prehistoric sites and subsistence strategies in eastern Jordan. In *Prehistory of Jordan* A. N. Garrard & H. G. Gebel (eds). 369–91: Oxford: BAR International Series 396.
Bintliff, J. L. & W. van Zeist (eds) 1982. *Paleoclimates, paleoenvironments and human communities in the eastern Mediterranean region in later prehistory.* Oxford: BAR International Series 133.
Byrd, B. F. & G. O. Rollefson 1984. Natufian occupation in the Wadi el Hasa, southern Jordan. *Annual of the Department of Antiquities, Jordan* **28**, 143–50.

Cauvin, J. 1982. L'oasis d'El Kowm au Néolithique. Bilan Après Trois Campagnes: Methodes, Problemes et Premiers Resultats. *Cahiers de l'Euphrate* **3**, 93–8.
Cauvin, J., M. C. Cauvin & O. Stordeur 1979. Recherches Prèhistorique à El Kowm (Syrie), Premiere Campagne 1978. *Cahiers de L'Euphrate* **2**, 80–117.
Cauvin, M. C. 1981. L'epipaleolithique de Syrie d'aprés les premières recherches dans la cuvette d'el Kowm (1978–1979). *Prehistoire du Levant,* J. Cauvin & P. Sanlaville (eds), 375–88. Paris: Colloques Internationaux du CNRS, Vol. 598.
Clark, G., J. Lindley, M. Donaldson, A. Garrard, N. Coinman, J. & S. Schuldenein 1988. Excavations at Middle, Upper, and Epipaleolithic Sites in the Wadi Hasa, West-Central Jordan. In *Prehistory of Jordan* A. N. Garrard & H. G. Gebel (eds) 209–85, Oxford: BAR International Series 396.

Garrard, A. N. & S. Price 1975–77, A Survey of Prehistoric sites in the Azraq Basin, Eastern Jordan. *Paléorient* **3**, 109–126.
Garrard, A. N., B. F. Byrd & A. Betts 1986. Prehistoric Environment and Settlement in the Azraq Basin, an interim report on the 1984 excavation season. *Levant* **18**, 5–24.
Garrard, A. N., A. Betts, B. Byrd & C. Hunt 1987. Prehistoric environment and settlement in the Azraq Basin: an interim report on the 1985 excavation season. *Levant* **19**, 5–25.
Garrard, A. N., B. Byrd, P. Harvey & F. Hivernel 1985. Prehistoric environment

and settlement in the Azraq Basin. A report on the 1982 survey season. *Levant* **17**, 1–28.

Garrard, A. N., A. Betts, B. Byrd, S. Colledge & C. Hunt 1988. Summary of Paleoenvironmental investigations in the Azraq Basin. In *Prehistory of Jordan* A. N. Garrard & H. G. Gebel, (eds) 311–37, Oxford: BAR International Series 396.

Goring-Morris, A. N. 1987. *At the edge: Terminal Pleistocene hunter–gatherers in the Negev and Sinai*. Oxford: BAR International Series 361

Hanihara, K. & T. Akazawa (eds) 1979. *Paleolithic site of Douara Cave and paleogeography of Palmyra Basin in Syria, Part II*. Bulletin of the University Museum, University of Tokyo, 16.

Hanihara, K. & T. Akazawa 1983. *Paleolithic site of Douara Cave and paleogeography of Palmyra Basin in Syria, Part III*. Bulletin of the University Museum, University of Tokyo, 21

Hanihara, K. & Y. Sakaguchi (eds). 1978. *Paleolithic site of Douara Cave and paleogeography of Palmyra Basin in Syria, Part I*. Bulletin of the University Museum. University of Tokyo, 14.

Henry, D. O. 1974. The Utilization of the microburin technique in the Levant. *Paléorient* **2** (1), 389–98.

Henry, D. O. 1982. The prehistory of southern Jordan and relationships with the Levant. *Journal of Field Archaeology* **9**, 417–44.

Henry, D. O. 1987. The prehistory and paleoenvironments of Jordan: an Overview. *Paléorient* **12** (2), 5–26.

Jones, M. L. 1985. The Qualkan and Hamran: two Epipaleolithic Industries from southern Jordan. Unpublished Dissertation, Southern Methodist University. University Microfilms, Michigan.

MacDonald, B., G. O. Rollefson, E. B. Banning, B. F. Byrd & C. D'Annibale 1983. The Wadi El Hasa archaeological survey 1982: a preliminary report. *Annual of the Department of Antiquities*, **27**, 311–24.

Marks, A. E (ed.) 1976. *Prehistory and paleoenvironments in the Central Negev. Israel. Vol. 1: The Avdat/Agev area, Part I*. Dallas: Southern Methodist University Press.

Marks, A. E. (ed.) 1977. *Prehistory and paleoenvironments in the Central Negev. Israel. Vol. 2: The Avdat/Agev area, Part 2 and the Har Harif*. Dallas: Southern Methodist University Press.

Marks, A. E. (ed.) 1983. *Prehistory and paleoenvironments in the Central Negev. Israel. Vol. 3: The Avdat/Agev area, Part 3*. Dallas: Southern Methodist University Press.

Muheisen, M. 1983. La Préhistoire en Jordanie. Recherches sur L'Epipaléolithique. L'exemple du Gisement de Kharaneh IV. Unpublished PhD Dissertation, L'Université de Bordeaux, France.

Muheisen, M. 1985. L'Epipaléolithique Dans le Gisement de Kharaneh IV. *Paléorient* **11** (2), 149–60.

Muheisen, M. 1988. Le Paléolithique et L'Epipaléolithic en Jordanie. Docteur D'Etat Es Sciences, L'Université de Bordeaux I, France.

Nelson, B. 1973. *Azraq: desert oasis*. London: Allen Lane.

Suzuki, H. & I. Kobori (eds) 1970. *Report of the Reconnaissance survey on Paleolithic sites in Lebanon and Syria*. Bulletin of the University Museum. University of Tokyo, 1.

Suzuki, H. & F. Takai (eds) 1973. *The Paleolithic site at Douara Cave in Syria. Part I*. Bulletin of the University Museum. University of Tokyo, 5.

Suzuki, H. & F. Takai (eds) 1974. *The Paleolithic site at Douara Cave in Syria. Part II*. Bulletin of the University Museum. University of Tokyo, 6.

(UNDP) United Nations Development Programme 1966. *General Report on the Groundwater Investigations of the Azraq Basin*. New York: UNDP.

Vries, H. L. de & G. W. Barendsen 1954. Measurements of age by the Carbon-14 technique. *Nature* **174**, 1138–41.

Waechter, J., V. Steton-Williams, D. Bate & L. Picard 1938. The excavations at Wadi Dhobai, 1937–1938 and the Dhobaian Industry. *Journal of the Palestine Oriental Society* **18**, 172–186, 292–8.

Zohary, M. 1973. *Geobotanical Foundations of the Middle East 1–2*. Stuttgart: Fischer.

5 Kebaran occupation at the Last Glacial Maximum in Wadi al-Hammeh, Jordan Valley

PHILLIP C. EDWARDS

The establishment of the Glacial Maximum as a temporal mark allows a global overview of archaeological evidence for human adaptations, at a time when many high-latitude environments must have presented marginal conditions for survival. As a contrast to these regions, this chapter details evidence of settlement from a low-latitude setting in the southern Levantine valley of Wadi al-Hammeh, which was well buffered from harsh environmental extremes.

In relating archaeological material from disparate regions of the Earth, a key question remains as to the units of measurement we should utilize to reckon human adaptive success in terms of the growth and radiation of populations. For the period of interest in this volume, and indeed for the Pleistocene in general, panglobal comparisons are largely restricted to considerations of faunal and floral remains, and very often only to flaked stone artefacts, their patterning within sites, and the locations of site hierarchies − as marked by these stone discards − in a landscape. This contribution stresses problems of intercomparability presented by stone artefact and site data, when these are compiled from regions widely spaced in time and space, for the purposes of reconstructing human populations in the Pleistocene.

This overview will primarily consider the palaeoenvironmental and pre-historic record of Wadi al-Hammeh on its own merits. The archaeological record in Wadi al-Hammeh during the LGM (*c.* 19500–16500 BP) is examined by concentrating on aspects of Kebaran settlement patterns and subsistence. Kebaran sites, together with an earlier Upper Palaeolitic site and a later Natufian site, are cited to discuss factors relevant to the measurement of occupation intensity.

Wadi al-Hammeh is an aquifer-fed stream which drains westward into the Jordan Valley. Deep incision by Wadi al-Hammeh and the ephemeral Wadi al-Himar, which runs parallel to it, have exposed Pleistocene sediments roughly coeval with the lifespan of the former Lake Lisan. The high density of sites and scattered archaeological artefacts, dating back at least to the Middle Palaeolithic, which are contained in these aggraded deposits indicate that a source of water persisted in the wadi during much of the last 100 000 years.

Since 1982 Wadi al-Hammeh has been the object of geological and archaeological attention by the University of Sydney expedition to Pella.[1] Other recent research projects conducted in wadi systems on both sides of the Jordan Valley, such as those in Wadi al-Hasa (McDonald *et al.* 1983), between Wadi Fazael and Wadi Salibiya (Bar-Yosef *et al.* 1974, Goring-Morris 1980, Schuldenrein & Goldberg 1981), Wadi Zarqa (Gordon & Villiers 1983), and Wadi Ziqlab (Banning & Fawcett 1983), have emphasized the magnitude of the Pleistocene as well as later sites pouring out of the Rift Valley exposures. The lower Wadi al-Hammeh appears to be highly unusual for its thick, horizontally bedded sequence of Pleistocene deposits (over 40 m), which contain superimposed sites spanning the period from 100 000 (?) to 12 000 BP. Another important trend emerging from these studies is the degree of microenvironmental diversity in this small region, which is reflected in the sedimentological and palynological records of the various wadi systems.

Definition of the region and geology of Wadi al-Hammeh

The catchment area of lower Wadi al-Hammeh (latitude 32° 27′; longitude, 35° 32′) from its source at the hot spring Hammamat Abu Dhabli (Fig. 5.1a) to its debouchment in the Jordan Valley 2 km away, is approximately 9 km². Another small springhead runs intermittently in Wadi al-Himar just upstream from its confluence with Wadi al-Hammeh (Fig. 5.1b). However, the rainfall caught in this basin has been of far less significance during the Pleistocene, as now, than the consistent groundwater outflow draining a large area of the Transjordanian plateau to the east.

The following preliminary descriptions of geology and palaeoenvironmental reconstructions are summarized from Macumber (1984, 1986).

Both wadis have incised through aggraded Pleistocene beds deposited in an ancestral valley. The approximate northern and southern boundaries of this valley are traceable as Cretaceous–Tertiary limestones and marls which outcrop respectively along the edge of the Tabaqat Fahl plain (Fig. 5.1c) and to the north of Wadi al-Hammeh (Fig. 5.1d).

The bed of the perennial Wadi al-Hammeh has cut deeper than that of the ephemeral Wadi al-Himar, though the latter deepens downstream from the aquifer source near the confluence of the two wadis. The narrow peninsula of land left as an interfluve (hereafter the 'plateau'; Figs 5.1e, 5.2) is particularly remarkable for the preservation in its eroded westerly cliff face of horizontally bedded deposits that overlap broadly in time with the lifespan of the formerly adjacent Lake Lisan. A series of north–south faults are visible in Wadi al-Hammeh sections marking the descent to the valley edge, which has resulted in inclination and overturning of beds in several places.

Capping the plateau is a 2–3 m thick travertine deposit (Fig. 5.3, unit 1).[2] This deepens in the down-valley direction to attain a thickness of 17 m at the residual butte called the 'knob' (Fig. 5.1f). Contemporaneous remnants of this

Figure 5.1 The Wadi al-Hammeh drainage system. North is to the left of the picture. Numbers refer to sites: a, Hammeh hot spring; b, Himar spring; c, southern margin of Tertiary valley; d, northern margin of Tertiary valley; e, the Plateau; f, the Knob; g & h, outcrops of Natufian landscape. Dashed line shows the up-valley limit of paludal facies; the dotted line shows the position of the Lisan shoreline.

ancient land surface are also preserved north of Wadi al-Hammeh (Fig. 5.1g) and west of Wadi al-Himar (Fig. 5.1h). Overlying the travertine unit at the northern end of the plateau is a dark grey, humic clay unit containing the Natufian site Wadi Hammeh 27 (−83.5 m). The uppermost phase of this site is dated *c.* 12 000 BP (11 920 ± 150 BP, OxA–393; 12 200 ± 160 BP, OxA–394; 11 950 ± 160 BP, OxA–507).

Figure 5.2   View east over Wadi al-Himar to the Plateau. North is to the left of the picture. The numbers refer to Wadi al-Hammeh sites.

Below the travertine unit 1 lies a suite of dark grey, silty clays (units 2–5). Unit 3 contains the Kebaran sites Wadi Hammeh 26 (dated 19 500 ± 600BP, SUA–2101) and Wadi Hammeh 33. Wadi Hammeh 26 overlies a weakly cemented conglomerate (unit 4), below which the dark silty clay (unit 5) continues for 3 m. From this point some 35 m down to the bed of Wadi al-Himar, the exposed deposits consist mainly of a fluviatile sequence of interfingering red, pebbly clays and conglomerates. A profusion of lithic debris, debitage, and retouched tools litter this face, including in its lower half many Levallois flakes. It is unclear how early the exposed sequence dates.

An artificial terrace has been created between the plateau and the knob where a section of the plateau has split off and slumped while rotating in the horizontal plane. Natufian flaked stone and basalt tools litter the surface of this slump zone, indentified as Wadi Hammeh 25 (Petocz & Villiers 1984), the material having been carried down from the overlying site Wadi Hammeh 27. Below this, a similar sequence to the one described above, of travertine and silty clay repeats itself. Low frequencies of caramel-coloured bladelet debitage are visible in the silty clays here, equivalent to units 2–5. This area is just north of the Kebaran site Wadi Hammeh 33 (Fig. 5.3).

Macumber (1986) notes that an important feature of the plateau sequence is

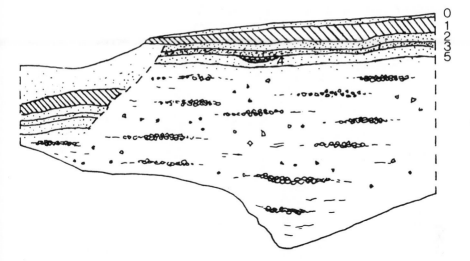

Figure 5.3 Schematic view of the westerly cliff face of the Plateau, indicating
Quaternary deposits. The numbers refer to units described in the text.

that it demonstrated a persistent cycle of aggradation up to the time of the
Natufian occupation at the top (*c.* 12 000 BP). Postdating the Natufian
occupation, the deep downcutting of the wadis began, initiating an erosive
cycle that continues at present. This was presumably a response to a new low
base-level formed by the desiccation of Lake Lisan. Schuldenrein & Goldberg
(1981, pp. 67–8) note that some Natufian sites in the lower Jordan Valley lie at
relatively lower altitudes, postdating the erosional event. Thus the evidence
from Wadi al-Hammeh supports the later postulated date of *c.* 11 000 BP
(Neev & Hall 1977) for the final disappearance of Lake Lisan.

The other two sites under consideration here, Wadi Hammeh 31 and Wadi
Hammeh 32, occur 1 km down-valley at the mouth of Wadi al-Hammeh,
stratified in the southern terrace of Wadi al-Hammeh, which is formed from
remnants of Quaternary deposits plastered against the ancient valley margin
(Fig. 5.1).

The more recent of the two, a Kebaran site (Wadi Hammeh 31), occurs in a
calcisiltite unit near the top of the sequence (*c.* − 136 m). The late Upper
Palaeolithic site, Wadi Hammeh 32, occurs beneath this in a dark clay unit
(− 141.5 m). The sites are positioned near a Lake Lisan shoreline. In the cliff
section on the opposite north terrace the calcisiltite unit can be seen interfingering with a beach deposit consisting of boulders, pebbles, and gravels (Fig. 5.1,
dotted line).

The calcisiltite and dark clay units repeat the depositional sequence of
travertine above dark clays recorded at the top of the plateau. According to its
flaked stone industry, the Kebaran site seems technologically similar to Wadi
Hammeh 26 (Table 5.1), yet it is ostensibly situated in a more recent
stratigraphic deposit. The key to this apparent anomaly is the recognition that

Table 5.1 Information on flaked stone tool industries

		WH 26 N	WH 31 N	WH 33 N	WH 27 N	WH 32 N
Debris						
chunks	(9% of total sample = 2777)		4	3	11 133	3
chips (miscellaneous)			122	5	29 699 368	13
subtotal			126	8	41 200	16
Debitage						
flakes		3072	140	16	20 211	45
blades		1475	354	18	7702	36
core-trimming elements		51	5	1	282	7
burin spalls		120	—	—	468	—
microburins		23	3	—	42	—
cores		41	16	5	260	11
subtotal		4782	518	40	28 965	99
Retouched tools						
scrapers		12	—	—	117	4
multiple tools		—	—	—	10	—
burins		11	—	1	544	9
retouched & backed blades		7	—	—	54	—
truncations		—	—	—	39	—
microliths		153	26	1	629	1
geometric microliths		1	1	—	359	—
notches & denticulates		6	4	—	300	—
various		4	—	—	163	—
subtotal		194	31	2	2 215	14
Total		4976★	675	50	72 380	129

★ Does not include Debris counts.

lateral deposition occurred diachronically from the mouth of Wadi al-Hammeh up-valley to the plateau.

Opposite the plateau on the westerly bank of Wadi al-Himar the travertine facies (unit 1) gives way to a fluviatile sequence, thus indicating the approximate up-valley limits of the lakeside paludal facies (Fig. 5.1, dashed line).

Evidence for the time-transgressive nature of the calcareous unit is seen in the plateau where the travertine unit thickens appreciably down-valley to a maximum thickness of 17 m at the knob. Whereas the Kebaran site Wadi Hammeh 26, dated 19 500 BP, underlies the travertine in dark clays, a site with apparent Levalloiso-Mousterian material, preliminarily examined by Villiers (Petocz & Villiers 1984), underlies the travertine by a similar distance in the knob. Here, however, the dark grey clays are lacking, and the site, which includes concentrations of charcoal, occurs in a red gypseous clay at the base of five cemented conglomerate bands (Macumber 1984).

An extensive series of samples taken for radiocarbon analysis will hopefully provide finer resolution in the near future for many of these deposits and sites.

Palaeoenvironmental reconstruction

In the plateau the boundary between the earlier fluviatile sequence of red pebbly clays and conglomerates, and the later dark grey, silty clays (unit 5), sandwiched between scatters of Levalloiso-Mousterian material and the Kebaran site dated 19 500 BP, must be dated sometime in the Upper Palaeolithic. Since the aquifers responsible for the deposition of these beds were ultimately dependent on winter precipitation over the Transjordanian plateau for their recharge, the transition from a higher to a lower energy hydrological regime may reflect the trend towards decreased precipitation during this period leading up to the LGM. Alternatively, a rise in the level of Lake Lisan during this period may have induced swampy conditions further up-valley giving rise to the dark grey clays, and thus more immediate topographical conditions may explain the change. The upper plateau sequence indicates that Lake Lisan reached its greatest size in the final millennia before its disappearance (Macumber 1986).

This evidence correlates well with the stratigraphic position of the Geometric Kebaran A site of Haon II, located near the eastern shore of Lake Tiberias in the Upper Jordan Valley. This site, dated 17 600 BP, occurs in a deposit that overlays a Lisan deposit marking the maximal expansion of the lake (Bar-Yosef 1975, p. 12; although the author questions the veracity of the date).

Within the area of the wadis investigated, there are two marked lateral facies changes discernible in the Kebaran period deposits, representing the boundaries of different environmental zones: namely the change from a lakeside to a paludal environment at the mouth of Wadi al-Hammeh (Fig. 5.1, dotted line), and the boundary between the up-valley limits of this backswamp and firm ground in the zone of groundwater discharge (Fig. 5.1, dashed line). Kebaran sites (not contemporaneous) are located both near the Lisan shore and the edge of the marshy area.

Other direct, though qualitative, evidence for palaeoenvironment in Wadi al-Hammeh during this period stems from the range of plants recovered as charcoal fragments from the Wadi Hammeh 26 hearth (Table 5.2; Willcox 1986). The presence of trees and shrubs such as oak, almond, pistachio, hawthorn, buckthorn, and hackberry indicates an open Mediterranean woodland near Wadi al-Hammeh rather than the depauperate flora which survives at present. The Wadi Hammeh 26 botanical remains are not irreconcilable with evidence suggesting an arid phase in the area during this period (Bottema & van Zeist 1981, Goldberg 1981) because an average 25% arboreal pollen,

Table 5.2   Botanical list

	Wadi Hammeh 26	Wadi Hammeh 27
Quercus sp.	+	+
Amygdalus sp.	+	−
Pistacia sp.	+	−
Rhamnus sp.	+	−
Crataegus sp.	+	−
Celtis sp.	+	−
Caryophyllaceae	−	+
Hordeum spontaneum	−	+
Chenopodium sp.	−	+
Bromus sp.	−	+
Echinochloa sp.	−	+
cf. *Cicer* sp.	−	+
cf. *Lens* sp.	−	+
cf. *Avena* sp.	−	+
cf. *Aegilops* sp.	−	+

including oak and other deciduous trees, is found during this phase in the Huleh column (Bottema & van Zeist 1981). The plant remains also demonstrate that considerable microenvironmental diversity probably existed along the margins of Lake Lisan at this time, and particularly around spring outlets.

Oxygen isotope evidence from the Gulf of Aqaba (Reiss *et al.* 1984) leads to estimates that mean winter temperatures at 18 000 BP were depressed by about 4°C. Environmental stress on human populations due to cold and aridity can not have been particularly severe at the glacial maximum in the Jordan Rift Valley. In Wadi al-Hammeh cold and aridity were buffered by the unusually low altitudes of the rift valley and the presence of a permanent and (hot!) water source.

The Kebaran sites

The most detailed information on the Wadi al-Hemmeh Kebaran is available from Wadi Hammeh 26. The Kebaran unit was investigated along the cliff section for 6 m. Within the excavated area lithic and bone fragments showed a similar, unimodal cluster with peak density occurring just south of an erosion gully that bisects the site (Fig. 5.4).

In the erosion gully and just to the north of it were two charcoal concentrations representing one or more hearths. Both were associated with groups of limestone pebbles. Otherwise no structural features were observed. Artefact densities were curtailed abruptly to the south but diminished more gradually to the north in the down-valley direction. This may indicate some movement of material out of the site by water, but other factors reveal the good state of *in situ* site preservation:

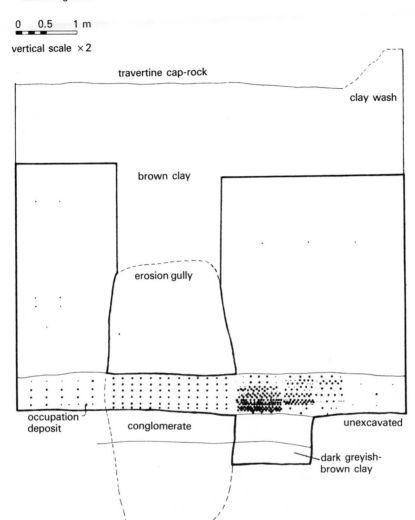

. bone fragment (× 10)
· bone fragment

0   0.5   1 m

vertical scale ×2

travertine cap-rock

clay wash

brown clay

erosion gully

occupation deposit

conglomerate

unexcavated

dark greyish-brown clay

Figure 5.4 Diagrammatic section of the Kebaran site Wadi Hammeh 26, showing the distribution of animal bone fragments. North (down-valley) is to the left. The excavated part of the site is within the thick black line.

(a)   The superimposed cluster of bone and stone tool fragments near to the hearth remnant,

(b)   The survival of small chert chips and small debitage peices. Nearly 9% of a total lithics sample ($N = 2777$) consisted of small chips, and 60% of a sample of flakes were smaller that 2 cm in largest dimension. This small

Table 5.3   Information on site area and density*

Site	Period	Estimated size	Lithic density (per m^3)
Wadi Hammeh 32	Upper Palaeolithic	6000 m^2	516
Wadi Hammeh 26	Kebaran	25 m^2	4930
Wadi Hammeh 31	Kebaran	25 m^2	6750
Wadi Hammeh 33	Kebaran	<25 m^2	5000
Wadi Hammeh 27	Natufian	>2000 m^2	4711

* All sites were dry-sieved through 0.5 cm mesh, except Wadi Hammeh 26 which was dry-sieved through a 0.3 cm mesh. All samples were then wet-sieved.

size fraction is generally lacking in sites that have been deflated by wind or water (Barton & Bergman 1982).

(c)   A full sequence of knapping products are represented by raw chert, chunks, cores, core-trimming elements, percussion shatter products, flakes, blades and bladelets, and retouched tools, demonstrating the preservation of an activity area (Table 5.1).

(d)   Two sets of conjoinable microliths were found less than 1 m away from each other in the area of peak artefact density.

(e)   The calcaneus and astragalus of a fox were found within 1 m of each other. The bones articulate well and may be derived from an individual animal.

Discovered during geological prospecting in the Kebaran unit, Wadi Hammeh 33 occurs some 50 m down-valley from Wadi Hammeh 26. Despite the small sample, artefact density and the flaked stone industry are similar to Wadi Hammeh 26 (Table 5.3). A few fragments of bone, which include artiodactyl remains, were also recovered. The area of the site is less than 25 m.^{2} In view of the good preservation of Wadi Hammeh 26, the occurrence seems to be a second site rather than deflated material from upstream. Wadi Hammeh 31 has a higher artefact density than these two sites, and the flaked stone industry is clearly similar to that of Wadi Hammeh 26 (Tables 5.1, & 5.3). Faunal remains were lacking except for the find of a piece of mammalian bone.

The Kebaran sites all have lithic artefact densities (calculated using debris, debitage, and retouched tools) between 4–6 × 10^3, and site areas of about 25 m^2.

Two additional sites are briefly described here to illustrate several comparative points. One is earlier and the other later than the Kebaran sites. The late Upper Palaeolithic site Wadi Hammeh 32 is a larger, diffuse site of up to 6000 m^2, which outcrops in various spots on top of the south Wadi al-Hammeh terrace near the wadi's mouth (Fig. 5.1). Artefact density is 516 lithics per m^3. No faunal remains were found.

The Natufian site, Wadi Hammeh 27, preserved on top of the plateau, but eroded at the edges, is an *in situ* site at least 2000 m² in area, though this is certainly a minimum estimate. Free-standing, oval and concentric-walled structures occur associated with other stone features, together with parietal engraved stone slabs, art mobilier consisting of geometric symbols incised in limestone pebbles and fragments, bone and marine shell ornaments, bone tools, basalt milling tools, and burials (Edwards *et al.* 1988). Faunal and floral remains have been retrieved. Artefact densities of 4711 lithics per m³ are similar to the Kebaran sites.

The archaeological landscape

Although the above descriptions have concentrated on the individual sites as discrete entities, a more accurate assessment is that archaeological material occurs more or less as a continuum throughout the Wadi al-Hammeh deposits.

This can be appreciated in the exposed plateau sequence. Figure 5.5 is a schematic visualization of the degree of dispersal of archaeological artefacts in the plateau deposits from the Middle Palaeolithic (?) up to the Natufian. The most recent site, Wadi Hammeh 27, remains as a well-preserved, single-period site. The Kebaran sites occur as small encampments with low frequencies of lithic artefacts in between. The sampling methods designed for outcrop strips at Koobi Fora by Isaac (1981, p. 148) should eventually provide better estimates of the degree of Kebaran artefact dispersal throughout unit 3, if this sequence is further investigated as planned. In view of the good preservation of

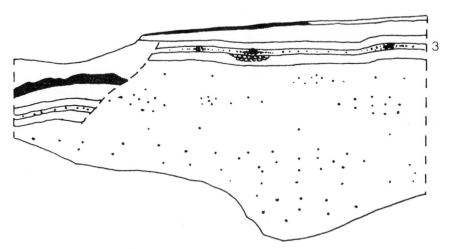

Figure 5.5 Schematic conception of the dispersal of archaeological material throughout the Quaternary deposits in the Plateau. The Natufian site, Wadi Hammeh 27, is shown as the black area. The Kebaran sites (in unit 3) are the earliest discovered sites which have recognizable site boundaries.

Wadi Hammeh 26, not all of this can be deflated material, but more likely represents activity on the periphery of sites, or away from the archaeologically visible site areas.

Wadi Hammeh 32 typifies many characteristics of the material scattered on the middle and lower parts of the plateau. The lithic density of Wadi Hammeh 32, which is ten times lower than the other sites (Table 5.3), might be expected to follow from less preoccupation with bladelet and microlith production, but this can only be partly true because bladelet cores and bladelet debitage are found in the site. More importantly, the frequency of small size-fraction material accounts for much of the difference in lithic density between Wadi Hammeh 32 and the overlying Wadi Hammeh 31 (Table 5.1). Chert chips are 10% compared to 18% and debitage under 2 cm is absent, compared to 4.6% in Wadi Hammeh 31.

These figures provide a rough guide to the increased degree of deflation of the earlier site, which is responsible for the lower artefact density and larger site size.

The same effect explains the scattered nature of the Middle Palaeolithic artefacts in the lower half of the plateau cliff. Although this area has not yet been systematically explored, it appears that the consistent presence of artefacts across the surface results from their lateral movement by water erosion, with the consequent blurring of many site boundaries. The pattern in this particular sequence corresponds to the overall trend of site size distribution through time noted by Hassan (1980, pp. 444–5) for sites along the Nile. Site sizes there show a decrease from the Lower Palaeolithic through the Middle Palaeolithic to the Late/Terminal Palaeolithic, a trend which is reversed in Predynastic times. The increase in Predynastic times is a process of genuine settlement expansion, rather than a result of increased deflation as in the Lower Palaeolithic sites.

In the plateau sequence, the equivalent period of settlement increase occurs during the Natufian. All of the *in situ* sites occur in the dark grey clay deposits under low energy conditions. The earlier dispersed sites occur in the fluviatile red clays deposited under higher energy conditions.

Kebaran settlement patterns

The average site size for Kebaran sites has been estimated at *c*. 200 m^2 (Bar-Yosef 1970, p. 183). Comparisons with some individual Kebaran sites from the Levant (Table 5.4) show the Wadi al-Hammeh sites to be similar in magnitude. They are also similar in kind, as very few Kebaran sites have yielded evidence for structures (Bar-Yosef 1970, p. 183). The larger Azraq sites may have undergone significant deflation (Garrard & Stanley-Price 1977).

The sites listed range over a long time-interval (*c*. 19 500–15 500 BP) and it is difficult to discern time-dependent trends. The site on Ein Gev I (dated 15 700 ± 415 BP), for example, is remarkable in having preserved traces of a dwelling (Bar-Yosef 1970, p. 110, 1981, p. 405) and heralds the trend towards

Table 5.4 Sizes of some Kebaran sites

Site	Estimated site size (m²)	Reference
Azraq 17	2000–8000	Garrard & Stanley-Price (1977, p. 119)
Azraq 20	1000–2000	Garrard & Stanley-Price (1977, p. 119)
Ein Gev I	100–150	Bar-Yosef (1981, p. 395)
Fazael III B	50	Goring-Morris (1980, p. 57)
Fazael III D	10–20	Goring-Morris (1980, p. 64)
Fazael III A	75–100	Goring-Morris (1980, p. 66)
Fazael VII	50	Goring-Morris (1980, p. 75)
Kebara C	200	Bar-Yosef (1970, p. 182)
Kefar Darom 8	350	Bar-Yosef (1981, p. 395)
Yabrud III	50	Rust (1950, p. 100)

increased numbers of structures and milling tools known from the Geometric Kebaran A.

The pattern of Kebaran sites in Wadi al-Hammeh may be visualized as a palimpsest of repeated, short occupation events of mobile hunter-gatherer bands attracted to a well-watered locality.

Kebaran subsistence patterns

The Wadi Hammeh 26 faunal complex of artiodactyl–small carnivore–bird–tortoise (Table 5.5) strongly resembles other Jordan Valley Kebaran faunas, for example from the Wadi Fazael and Ein Gev I (Davis 1974, Goring-Morris 1980, pp. 67, 76). *Gazella* and *Vulpes* bone remains predominate but minimum individual numbers (MIND) are restricted to either one or two. Since the sample is small, MIND estimations are probably underrated for the more frequent taxa (Garrard 1982, p. 175).

The Capsian escargotières (Lubell & Gautier 1979) serve as a reminder that small terrestrial snails may constitute part of a human group's diet. It seems doubtful, though, that the small *Melanopsis praemorsa* shells were utilized for food by the Kebarans. All of the other species listed in Table 5.5 were found concentrated around the hearth in the Kebaran unit, and while it is true that *Melanopsis* shells were also present, they are much more evenly dispersed throughout the silt units. Plentiful nearby groundwater sources are probably the reason for their occurrence. Certainly, their total numbers at the site, 75, would represent but a meagre addition to caloric intake, about 6 g of flesh.

Bones of both gazelle and tortoise from Wadi Hammeh 26 are burnt. One piece of mammal bone shows characteristic rodent incisor marks, and the presence of rodents at the site is probably explained by their role as scavengers.

Complete elements are restricted to small bones no larger than a few centimetres in dimension: mandibles of hare and rodents, phalanges, podial

Table 5.5 Faunal list

	Wadi Hammeh 26	Wadi Hammeh 27
Equus sp.	−	+
Cervus elaphus	−	+
Dama mesopotamica	−	+
Capreolus capreolus	−	+
Sus scrofa	+	+
Bos primigenius	−	+
Ovis/Capra	+	+
Capra sp.	−	+
Gazella sp.	+	+
Canis lupus	−	+
Vulpes vulpes	+	+
Felis sp.	+	+
Lepus capensis	+	+
Rodentia (large)	+	−
Rodentia (small)	+	−
Aves	−	+
Phasianidae	+	−
Passeriformes	+	−
Testudo sp.	+	+
Potamon potamon	−	+
Dentalium vulgare	−	+
Melanopsis praemorsa	+	+

Table 5.6 Survival patterns of mammalian bone elements

		Wadi Hammeh 26				Wadi Hammeh 27*			
		C.	Fr.	Prox.	Dist.	C.	Fr.	Prox.	Dist.
horn core		−	−	−	−	1	−	−	−
mandible		2	−	−	−	1	−	−	−
teeth		4	11	−	−	3	9	−	−
scapula		−	−	−	−	−	−	−	1
humerus		−	−	2	−	−	−	2.	−
ulna		−	−	2	−	−	−	3	−
radius		−	−	−	−	−	−	1	−
vertebrae		−	7	−	−	18	−	−	−
metapodials		−	−	1	2	−	−	−	7
carpals		6	−	−	−	2	−	−	−
tarsals		9	−	2	−	−	−	−	−
phalanges	1st	5	−	−	7	4	−	1	3
	2nd	6	−	−	−	3	−	2	−
	3rd	2	−	1	−	2	−	−	−

C., Complete; Fr., fragment; Prox., proximal fragment; Dist., distal fragment.
 * These figures for Wadi Hammeh 27 do not cover all of the species listed in Table 5.5, some of which were newly identified taxa from the 1985 season.

elements, vertebrae, and teeth. Recent ethnographic studies of the deterioration of animal bones in archaeological sites (Yellen 1977, Stallibrass nd) show that much of the patterning observed in faunal residues is attributable to differential survival of bone elements. This seems to be the case at Wadi Hammeh 26 and Wadi Hammeh 27. Bone element frequencies from these sites, which differ in kind and in scale, are extremely similar (Table 5.6). Only those elements which are small, dense, or poor in marrow or blood vessels have survived intact.

Botanical remains from Wadi Hammeh 26 are all wood charcoal fragments retrieved from a fireplace. It is not possible to simply extrapolate that the trees and shrubs concerned were sources of food (Table 5.2), but the taxa present at least show the site occupants' familiarity with nut-bearing trees such as oak, pistachio, almond, and hackberry. Recent finds of charred nut, seed, fruit, and pulse remains, for example at sites Wadi Jilat 6 and 8 (Garrard et al. 1986), Mushabi XIV (Bar-Yosef & Phillips 1977, p. 155), Douara Cave (Akazawa & Ohnuma 1988) and Kebara Cave (Kislev & Bar-Yosef 1988) show positive evidence for the use of plant foods in the Levant from the Middle Palaeolithic through Late Epi-Palaeolithic times.

The Natufian site Wadi Hammeh 27, where the deposit matrix is similar to Wadi Hammeh 26, has in addition to oak charcoal yielded the remains of grasses, legumes, and other seed-bearing plants. (Table 5.2), which require milling to be easily edible. Here, as at many Natufian sites (Henry 1981), basalt milling tools, bone sickle hafts, and many blades bearing silica sheen have been found. It can be conjectured that while nuts, fruits, pulses, bulbs, and tubers were regularly used as food sources in the Kebaran, the widespread adoption of cereals does not appear to have occurred before the Natufian, and there is no substantial evidence for cereal exploitation, direct or indirect, before the reaping equipment found at Ein Gev I (c. 15 700 BP).

The blanks used for bladelet cores in the Kebaran sites were selected from the abundant chert cobbles nearby. Unlike the situation in the Natufian site, there are no materials not immediately procurable in the Tabaqat Fahl area found at the Kebaran sites.

Measuring occupation intensity

The evidence cited above concerning the depositional environment, taphonomy, and stone-tool technology of the Wadi al-Hammeh sites suggests two factors that hinder the use of artefact density as an index of occupation intensity in Palaeolithic times.

Firstly, if depositional conditions are equal, progressively older sites may be expected to suffer increased rates of deflation, with the differential removal of small size-fraction material. In Wadi al-Hammeh, this trend has been exacerbated because some sites of Upper Palaeolithic and earlier date were deposited under high-energy fluviatile conditions conducive to deflation, whereas sites of Kebaran and later date were deposited under low-energy paludal conditions conducive to preservation.

Secondly, the technological transition from predominantly flake to blade and bladelet production from the Mousterian through to the epi-Palaeolithic may have resulted in progressively greater quantities of debitage being discarded in archaeological sites. The cumulative effect of both factors, if not controlled for, is to create the illusion of increased occupation density through time.

Within the similar technological bladelet traditions of the various Levantine Epi-Palaeolithic culture units, comparisons of lithic density would seem to be more realistic. Assemblages from many industries and regions, such as the Sinai (Bar-Yosef & Phillips 1977), the Negev (Marks 1977), the Ras an-Naqb (Henry 1982), Azraq (Garrard et al. 1986), and Palestine (Bar-Yosef 1970) exhibit similar high rates of discard of bladelet core reduction debitage.

More intractable problems remain in transferring artefact density, as an index of occupation intensity, across the mobile/sedentary transition, or even from small hunter–gatherer camp sites to large and complex hunter-gatherer residential sites.

Wadi Hammeh 27 is a hundred times bigger than Wadi Hammeh 26, shows several reconstruction phases of the same building, possesses burials with grave goods, which include exchanged exotic items, elaborate symbolism, and sophisticated ground stone and bone tool industries. These would generally be regarded as signs of increased subsistence and ritual intensification, as well as greatly increased occupation intensity. Its artefact density, however, is only equivalent in magnitude, and in fact slightly lower, than the Kebaran sites.

Fletcher (1981, p. 98–9) has raised the issue that site area cannot be taken as a neutral referent for settlement population, since both variables are not static, but interact. Similarly, artefact density cannot be assumed to be a neutral referent for occupation intensity. Mobile human groups may occupy a base camp for a short span without the need to resort to refuse redistribution or management, and thereby dense artefact accumulations may result in a small area. In sedentary or long-term, seasonally occupied sites there may ultimately be a ceiling at which problems of hindrance of movement and tasks, pollution of foodstuffs and disease render successful settlement inoperable unless refuse management is undertaken.

The Natufian structure at Jericho is notable for its low quantities of refuse (Kenyon 1981, p. 273) and has been interpreted as a 'shrine' (Kenyon 1960). It is an intriguing speculation that a more prosaic and sufficient interpretation of its function, considering the presence of large pits in its floor, might be as a grain storage area which would obviously have been incompatible with the presence of thousands of stone tool fragments. The agricultural 9th millennium BP settlement of Ali Kosh appears to have early evidence for an attempt at secondary refuse disposal, in the form of a concentration of animal bones thrown in a narrow alley between two structures (Hole et al. 1969, p. 42).

Isaac and colleagues (Isaac et al. 1981, pp. 118–19) described outcrop strips at

Koobi Fora where small sites marked by clusters of stone tools occurred amidst intercalated scatters; a similar archaeological landscape to the Kebaran unit in Wadi al-Hammeh. In the Koobi Fora sites artefact densities were of the order of 10 per m^3, as opposed to 10^3 per m^3 at Wadi al-Hammeh. Clearly there were not tens, or even hundreds more hominids crowded around the Kebaran camp sites than in the Koobi Fora ones. Nor is there any intrinsic evidence to show that any single Kebaran camp was occupied longer than any Koobi Fora site.

The ethnographic site of Ngarulutra in the Lake McDonald region of the Northern Territory, Australia, recorded by Hayden (1979, pp. 139–49), consisted of a few hearths around which four people camped for a week, in which time they cooked animals and made, used, and discarded stone tools (an informant's recollection). The archaeologically visible area totalled no more than 20 m^2, and stone tools numbered only 98.

Counting gross tallies of sites per period in a survey area also appears to be a seriously flawed method of calculating regional occupation intensity. How does one compare the intensity value of two small Kebaran camp sites with one large Natufian residential settlement?

It may be supposed that a more accurate relationship between the intensity of the Kebaran camp sites and the Natufian settlement is to measure more rigorously the total area covered by the settlements of the two periods. Obviously in this procedure one must first take into account the relative areas of different periods that are today exposed.

Within an arbitrary area of 1 km^2 centred on the plateau, the exposed vestiges of Natufian landscape totals about 9 ha. The single Natufian residential site in the square, and the Natufian sites and scatters located north and west of the two wadis (Wadi Hammeh sites 9, 12, 22, and 23; Petocz & Villiers 1984) total 17% of the contemporary landscape. The small Kebaran camp sites comprise 0.08% of the contemporary Kebaran landscape exposed in the narrow outcrop strips (This estimate does not include intercalated scatters between the sites.) Once the imbalance in the exposures is corrected for, then the Natufian occupation area is calculated as 213 times larger than the Kebaran.

Stated algebraically, this procedure can be described as:

$$Ir = \frac{S_{(1-n)} \left(\Sigma As_{(1-n)} \right)}{Al(t)}$$

where

Ir = relative index of area under settlement;
$S_{(1-n)}$ = number of sites;
$As_{(1-n)}$ = areas of the sites;
Al = area of contemporary archaeological landscape;
t = time for accumulation of exposed deposits.

Although total settlement area in a region might be considered as a relevant way to mark regional occupation intensity, there is still a fundamental objection to it, even if it is accepted, for argument's sake, that area is indeed a neutral referent for population.

In Wadi al-Hammeh the Natufian settlement pattern may be modelled as a miniature implosion event in the landscape, compared to the dispersed, laterally shifting nature of repeated Kebaran occupations. The phenomenon of growth in a nucleated settlement centre causing a consequent decline and even extinction of many of its satellite settlements has been postulated for the Warka region in Mesopotamia during the Early Dynastic period (Adams & Nissen 1972). It has also characterized the growth of many of the great cities of the Third World (Vining 1985). Future work is needed to resolve whether this model is applicable to Wadi Hammeh 27, by determining whether the surface material north and west of the wadis represents artefacts discarded at the periphery of a single residential site, or whether these sites are indeed further large residential sites.

Economic and social stratification, and population growth may actually correspond to a decrease in the total number of settlement sites and total residential area. In the Natufian period, sites such as Wadi Hammeh 27 and Ain Mallaha (Perrot 1966) represent the initial stages of the phenomenon of the *tell* in Southwest Asia. In these sites, buildings and features are rebuilt over several reconstruction phases. Human settlement is now linked to the constraints imposed by durable structures, which, if continually reoccupied, somewhat control a group's residential shifts in the immediate locale on its return to a settlement.

These considerations suggest that better archaeological indices for occupation intensity lie elsewhere, particularly if the aim is to compare simple and complex hunter–gatherer sites.

Site size distributions for all periods have been shown to consist of a full range of sizes from very small to large, contingent upon the use of the site as a residential base or activity-specific locus. More reliable estimates of the rate, timing, and magnitude of occupation intensity changes may be obtained from the examination of the numbers of sites in the larger or largest site-size intervals, and subsequent calculation of the largest average site size for any archaeological culture or period (Fletcher 1986).

For mobile groups whose settlement pattern is marked by lateral shifts upon return to a favoured locale, calculation of Ir, the relative index of settlement area for a given culture in a unit region, may at least prove a more rigorously comparable index for use in situations where site boundaries can be recognized.

Conclusions

The Kebaran settlement pattern in Wadi al-Hammeh is characterized by a series of small (c. 25 m^2) camp sites at which the cooking of animals and stone tool-making were carried out around fireplaces. Kebaran encampments occur in both lakeside and marshy environments.

Environmental stress due to cold and aridity cannot have been particularly severe in Wadi al-Hammeh during the glacial maximum, where the effects of cold and aridity were buffered by the low altitude of the Jordan Valley and a permanent water source. A wide variety of animal taxa were hunted, and probably nuts and other plant foods were collected.

Once the results of several recent research projects are assimilated, future settlement maps of the Kebaran period in Jordan will probably show concentrations of sites along the margins of the Jordan Rift Valley. This is largely because of the serendipitous nature of the Rift Valley exposures, but it is also due to the chain of aquifers that rise along the valley's edge. These factors, and the setting of many of these sites in rugged terrain, tend to distract us from consideration of prehistoric site placements due to the other un-doubted ecological attractions of the region.

The use of raw artefact densities and site numbers as valid comparative indicators of occupation intensity have been criticized in this chapter. Instead it is suggested that calculation of a relative index of total area under settlement, adjusted for differential time periods and exposures, is a more suitable starting point. Also, the use of the largest average site-size for a given culture or period may lead to a better understanding of rates of change of occupation intensity.

Notes

1   Investigations in Wadi al-Hammeh constitute one of the projects being conducted by the University of Sydney Expedition to Pella, which has proceeded thanks to the courtesy of Dr A. Hadidi and the Department of Antiquities of the Hashemite Kingdom of Jordan. The work referred to here was conducted under the directorships of the late Dr A. McNicoll and Mr T. F. Potts.

This paper is dedicated to the memory of Tony McNicoll. Though his particular research interests spanned the Hellenistic and later periods, Tony's vision was largely responsible for the inclusion of the prehistory of the Tabaqat Fahl region within the Pella Expedition's ambit.

2   Numbering of these units is preliminary and made in order to clarify the text.

References

Adams, R. McC. & H. J. Nissen 1972. *The Uruk Countryside: the natural setting of urban societies*. Chicago & London: The University of Chicago Press.

Akazawa, T. & K. Ohnuma 1988. Site catchment analysis of the Early Middle Palaeolithic occupation at Douara Cave, Syrian Desert. Paper read at the CNRS colloquium Prehistory of the Levant 2, Lyons.

Banning, E. B. & C. Fawcett 1983. Man-land relationships in the ancient Wadi Ziqlab: report of the 1981 survey. *Annual of the Department of Antiquities of Jordan* **XXVII**, 291–309.

Barton, R. N. E. & C. A. Bergman 1982. Hunters at Hengistbury: some evidence from experimental archaeology. *World Archaeology* **14**(2), 237–48.

Bar-Yosef, O. 1970. The Epi-Palaeolithic cultures of Palestine. Unpublished PhD thesis, Hebrew University, Jerusalem.

Bar-Yosef, O. 1975. Les gisements 'Kébarien Géométrique a' d'Haon, vallée du Jordain, Isräel. *Bulletin de la Société Préhistorique Francaise* **72**, 10–14.

Bar-Yosef, O. 1981. The Epi-palaeolithic complexes in the southern Levant. In *Préhistoire du Levant: chronologie et organisation de l'espace depuis les origins justqu'au au VIe millénaire*. J. Cauvin & P. Sanlaville (eds), 389–408. Paris: CNRS.

Bar-Yosef, O. & J. L. Phillips (eds) 1977. *Prehistoric investigations in Gebel Maghara, Northern Sinai, Qedem* 7. Hebrew University, Jerusalem.

Bar-Yosef, O., P. Goldberg & T. Leveson 1974. Late Quaternary stratigraphy and prehistory in Wadi Fazael, Jordan Valley: a preliminary report. *Paléorient* **2**(2), 415–28.

Bottema, S. & W. van Zeist 1981. Palynological evidence for the climatic history of the Near East, 50 000–6000 BP. In *Préhistoire de Levant: chronologie et organisation de l'espace depuis les origines jusqu'au au VIe millénaire*, J. Cauvin & P. Sanlaville (eds), 111–143. Paris: CNRS.

Davis, S. 1974. Animal remains from the Kebaran site of Ein-Gev I, Jordan Valley, Israel. *Paléorient* **2**(2), 453–62.

Edwards, P. C., S. J. Bourke, S. M. Colledge, J. Head & P. G. Macumber 1988. Late Pleistocene prehistory in the Wadi al-Hammeh, Jordan Valley. In *The prehistory of Jordan; the state of research in 1986* A. N. Garrard & H. G. Gebel (eds), 525–65. Oxford: BAR International Series 396 (ii).

Fletcher, R. J. 1981. People and space: a case study on material behaviour. In *Pattern of the Past*, I. Hodder, G. Isaac & N. Hammond (eds), 97–128. Cambridge: Cambridge Univeristy Press.

Fletcher, R. J. 1986. Settlement archaeology: world-wide comparisons. *World Archaeology* **18**, 59–83.

Garrard, A. N. 1982. The environmental implications of a reanalysis of the large mammal fauna from the Wadi el-Mughara caves, Palestine. In *Palaeoclimates, palaeoenvironments and human communities in the Eastern Mediterranean region in later prehistory*, J. L. Bintliff & W. van Zeist (eds), 105–29. Oxford: BAR International Series 133.

Garrard, A. N. & N. P. Stanley-Price 1977. A survey of prehistoric sites in the Azraq Basin, eastern Jordan. *Paléorient* **3** (1975–1976–1977), 109–26.

Garrard, A. N., B. Byrd & A. Betts 1986. Prehistoric environment and settlement in the Azraq Basin. An interim report on the 1984 excavation season. *Levant* **XVIII**, 5–24.

Goldberg, P. 1981. Late Quaternary stratigraphy of Israel: an eclectic view. In *Préhistoire de Levant; chronologie et organisation de l'espace depuis les origines jusqu'au au VIe millénaire*, J. Cauvin & P. Sanlaville (eds), 111–32. Paris: CNRS.

Gordon, R. L. & L. E. Villiers 1983. Telul edh Dhahab and its environs surveys of 1980 and 1982. A preliminary report. *Annual of the Department of Antiquities of Jordan* **XXVII**, 275–89.

Goring-Morris, A. N. 1980. Late Quatenary sites in Wadi Fazael. Lower Jordan Valley. Unpublished MA thesis, Hebrew University, Jerusalem.

Hassan, F. A. 1980. Prehistoric settlements along the Main Nile. In *The Sahara and the Nile*, M. A. J. Williams & H. Faure (eds), 421–50. Rotterdam: A. A. Balkema.

Hayden, B. 1979. *Palaeolithic reflections*. Australian Institute of Aboriginal Studies. New Jersey: Canberra/Humanities Press Inc.

Henry, D. O. 1981. An analysis of settlement patterns and adaptive strategies of the Natufian. In *Préhistoire du Levant: chronologie et organisation de l'espace dupuis les origines jusqu'au au VIe millénaire* J. Cauvin & P. Sanlaville (eds), 421–32. Paris: CNRS.

Henry, D. O. 1982. The prehistory of southern Jordan and relationships with the Levant. *Journal of Field Archaeology* **9** (4), 417–44.

Hole, F., K. V. Flannery & J. A. Neely 1969. *Prehistory and human ecology of the Deh Luran plain: an early village sequence from Khuzistan, Iran.* Museum of Anthropology, University of Michigan. Memoir no.1, Ann Arbor.

Isaac, G. 1981. Stone Age visiting cards: approaches to the study of early land use patterns. In *Pattern of the Past*, I. Hodder, G. Isaac & N. Hammond (eds), 131–55. Cambridge: Cambridge University Press.

Isaac, G., J. W. K. Harris & F. Marshall 1981. Small is informative: the application of the study of mini-sites and least effort criteria in the interpretation of the early Pleistocene Archaeological record at Koobi Fora, Kenya. UISPP Tenth Congress, Mexico City, 101.

Kenyon, K. M. 1960. Excavations at Jericho, 1957–58. *Palestine Exploration Quarterly* **92**, 88–108.

Kenyon, K. 1981. *Excavations at Jericho*. Vol. III: *The architecture and stratigraphy of the Tell*. London: British School of Archaeology at Jerusalem.

Kislev, M. E. & O. Bar-Yosef 1988. The legumes. The earliest domesticated plants in the Near East? *Current Anthropology* **29**(1), 175–8.

Lubell, D. & A. Gautier 1979. Holocene environment and Capsian subsistence in Algeria. *Palaeoecology of Africa and the surrounding islands* **11**, 171–8.

MacDonald, B., G. O. Rollefsen, E. B. Banning, B. F. Byrd & C. d'Annibale 1983. The Wadi el-Hasa archaeological survey 1982: a preliminary report. *Annual of the Department of Antiquities of Jordan* **XXVII**, 311–23.

McNicoll, A., W. Ball, S. Bassett, P. Edwards, P. Macumber, D. Petocz, T. Potts, L. Randale, L. Villiers & P. Watson (eds) 1984. Preliminary report on the University of Sydney's fifth season of excavation at Pella in Jordan. *Annual of the Department of Antiquities of Jordan* **XXVIII**, 55–86.

Macumber, P. G. 1984. Geology and geomorphology of the lower Wadi Hammeh sites. In Preliminary report on the University of Sydney's fifth season of excavations at Pella in Jordan, A. W. McNicoll et al. (eds). *Annual of the Department of Antiquities of Jordan* **XXVIII**, 81–6.

Macumber, P. G. 1986. Environmental reconstruction of the Wadi Hammeh region in the Late Pleistocene. In Preliminary report on the University of Sydney's seventh season of excavations at Pella (Tabaqat Fahl) in 1985, A. W. McNicoll, P. C. Edwards, J. Hosking, P. G. Macumber, A. G. Walmsley & P. M. Watson (eds). *Annual of the Department of Antiquities of Jordan* **XXX**, 156–7.

Marks, A. E. (ed.) 1977. *Prehistory and paleoenvironments in the Central Negev, Israel.* Volume II: *The Avdat/Agev area, part 2 and the Har Harif.* Dallas: Southern Methodist University Press.

Neev, D. & J. K. Hall 1977. *Climatic fluctuations during the Holocene as reflected by the Dead Sea levels.* Paper presented at the International Conference on Terminal Lakes. Utah: Ogden

Perrot, J. 1966. Le gisement Natoufien de Mallaha (Eynan) Isräel. *L'Anthropologie* **70**, 437–83.

Petocz, D. & L. Villiers 1984. Wadi Hammeh survey. In Preliminary report on the University of Sydney's fifth season of excavations at Pella in Jordan, A. W. McNicoll et al. (eds). *Annual of the Department of Antiquities of Jordan* **XXVIII**, 77–81.

Reiss, Z., B. Luz, A. Almogi-Labin, E. Halicz, E. Winter, & J. Erez 1984. Paleoceono-graphy of the Gulf of Aqaba during the last 150 000 years. *Palaeoecology of Africa and the surrounding islands* **16**, 55–65.

Rust, A. 1950. *Die Höhlenfunde von Jabrud (Syrien)*. Neumunster: Wachholtz.

Schuldenrein, J. & P. Golberg 1981. Late Quaternary paleoenvironments and pre-historic site distributions in the Lower Jordan Valley. *Paléorient* **7**(1), 57–71.

Stallibrass, S. n.d. The distinction between the effects of small carnivores and hunters on post-glacial faunal assemblages. A case study using scavenging of sheep carcasses by foxes. Department of Archaeology, University of Sheffield.

Vining, D. R. 1985. The growth of core regions in the Third World. *Scientific American* **252**(4), 24–31.

Willcox, G. 1986. Preliminary report on plant remains from Pella. In *Pella in Jordan 2*. A. McNicoll, J. B. Hennessy & R. H. Smith (eds), in press.

Yellen, J. E. 1977. Cultural patterning in faunal remains. In *Experimental Archaeology* D. Ingersoll, J. E. Yellen & W. McDonald (eds), 271–331. New York: Academic Press.

SUB-SAHARAN
AFRICA

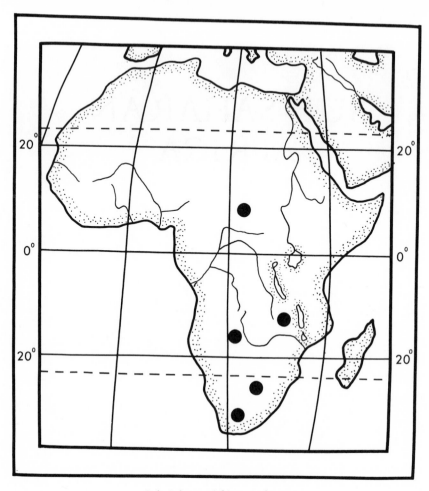

Sub-Saharan Africa: study area

6 The Glacial Maximum in Tropical Africa: 22 000–12 000 BP

ALISON S. BROOKS & PETER ROBERTSHAW

Introduction

Late Pleistocene human adaptations in the tropics and subtropics of sub-Saharan Africa, from the southern edges of the Saharan south to the Limpopo River, are perhaps the least well known of any major area in the Old World. For some parts of this area, for instance, Kenya and Ethiopia, research has focused primarily on earlier periods, to the extent that more excavated archaeological sites are known from the early Pleistocene than from the Late Pleistocene hypothermal, around 18 000 BP. In the more forested areas in or adjacent to the Zaire Basin, exploration has been very limited, and only a few archaeological sequences are known from any time period. West Africa south of the Sahel is almost completely unknown during this interval, and the few regional surveys conducted suggest that human settlement was sparse or absent in this area during the hypothermal. For the southern part of tropical Africa, preliminary regional sequences of Later Pleistocene industries have resulted from more intensive work in limited areas of Zambia, Zimbabwe, and Namibia, although one cannot assume the applicability of these sequences to the relatively unexplored adjacent regions of Botswana, Angola, or Mozambique.

The chronology of those late glacial sequences that have been studied is problematic throughout the area, owing to the relatively poor preservation of most organic materials. Often, in a deeply stratified site, there are no radiocarbon determinations at all that fall in the period around 20 000–16 000 BP with which this volume is particularly concerned. Even when such determinations do exist, they are obtained from inorganic materials or inorganic fractions of organic materials: bone apatite, shell carbonates, and calcretes. Contamination with inorganic 'old' carbon is a problem during the formation of the latter two materials, while post-depositional diagenetic contamination through groundwater exchange may invalidate ^{14}C dates on all three. Thus deposits for which radiocarbon determinations indicate an age within the period in question may, in reality, not date to the period at all. To remind the reader of this problem, the material used as the basis of each radiocarbon date cited in this chapter is shown in Table 6.1.

Table 6.1 Absolute dates from tropical Africa for the LGM and Late Pleistocene

Country	Site	Level	Industry	Lab	Age BP	Material	Comments	References
Botswana	Gi	2B	sterile, pre-LSA	Sl-4090	23 980 ± 590	limestone		Helgren & Brooks (1983)
		2B	sterile, pre-LSA	Sl-4647	22 250 ± 290	limestone	minimum age	Helgren & Brooks (1983)
		2C	post-MSA	AA-3302	33 200 ± 1100	ostrich eggshell	accelerator measurement	Brooks et al. (in prep.)
		3	sterile	Sl-4089	10 255 ± 80	limestone	not in sequence with other date	Helgren & Brooks (1983)
		3	sterile	Sl-4648	31 470 ± 1010	limestone	minimum age	Helgren & Brooks (1983)
	Depression Cave	160–170 cm	LSA	Beta-2281	10 900 ± 420	charcoal		Robbins & Campbell (in press)
		200–210 cm	LSA	Beta-22882	13 060 ± 280	charcoal		Robbins & Campbell (in press)
		270–280 cm	LSA	Beta-22883	18 910 ± 180	charcoal	accelerator (ETH-3531)	Robbins & Campbell (in press)
Zimbabwe	Pomongwe		Pomongwan	SR-12	9 400 ± 100	charcoal		C. K. Cooke (1971, 1984)
		over rockfall	Tshangula	Pta-2300	11 020 ± 60	charcoal		Walker (1980)
		over rockfall		Pta-2299	14 860 ± 115	charcoal		Walker (1980)
		over rockfall		SR-11	15 800 ± 200	charcoal	terminus post quem	C. K. Cooke (1963, 1984)
		under rockfall	Tshangula	SR-10	21 700 ± 400	charcoal		C. K. Cooke (1963, 1984)
	Tshangula		Pomongwan	UCLA-629	12 200 ± 250	charcoal		C. K. Cooke (1963, 1984)
	Nswatugi	under 'Pomongwan'	Pomongwan sterile	Pta-1771	9 790 ± 90	charcoal		Walker (1977)
				Pta-2218	10 265 ± 90	charcoal		Walker (1980)
	Redcliff	above rockfall (e, f)	'Tshangula'	I-3726	25 560 ± 1800	'bone'		C. K. Cooke (1978)

Table 6.1 cont.

Country	Site	Level	Industry	Lab	Age BP	Material	Comments	References
Zimbabwe	Duncombe Farm	3 (128 cm)	microlithic	SR-243	18 970 ± 275	charcoal		Walker & Wadley (1984)
	Zombepata	above rockfall (30–37 cm)	Tshangula	SR-186	13 100 ± 90	charcoal	mixed level ?: MSA/LSA	C. K. Cooke (1971)
		above rockfall (61–68 cm)	Tshangula	SR-187	13 900 ± 140	charcoal		C. K. Cooke (1971)
		above rockfall (61–68 cm)	Tshangula	SR-188	21 360 ± 170	charcoal		C. K. Cooke (1971)
		in rockfall (76–84 cm)	Tshangula	SR-189	22 850 ± 170	charcoal		C. K. Cooke (1971)
Zambia	Diana's Vow	150–160 cm	microlithic	Pta-1857	10 650 ± 80	charcoal		C. K. Cooke (1979)
	Leopard's Hill Cave	114–122 cm	Nachikufan IIa	UCLA-1290	9 700 ± 85	charcoal		Miller (1969)
		183–190 cm	Nachikufan I	SR-138	16 715 ± 95	charcoal		Miller (1969)
		213–221 cm	Proto-LSA	GX-0957	21 550 ± 950	charcoal		Miller (1969)
		267–290 cm	Proto-LSA	UCLA-1429B	22 600 ± 510	charcoal		Miller (1969)
		297–300 cm	Proto-LSA	UCLA-1429A	23 600 ± 360	charcoal		Miller (1969)
	Mwela Rocks shelter	137–213 cm	Nachikufan I	Y-808	10 820 ± 340	charcoal		Miller (1969)
					11 700 ± 280	charcoal	alkaline soluble residue	Miller (1969)
	Chifubwa Stream	post Nachikufan I	post-Nachikufan I	Y-620B	9 720 ± 550	charcoal		Miller (1969)
	Nachikufu Cave	91–107 cm		C-663	6 310 ± 250			Miller (1969)
	Kalemba	N middle	mode 5	GX-2769	15 330 ± 1100	bone apatite	published as bc dates	Phillipson (1976)
		M middle	mode 5	GX-2768	26 300 + 1500 − 1200	bone apatite	too old?	Phillipson (1976)
		L middle	mode 5	GX-2767	>3 1000	bone apatite		Phillipson (1976)
		K top	mode 5	GX-2766	14 800 ± 1000	bone apatite	too old?	Phillipson (1976)
		K lower	Transtl mode 3/5	GX-2611	24 420 + 2000 − 1000	bone apatite		Phillipson (1976)
		H top	mode 3	GX-2610	24 600 + 2000 − 1000	bone apatite		Phillipson (1976)
		G bottom	mode 3	GX-2609	>37 000	bone apatite		Phillipson (1976)
	Mwambacimo	III–130 cm	Group I (c. Nch I)	Pta-2454	9 830 ± 90	charcoal		Musonda (1984)
		III 140–150 cm	Group I	N-3434	12 900 ± 110	charcoal		Musanda (1984)
		III–190 cm	Group I	N-3435	12 000 ± 90	charcoal		Musonda (1984)
		III–200 cm	Group I	Pta-2453	19 080 ± 180	charcoal		Musonda (1984)

Table 6.1 cont.

Country	Site	Level	Industry	Lab	Age BP	Material	Comments	References
Zambia	Kalambo Falls	A 3, top rubble 1	post-'Magosian'	L-395D	9 550 ± 210	charcoal	terminus ante quem	Clark (1969)
		A 1, rubble I C	? Lupemban	L-3991	30 500 ± 2000	charcoal	residue	Clark (1969)
				L-3991	27 500 ± 2300	charcoal	humic acid	Clark (1969)
		A 4, clay over rubble II	? Lower Lupemban	GrN-4261	31 660 ± 600	charcoal		Clark (1969)
Tanzania	Kisese II		Middle LSA	NPL-35	14 760 ± 202	charred OES		Callow et al. (1964)
			Early LSA	NPL-36	10 720 ± 132	charred OES	too young, out of seq.	Callow et al. (1964)
			Transtl 1st (sic) Intermediate/LSA	NPL-37	18 190 ± 306	charred OES		Callow et al. (1964)
			Mid. 2nd Intermed.	NPL-38	31 480 + 1640			Callow et al. (1964)
					– 1350	charred OES		Callow et al. (1964)
	Naisiusiu Beds, Olduvai Gorge	17–23 cm above artefacts		UCLA-1695	17 550 ± 1000	'bone geletin'	collagen?	Leakey et al. (1972)
		17–23 cm above artefacts			17 000	OES	no error or lab no. given	Leakey et al. (1972)
	Nasera	4	Early LSA (Capsian)	ISGS-449	14 780 ± 250	collagen		Mehlman (1977)
				ISGS-449	22 460 ± 50	apatite		Mehlman (1977)
		4	Early LSA (Capsian)	GX-6618A	18 280 ± 645	apatite		Mehlman (1977)
		4	Early LSA (Capsian)	GX-6618A	c.20 000	bone protein	amino acid racemization (Bada)	Bada (1981)
		5A	Early LSA	ISGS-445	21 600 ± 400	collagen		Mehlman (1977)
				ISGS-445	21 700	apatite		Mehlman (1977)
		6	Naseran	GX-6619A	18 475 ± 860	apatite		Mehlman (1977)
		6	Naseran	ISGS-425	22 910 ± 400	collagen		Mehlman (1977)
				ISGS-425	22 350 ± 380	apatite		Mehlman (1977)
		6		ISGS-425	25 599 + 600 / – 350	bone	uranium series (Bischoff)	Mehlman (1977)
		6	Nasseran	ISGS-425	c.26 000	bone protein	amino acid racemization (Bada)	Bada (1981)

Table 6.1 cont.

Country	Site	Level	Industry	Lab	Age BP	Material	Comments	References
Tanzania	Nasera	7	Naseran	ISGS-500	20 360 ± 330	collagen		Mehlman (1977)
				ISGS-500	17 080 ± 130	apatite		Mehlman (1977)
		17	MSA	ISGS-500	55 960 + 2675 − 2300	rhino tooth	uranium series (Bischoff)	Mehlman (1977)
	Mumba-Hohle	III-Low. 160–180 cm	?Naseran	ISGS-566	26 960 ± 760	OES		Mehlman (1979, pers. comm.)
		III-Low 190–200 cm	?Naseran	AA-3299	33 200 ± 900	OES	accelerator measurement	Brooks et al. (in prep.)
		IV 230–240 cm	beach dep.	USGS-1505	25 130 ± 320	tufa		Mehlman (pers. comm.)
		IV 230–240 cm		ISGS-498	36 900 ± 800	snail shell	land snail (Achatina) reworked from Bed V	Mehlman (pers. comm.)
		V-top	Intrmed. MSA/LSA	ISGS-498	23 620 + 1099 − 851			Mehlman (pers. comm.)
				ISGS-498	23 800 + 2538 − 1414	bone	uranium series (Th-230)	Mehlman (pers. comm.)
		V-Mid	Intrmed. MSA/LSA	GX-6620A	37 000	snail shell	uranium series (Pa-231)	Mehlman (1987, pers. comm.)
		V-Mid	Intrmed. MSA/LSA	ISGS-498	31 070 ± 500	snail shell		Mehlman (1979, 1987)
		V-Mid	Intrmed. MSA/LSA	ISGS-498	65 686 + 6049 − 5426	bone	uranium series (Th-230)	Mehlman (1979, 1987)
		V-Mid	Intrmed. MSA/LSA	GX-6621A	29 570 + 1400 − 1100	'bone'		Mehlman (1979, 1987)
		V-Mid	Intrmed. MSA/LSA	GX-6621A	46 600 + 2050 − 1725	bone	uranium series (Th-230)	Mehlman (1979, 1987)

Table 6.1 cont.

Country	Site	Level	Industry	Lab	Age BP	Material	Comments	References
Tanzania	Mumba-Hohle	V-Lower	Intrmed. MSA/LSA	GX-6622A	20 995 ± 680	'bone'		Mehlman (1979, 1987)
		V-Lower	Intrmed. MSA/LSA	GX-6622A	35 291 + 749 − 476			Mehlman (1979, 1987)
				GX-6622A	39 777 + 4162 − 3753	bone	uranium series (Th-230)	Mehlman (1979, 1987)
		VI-B-top	MSA	GX-6623A	19 820 ± 750	'bone'	uranium series (Pa-231)	Mehlman (1979, 1987)
		VI-B-Middle	MSA	GX-6623A	109 486 + 44 404 − 2302	bone		Mehlman (1979, 1987)
				GX-6623A	131 710 + 6924 − 6026	bone	most acceptable dates for this level	Mehlman (1979, 1987)
Kenya	Twilight Cave (Enkapune ya Muto)	DBL1 c. 335 cm	early LSA	UCLA-	16 300 ± 1000	charcoal	small sample, mini-counters	Ambrose
		DBL1 c. 335 cm	early LSA	UCLA-	35 800 ± 550	charcoal	large sample	Ambrose
		RBL4-1 c. 420 cm	pre-LSA	GX-9948	>26 000	charcoal	minimum age	Ambrose (pers. comm.)
	Lukenya Hill GvJm22	Zone E: 135–140 cm	early LSA	UCLA-1709A	17 670 ± 800	collagen		Gramly & Rightmire (1973)
		Zone E: 140–145 cm	early LSA	UCLA-1709B	17 700 ± 760	collagen		Gramly & Rightmire (1973)
		Zone F: 180–185 cm	early LSA	GX-3699	15 320 ± 450	collagen	humic acid contamination?	Gramly & Rightmire (1973)
		Zone F: 190–200 cm	early LSA	GX-3698	13 730 ± 430	collagen	humic acid contamination?	Gramly & Rightmire (1973)
		Zone F: 190–195 cm	early LSA	HEL-535	9 910 ± 300	collagen	humic acid contamination?	Gramly & Rightmire (1973)

Table 6.1 cont.

Country	Site	Level	Industry	Lab	Age BP	Material	Comments	References
Uganda	Munyama Cave	70–80 cm	early LSA	GrN-5708	14 480 ± 130	charcoal		van Noten (1971)
		80–90 cm	early LSA	GrN-5850	14 925 ± 80	charcoal		van Noten (1971)
Ethiopia	Lake Ziway, Bulbula R.	exp. palaeosol	microlithic	SUA-588	27 050 ± 1540	charcoal		Gasse et al. (1980)
		palaeosol under lake dep.	LSA	SUA-494	11 870 ± 300	charcoal		Gasse & Street (1978)
	Lake Besaka, Fejx1–4	sand under cult. horiz.	under LSA	UW-494	19 280 ± 215	OES		Brandt (1982, 1986)
		sand under cult. horiz.	under LSA	UW-493	19 460 ± 205	OES		Brandt (1982, 1986)
		sand under cult. horiz.	under LSA	UW-495	22 080 ± 305	OES		Brandt (1982, 1986)
	K'one Caldera	top, upper loam	Transl LSA/MSA	I-8322	14 670 ± 200	OES		Clark & Williams (1978)
	Laga Oda	80–110 cm	LSA?	SUA-474	10 270 ± 170	charcoal		Clark & Prince (1978)
		110–140 cm	LSA	SUA-475	15 590 ± 460	charcoal		Clark & Prince (1978)
	Gobedra	IV-C 65–75 cm	LSA	P-2238	10 160 ± 140	charcoal		Phillipson (1977b)
	Aladi Springs	tufa	LSA	I-7970	11 070 ± 160	shell		Williams et al. (1977)
	Macho ETH–73–3–III	30–35 cm	LSA	SMU-86	10 330 ± 90	charcoal		Humphreys (1978)
Somalia	Midhishi 2		'Hargeisan'?	UW-787	18 790 ± 340	charcoal		Brandt (1986)
			MSA	UW-761	> 40 000	charcoal		Brandt (1986)
Zaire	Matupi	c. 50–70 cm	LSA	GrN-7343	12 050 ± 250	charcoal		van Noten (1977)
		c. 70–75 cm	LSA	GrN-6917	14 230 ± 220	charcoal		van Noten (1977)
		c. 90–100 cm	LSA	GrN-3344	16 740 ± 150	charcoal		van Noten (1977)
		c. 120 cm	microlithic	GrN-6918	21 210 ± 400	charcoal		van Noten (1977)
		c. 140–150 cm	microlithic	GrN-7347	21 630 ± 410	charcoal		van Noten (1977)
		c. 160–170 cm	microlithic	GrN-7348	22 100 ± 240	charcoal		van Noten (1977)
		c. 180–190 cm	microlithic debit.	GrN-7349	33 000 ± 1900 – 1500	charcoal		van Noten (1977)
		c. 200–210 cm	microlithic debit.	GrN-7246	> 40 700	charcoal		van Noten (1977)

Table 6.1 cont.

Country	Site	Level	Industry	Lab	Age BP	Material	Comments	References
Zaire	Ishango 11	Niv. Tufaces	'Ishangian III'	SI-7062	20 155 ± 245	mollusc shell		Brooks & Smith (1987)
		Niv. Foss. Princ.	'Ishangian II'	W-283	21 000 ± 500	mollusc shell	modern shell (W-284, SI-7061, SI-7063 dated to between 1700 & 3000 BP)	Brooks & Smith (1987) de Heinzelin (1957)
		Niv. Foss. Princ.	'Ishangian II'	SI-7064	23 760 ± 385	mollusc shell		Brooks & Smith (1987)
		Niv. Fos. Princ.	'Ishangian II'	SI-7065	19 870 ± 240	mollusc shell		Brooks & Smith (1987)
		Niv. Foss. Princ.	'Ishangian II'	Beta-22047	19 920 ± 450	mollusc shell		Brooks (pers. comm.)
		Niv. Foss. Princ.	'Ishangian II'	AA-3300	25 290 ± 350	OES	accelerator measurement	Brooks (pers. comm.)
	Ishango 14	cultural level	'Ishangian III'	Beta-22050	16 840 ± 480	crab claws		Brooks (pers. comm.)
		cultural level	'Ishangian III'	Beta-22051	20 610 ± 530	mollusc shell		Brooks (pers. comm.)
		cultural level	'Ishangian III'	Beta-22052	22 530 ± 500	mollusc shell		Brooks (pers. comm.)
	Gombe Point	yellow sand	Djokocian	GrN-7220	8 095 ± 50	charcoal		Brooks (pers. comm.)
		yellow sand	Djokocian	GrN-7276	14 840 ± 80	charcoal		Brooks (pers. comm.)
		angular gravel below sand	Kalinian	GrN-7221	27 240 ± 280	charcoal		Cahen (1976)
		angular gravel below sand	Kalinian	GrN-7277	>43 800	charcoal		Cahen (1976)
	Kinshasa Plain		Tshitolian	Lv-164	9 730 ± 280	charcoal		van Moorsel (1968)
			Tshitolian	Lv-165	8 920 ± 160	charcoal		van Moorsel (1968)
			Lupemban 'moyen'	Lv-287	12 230 ± 450	charcoal		van Moorsel (1968)
			Lupemban 'moyen'	Lv-166	15 080 ± 480	charcoal		van Moorsel (1968)
			Lupemban 'ancien'	Lv-47	>30 000	charcoal		van Moorsel (1968)
			Lupemban 'ancien'	Lv-163	>26 000	charcoal		van Moorsel (1968)

Table 6.1 cont.

Country	Site	Level	Industry	Lab	Age BP	Material	Comments	References
Zaire	Lake Tumba area sites:							
	Wafanya, Luilaka R.	sands under artefacts	pre-artefacts	Hv-12944	37 640 ± 860	charcoal		Fiedler & Preuss (1985)
	Nkoyakoni, Busira R.	sands under artefacts	pre-artefacts	Hv-12947	24 860 ± 290	charcoal		Fiedler & Preuss (1985)
	Imbonga, Momboyo R.	org. horiz. w/pollen		Hv-12945	19 920 ± 765	charcoal		Fielder & Preuss (1985)
	Bokuma-Isoku, Ruiki R.	org. horiz. (top)		Hv-11776	17 735 ± 135	charcoal		Fiedler & Preuss (1985)
	Imbonga	surface deposit	contemp w/tools?	Hv-12948	15 880 ± 340	charcoal		Fiedler & Preuss (1985)
	Lokolo R.	surface deposit	contemp w/tools?	Hv-12951	11 505 ± 190	charcoal		Fiedler & Preuss (1985)
Angola	Calunda 3	low sand/yngst gravels	Tshitolian (early)	UCLA-172	12 970 ± 250	charcoal		Clark (1963)
	Mufo	upper gravel under sand	Lupembo-Tshitolian	C-580	11 189 ± 490	wood		Clark (1963)
		upper gravel under sand	Lupembo-Tshitolian	C-581	14 503 ± 560	wood		Clark (1963)
		lower gravels 105–110 cm	Lower Lupemban	UCLA-169	>34 000	wood		Clark (1963)
		lower gravels 105–110 cm	Lower Lupemban	UCLA-168	38 000 ± 2500	peat		Clark (1963)
Cameroon	Mayo Louti	yellow sand over gravel	above MSA horiz.	Gif-2233	8 400 ± 110	calcrete		Marliac (1973, 1974)
		yellow sand over gravel	above MSA horiz.	Gif-2234	14 720 ± 200	calcrete		Marliac (1973, 1974)
		yellow sand over gravel	above MSA horiz.	Gif-2236	15 320 ± 210	calcrete		Marliac (1973, 1974)

The archaeological record of the sub-Saharan African interior, however scanty, does suggest that *following* the late glacial hypothermal, from about 13 000 BP on, the number of dated archaeological sites rose exponentially. Many of these assemblages were once considered to exhibit new technological and economic capacities, such as backed microliths and fishing equipment, innovations which may have made their first appearance earlier during the hypothermal itself. Even the limited evidence available may allow a preliminary examination of three questions of interest to this examination of worldwide adaptations during the Late Glacial:

(a)   What was the nature of late Pleistocene environmental change in tropical sub-Saharan Africa, with particular reference to the amount of forest cover, and how do environmental changes during this interval correlate with those in other areas considered in this volume?

(b)   What is the evidence for the development of specialized economies and technologies in this region, and how does it compare with that of other regions?

(c)   Did hunter–gatherers occupy the tropical forest before the onset of agriculture, or is human survival in this ecozone necessarily linked to domesticated sources of carbohydrates, as some authors have recently argued (Headland 1987, Bailey & Peacock 1988)? This question is of particular relevance in the debate over the applicability of modern hunter–gatherer studies to the reconstruction of past hunter–gatherer lifeways (e.g. Schrire 1984).

Palaeoclimatic reconstruction

Palaeoclimatic reconstruction in the interior of sub-Saharan Africa derives primarily from two bodies of data: pollen and other biological and sedimentological indicators recovered from deep lake cores and high-altitude peat bogs, and studies of terrestrial sediments, often in association with archaeological materials. Correlation between these two data sets is often problematic. Pollen data in tropical areas are subject to particular interpretative problems (e.g. Hamilton 1982), in view of the large number of trees and other tropical species that contribute little to the pollen rain. For lake cores, the analyses of diatoms, ostracods, chemistry, and sedimentology, together with fossil pollen, have contributed to a more complete, but often more complex and contradictory reconstruction of palaeoclimates (e.g. Haberyan & Hecky 1987, Richardson & Dussinger 1986). Many lake cores, however, do not extend to or beyond the hypothermal, and may reflect fluctuations in lake-level due to local conditions or to tectonic movements, rather than entirely to climatic shifts. The most significant problem for the archaeologist is the difficulty of correlating the lake-level and vegetation fluctuations reflected in the deep-lake cores, with the environments actually experienced by the prehistoric inhabitants of a site,

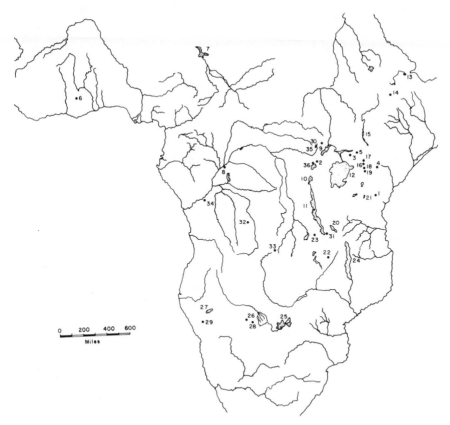

Figure 6.1 Locations of palaeoenvironmental studies mentioned in the text. Mountains: 1, Mt Kilimanjaro; 2, Ruwenzoris; 3, Mt Elgon; 4, Mt Kenya; 5, Cherangani Hills. Lakes: 6, Bosumtwi; 7, Chad; 8, Tumba; 9, Mobutu; 10, Kivu; 11, Tanganyika; 12, Victoria; 13, Abhe; 14, Ziway-Shala; 15, Turkana; 16, Bogoria; 17, Baringo; 18, Nakuru-Elementeita; 19, Naivasha; 20, Rukwa; 21, Manyara; 22, Ishiba Ngandu; 23, Chesi; 24, Malawi; 25, Makgadikgadi Pans; 26, Gi; 27, Etosha Pan. Caves: 28, Kwihabe (Drotsky's Cave); 29, Rossing; 30, Mt Hoyo. Archaeological sites: 31, Kalambo Falls; 32, Dundo; 33, Kamoa; 34, Gombe Point; 35, Matupi; 36, Ishango.

which may be located at a considerable distance from a lake margin. Data from glacial deposits at high altitudes, as well as the analysis of travertines and cave sinters, may also be difficult to correlate with the archaeological record.

Despite the suggestion in a recent global climatic simulation that eastern Africa was wetter during the hypothermal at 18 000 BP (COHMAP 1988), the available data from specific sites indicates otherwise. Since the summaries by van Zinderen Bakker (1967), Butzer *et al.* (1972), Livingstone (1975), Street & Grove (1976) and Moeyersons & Roche (1977–78, 1982) of late Quaternary climatic change in sub-Saharan Africa, excellent compendia have been published for southern Africa (Vogel 1984) and for eastern Africa (Hamilton 1982). Most recently, several individual studies have appeared that add significantly to the body of data for eastern Africa (e.g. Hastenrath & Kutzbach 1983, Richardson & Dussinger 1986, Haberyan 1987, Haberyan & Hecky 1987). In addition, archaeological exploration of the Zaire Basin has begun to suggest the extent and age of old sand sheets in areas presently under tropical forest cover (Cahen 1976, Preuss 1986).

Palaeotemperatures

The worldwide temperature drop of 4–7°C during the last hypothermal is directly reflected in this region only at the highest altitudes in the presence of moraines on Mt Kenya, Kilimanjaro, and the Ruwenzoris which mark the glacial maxima. These have rarely been dated, so their equivalence to the late glacial maxima of the northern hemisphere at 18 000 BP is assumed rather than proven. An indirect age for the basal layers of a core from Lake Mahoma, above the most extensive terminal moraine in the Ruwenzoris, suggests that glacial retreat must have begun before 14 750 BP (Livingstone 1971). Osmaston (1965, reviewed in Livingstone 1975) argued that the descent of the snowline from its present altitude to a point 2400 m lower, indicated by the Mahoma moraines, would have required a temperature drop of 4°C in the *absence* of any change in precipitation. Since there is widespread evidence for a decrease in precipitation during this interval (see below), an even greater lowering of temperature may be inferred. Despite arguments for changes in atmospheric circulation patterns, the position of the Ruwenzori moraines relative to the current ice cap, suggests that in this area at least, the rainfall pattern and direction during the Last Glacial Maximum (LGM) was similar to that of the present day.

Further confirmation of the presence of cold and arid climatic conditions over much of eastern Africa has been obtained from pollen cores taken from high-altitude swamps scattered across the region from Rwanda and the Ruwenzoris to Mt Elgon and the Cherangani Hills (Hamilton 1982 and references therein). All these pollen spectra contain high percentages of grass pollen but relatively rare tree pollen, indicating that the climate was generally more arid than that of the present. Forest was particularly restricted on Mt Elgon (Hamilton 1982), where confirmation of aridity was provided both by high percentages of grasses (55–90%) and by dominance of the very small arboreal fraction by *Juniperus* and other dry montane forest trees. The substantial quantities of Ericaceous zone pollens (*Artemesia, Anthrospermum, Ericacea*) in the core from Sacred Lake, Mt Kenya (Coetzee 1967), imply a lowering of the upper forest boundary by at least 700 m from its present position; a reduction in mean air temperatures compared to the present of at least 4.4°C is surmised (Coetzee 1967, van Zinderen Bakker 1967). Livingstone, however, argues that global percentages of grass pollen cannot be used as a climatic indicator in many areas of eastern and southern Africa, particularly in the absence of data on the modern pollen rain in which the leguminous trees of the savanna belt may be poorly represented (Livingstone 1975). A temperature reduction of similar scale is suggested by the presence of pollen of giant groundsels (*Dendrosenecio*) in the core from Lake Mahoma (altitude 2960 m) in the Ruwenzoris (Livingstone 1967, Hamilton 1982).

Other direct indicators of lower palaeotemperatures may include a larger body size of some mammals, especially carnivores (see Klein 1980, Peters 1989) as well as $^{16}O : {}^{18}O$ ratios in mollusc shells (Shackleton 1982), ostrich eggshell (Brooks *et al.* in press) and soil carbonates (Labeyrie *et al.* 1967, Cerling 1984, Cerling & Hay 1986). Regional studies, using these techniques, are still in the experimental stages, but may be expected to yield better direct estimates of effective palaeotemperatures at archaeological sites.

Palaeolimnology and stratigraphy in African lakes

Evidence of fluctuating vegetation zones, alkalinity and/or shorelines have been recovered from Lakes Chad (Servant *et al.* 1969, Servant & Servant-Valdary 1980), Bosumtwi (Talbot *et al.* 1984), Mobutu (Hecky & Degens 1973, Harvey 1976), Kivu (Livingstone 1965, Haberyan & Hecky 1987), Tanganyika (Livingstone 1965, Haberyan & Hecky 1987), Chesi (Stager 1984), Ishiba Ngandu (Livingstone 1971), Victoria (Kendall 1969, Stager 1984), Abhe (Gasse 1980), Ziway-Shala (Gasse 1980), Turkana (Butzer 1971, Butzer *et al.* 1972), Bogoria (Tiercelin *et al.* 1981), Baringo (Renaut & Owen 1980), Nakuru-Elmenteita (Richardson & Dussinger 1986), Naivasha (Richardson & Richardson 1972, Richardson & Dussinger 1986), Rukwa (Haberyan 1987), Manyara (Holdship 1976), and Malawi (Scholz & Rosendahl 1988). Further to the south, a chronology of the palaeoshorelines of Lake Makgadi, which once covered *c.* 37 000 km^2, has been developed by H. J. Cooke (1984).

All of the rift lake studies (Fig. 6.2) together with those of Lakes Chad and Bosumtwi show a remarkably consistent picture of very low lake-levels associated with reduced vegetation cover for a significant portion of the late glacial hypothermal, particularly around 15 000 to *c.* 13 000 BP. The magnitude of this dry phase may be reflected in ancient shorelines at least 400 m below the present shoreline, which have been identified using seismic data in lakes Tanganyika and Malawi (Scholz & Rosendahl 1988). Sedimentation rates calculated for these lakes suggest that the dry phase may have begun 25 000 years ago and lasted for the rest of the Pleistocene. Between 19 500 and 16 000 BP, however, somewhat higher lake-levels are reflected in the data from lakes Mobutu and Manyara, and, to a lesser extent, in the diatom evidence only from Lake Naivasha. For Lake Mobutu, however, the existence of more humid conditions around 18 000 BP has been contradicted by more recent pollen analyses (Sowunmi 1986). Other rift lakes (e.g. Elmenteita-Nakuru) show no significant change from low levels and more open vegetation over the entire period. Local differences among lake histories may be due to greater buffering of some lakes from environmental perturbations due to greater depth, or degree of closure (L. C. Beadle 1981, Haberyan & Hecky 1987).

At the southern margin of the area considered here, the picture is more

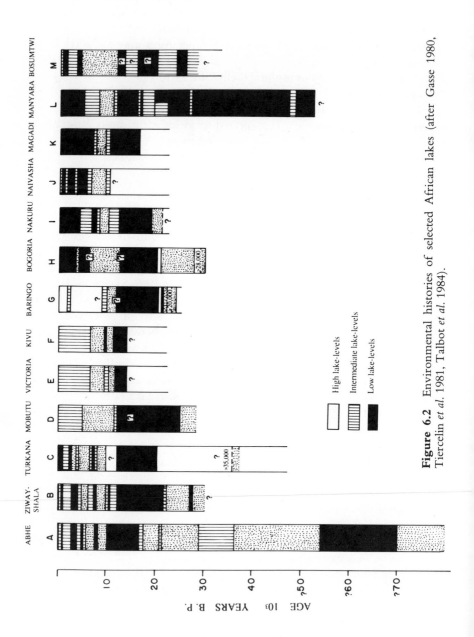

Figure 6.2 Environmental histories of selected African lakes (after Gasse 1980, Tiercelin et al. 1981, Talbot et al. 1984).

complex, and does not correlate well with the East African evidence. The recent desiccation of the Lake Makgadi basin in Botswana is due primarily to the tectonic shifts which ponded the Okavango River behind a NE–SW trending ridge, and allowed capture of much of the catchment area in Angola by the Zambezi (Grove 1969, H. J. Cooke 1978, Ebert & Hitchcock 1978). The chronology of ancient shorelines has been determined largely through radiocarbon dating of calcretes at various heights. Both the calcrete dates themselves and their association with particular lake-levels can be questioned, although it is clear, as H. J. Cooke points out (1984, p. 274) that calcretes probably indicate that the lake was lower than the level sampled at that particular time, and that any beach features overlying the calcrete formed during a subsequent rise in lake-level. The lowest elevation (910 m) is associated with dates around 20 000 to 19 000 BP. A peat at 910 m, also dated to around 19 000 BP, suggests that the lake was in proximity to the 910 m shoreline at this date. The 912 m shoreline is particularly problematic, with clusters of dates around 3000 BP and 22 000–35 000 BP. Higher shorelines, at 920 and 945 m, are mostly associated with dates in the range from 26 000 to 40 000 BP. The lake may not have been at this height during the period prior to the hypothermal, but the available evidence would suggest that during the onset of the hypothermal, the lake was at a minimum level.

Dates on calcretes from an ephemeral lake at Gi on the Botswana–Namibia border also suggest that the last high lake stand was at about 23 000–22 000 BP, followed by a period of prolonged desiccation, calcrete formation, and aeolian transport (Helgren & Brooks 1983). The southwestern Kalahari was also drier after *c.* 19 000 BP (Heine 1982, Deacon *et al.* 1984). Dates between 22 000 and 18 000 BP on pedogenic calcretes from Etosha pan in northern Namibia are interpreted by Rust (1984) as evidence for a period of more evenly distributed rainfall and greater vegetation cover, followed by a time of aeolian activity in conditions of low and/or highly erratic rainfall and reduced vegetation cover between 18 000 and 10 000 BP.

The evidence from South Africa itself is quite varied and suggests that a number of locations may have experienced higher rainfall during and immediately following the late glacial hypothermal (Butzer 1984, Deacon *et al.* 1984). The available evidence from tropical southern Africa, however, is more or less consistent with the late glacial dry period suggested by the rift lake sequences further to the north. Differences in timing of minimum levels in the several lake and pan basins discussed above may be attributable to localized differences in rainfall and drainage patterns, to a west–east and/or south–north gradient in the actual timing of the minimum rainfall period, or to problems in age determination, particularly in view of a probable lag time between the rainfall minimum and formation of the dated material in many cases.

Palaeoclimatic inferences from cave sinters and other speleotherms

Deposition of cave sinters in karstic terrain should correlate with periods of humid conditions sufficient to account for the downward movement of water through the cavern system. The dating of these by ^{14}C, however, may be subject to some of the same interpretative problems as the dating of calcretes in regard to the ultimate origin of the carbonate fraction. A series of cave sinter dates from the Kwihabe Hills (Drotsky's Cave) in northwestern Botswana (H. J. Cooke 1975, 1984) have indicated the presence of humid conditions around 30 000 BP and again between 16 000 and 13 000 BP. These determinations are in accord with other evidence suggesting dry conditions around the hypothermal at 18 000 BP. The wetter conditions reflected at the nearby pan site of Gi at *c*. 22 000 BP, however, are not represented at Kwihabe, and the wetter conditions at 16 000 BP indicated at Kwihabe are not seen in the lake and pan data from tropical southern Africa. Speleotherms from the Rossing cave in the Namib Desert (Heine & Geyh 1984) indicate that active formation and inferred humid conditions were in effect until 26 500 BP, followed by a period of increasing aridity from 25 000 to 19 000 BP. Conditions of extreme aridity prevailed after 19 000 BP; this situation is also reflected in pollen data from the Namib (van Zinderen Bakker 1984a, b, see also Rust *et al.*, 1984). Other data on cave sinters in the Mt Hoyo massif in eastern Zaire are presently being studied by George Brook, and may be expected to yield information on Late Pleistocene rainfall patterns in Central Africa.

Palaeoclimatic data from archaeological sites

Relatively little palaeoclimatic information is available for archaeological sites during the interval in question. Pollen is poorly preserved in most tropical rockshelters and many open-air sites in desert and savanna ecozones. Pollen diagrams are available from Kalambo Falls (Zambia), Dundo (Lunda District, Angola), Kamoa (Shaba Province, Zaire), and several sites in the Lac Tumba area (Equateur Province, Zaire).

During the late Pleistocene hypothermal, the Kalambo Falls pollen spectra indicate an open grassland with few trees, which in turn implies a downward shift in vegetation belts of some 800 m, corresponding to a temperature drop of *c*. 4°C, in the absence of shifts in rainfall (Clark & van Zinderen Bakker 1964, van Zinderen Bakker 1967). The Dundo spectrum from this time-interval also appears to suggest a very similar lowering of vegetation belts in response to lowered temperature and rainfall. Here the reconstructed vegetation during the hypothermal indicates a riverine forest of montane evergreen type with abundant *Podocarpus*. Both sites are currently situated in *Brachystegia* woodland.

In Zaire, a pollen profile from the Kamoa River in Shaba Province, also currently characterized by open woodland of *Brachystegia* type, is less informative since it is not associated with radiocarbon dates (Roche 1975, Moeyersons & Roche 1977–78). An approximate date of 15 000 BP, based on sedimentation rates, is associated here with a reduction in surface erosion, the deposition of red sands from the plateau, and the eventual formation of a palaeosol in association with a gallery forest vegetation, all indicative of increasing humidity and decreasing seasonality of rainfall. Moeyersons & Roche (1977–78) correlate the climax of this phase, associated with a 'transitional' [Middle Stone Age–Late Stone Age (MSA–LSA)] industry with the rising lake-levels of the rift around 12 000 BP. Prior to this transition, the climate was more arid, and the vegetation more open.

A more securely dated set of analyses, also by E. Roche (Fiedler & Preuss 1985, Preuss 1986), has recently been carried out on samples from the Lac Tumba area in Equateur Province, part of the central 'refugium' of the lowland tropical forest in most reconstructions of late Pleistocene forest retreat. In two samples from Imbonga and Bokuma-Isoku, dated to 19 920 BP and >17 735 BP respectively, the pollen spectra suggest the dominance of woodland savanna, with nearby swamps and gallery forest, and constitute the first direct evidence for savanna penetration into the central forest areas during the glacial maximum. These spectra are in possible association with surface collections of small quartz artefacts of the type also described from Matupi Cave, Ituri Province, Zaire (see below).

Arid conditions at archaeological sites dating to this interval are also inferred on the basis of sediment analyses. Invasion of the southern margins of the Zaire Basin by 'Kalahari' sands, documented at archaeological sites such as Gombe Point on the Kinshasa Plain (Zaire), implies greater aridity during the period beginning before 20 000 BP and extending to c. 12 000 BP. The chronology is based on dates from associated charcoal samples, although the stratigraphic integrity of this site in particular, and of sites located in Kalahari sand in general, has been questioned (Cahen & Moeyersons 1977). Sand also underlies current forests and forest soils in the central basin of Zaire (Preuss 1986).

Most frequently, environmental reconstruction at archaeological sites in sub-Saharan tropical Africa is based in large part on faunal analyses, primarily of large mammals. Even without the cultural bias of human hunting and exploitation, which resulted in the accumulation of at least some of this faunal material, large mammals are notoriously poor climatic indicators. The presence of bones of savanna mammals, for example, when recovered from sites currently in tropical forest environments (e.g. Matupi, Zaire), is taken to indicate the close proximity of savannas to the site in the past, without adequate consideration for the distances of up to 100 km that human hunters have frequently covered over a few days' time in ethnographic accounts (Lee 1979, Silberbauer 1981). The effect of recent intensive hunting of large African mammals on their former distribution is also not always taken into account. A more promising approach deals with differences in size between late Pleistocene and Holocene forms as indicators of palaeotemperatures (Klein 1980). A re-analysis of the mammalian fauna from Ishango, Kivu Province, Zaire, by Peters (1989), has shown that most specimens fall outside the range of size variability of their modern counterparts, a difference which could well be attributed to colder temperatures in the interval under consideration. Whether changes in size are connected primarily to temperature differences or to some other factor, such as increasing abilities of human predators to track and kill larger specimens, is not resolved at present. Micromammals, more sensitive indicators of both temperature and ecology, have been studied at several sites in South Africa itself (Avery 1984), but rarely at sites in the tropical area (but see Brain 1974).

Consideration of several lines of evidence confirms an overall impression of greater aridity over most of tropical Africa during the late glacial hypothermal. The timing of this event varies, however, with some sites suggesting an onset of arid conditions by 20 000 BP, while others indicate maximum aridity around 15 000–13 000 BP. The effect of increased aridity, together with the global decrease in temperature, was a lowering or compression of altitudinally controlled vegetation belts, together with a contraction of forest and woodland–savanna zones toward the equator, and an expansion of desert or semiarid vegetation. According to several reconstructions (Fig. 6.3), the net reduction in forested environments may have resulted in the creation of at least three forest 'refugia' in the Zaire Basin, one in the Ituri forest region to the east, one in the *'cuvette centrale'* near Lac Tumba, and one near the river mouth on the west. Recent evidence from the presumed 'refugia', however, indicates that even these areas may have been affected by increased sand cover and savanna vegetation during the hypothermal.

Archaeological evidence for cultural complexity: 24 000–12 000 BP

Southern Africa: Namibia, Botswana, Zimbabwe

Very little evidence exists for archaeological occupation of the Kalahari during the late glacial hypothermal. Although occupation at Apollo 11 (Namibia) and possibly also at Poggenbank, on the southern border of this region, was apparently continuous throughout the late Pleistocene (Wendt 1972, 1974, 1976), the absence of occupation sites in the more arid areas to the north and east may reflect a gap in the archaeological record of human occupation (Sandelowsky 1983). An occupation horizon, characterized by small blades, at the open-air site of Gi, in northwestern Botswana (Helgren & Brooks 1983, Brooks *et al.* 1985), is dated to an interval between 22 000 and 33 000 BP (see Table 6.1), and is followed by a lengthy period of calcrete formation and landscape erosion consistent with an arid climate. Further occupation of this area is not documented until the end of the Pleistocene, where a small, typologically indefinite assemblage from Kwihabe (Drotsky's Cave) has been dated to 12 200 BP on charcoal (Yellen *et al.* 1987). The fauna at the latter site reflect human utilization of a wide range of species, and the presence of blesbok (*Damaliscus dorcas albifrons*) may reflect a wetter climate than at present. Further to the northeast, a sequence from Depression Cave, in the Tsodilo Hills, (Robbins & Campbell in press) has provided one of the best series of

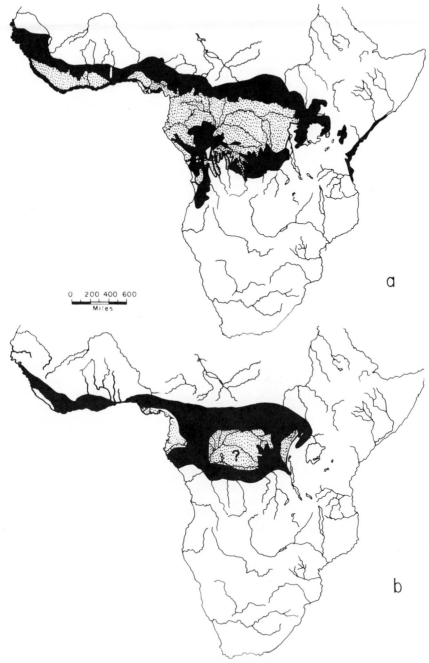

Figure 6.3 Limits of tropical forest (light) and forest–savanna (dark) vegetation zones. (a) present-day (after Clark 1967); (b) *c.* 18 000 BP (after Clark 1967, Moeyersons and Roche 1982).

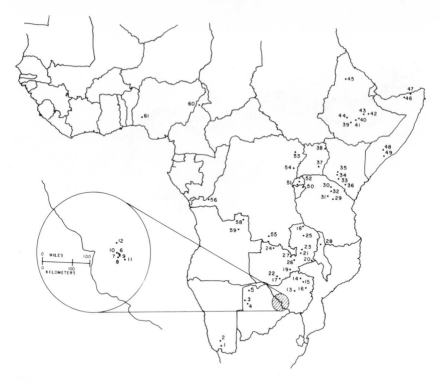

Figure 6.4   Archaeological sites mentioned in the text. Namibia; 1, Apollo 11; 2, Poggenbank. Botswana: 3, Gi; 4, Kwihabe (Drotsky's Cave); 5, Depression Cave. Zimbabwe: 6, Pomongwe; 7, Nswatugi; 8, Tshangula; 9, Shashabugwa; 10, Bambata; 11, Amadzimba; 12, Khami; 13, Redcliff; 14, Zombepata; 15, Duncombe Farm; 16, Pfupi. Zambia: 17, Twin Rivers; 18, Kalambo Falls; 19, Leopard's Hill Cave; 20, Kalemba; 21, Nsalu Cave/shelter; 22, Mumbwa Cave; 23, Nachikufu Cave/shelter; 24, Cifubwa Stream; 25, Mwelu Rocks shelter; 26, Mufulwe; 27, Mwambacimo. Malawi: 28, Hora Mountain rockshelter 7. Tanzania: 29, Kisese II; 30, Nasera Rock; 31, Mumba-Hohle; 32, Olduvai Gorge. Kenya: 33, Twilight Cave (GtJi 12); 34, Gamble's Cave; 35, Nderit Drift; 36, Lukenya Hill sites (GvJm 16, 22, 46). Uganda: 37, Munyama Cave; 38, Magosi. Ethiopia: 39, Lake Ziway; 40, Lake Besaka; 41, K'one (Garibaldi) Caldera Complex; 42, Laga Oda rockshelter; 43, Aladi Springs; 44, Kella; 45, Gobedra Rockshelter. Somalia: 46, Midhishi 2; 47, Karin Heegan; 48, Buur Heybe (Bur Eibe); 49, Gogoshiis Qabe (Gure Makeke). Burundi: 50, Nyarunazi. Rwanda: 51, Campion site; 52, Rutonde. Zaire: 53, Matupi cave; 54, Ishango (11 and 14); 55, Kamoa; 56, Gombe Point and Kinshasa plain; 57, Lake Tumba. Angola: 58, Mufo, Lunda Province; 59, Calunda, Lunda Province. Cameroon: 60, Mayo Louti. Nigeria: 61, Odo Ogun.

radiocarbon dates in tropical Africa covering the late glacial hypothermal. All dates so far are on charcoal, and reflect occupation beginning well before 18 910 BP, as this lowest date is underlain by *c.* 2 m of culture-bearing horizons. The earliest crescent (segment) in the sequence lies below the 18 910 BP date at just over 3 m, while microlithic technology reflected in cores and small bladelets extends to the base of the cultural deposits, with a possible age, based on extrapolated sedimentation rates, of *c*. 37 000 BP. The 25 cm immediately above the 18 910 BP date are characterized by an absence of cultural materials. While this hiatus in cultural occupation may be an effect of the small area sampled at this depth, it may also reflect the general depopulation or reduction in occupation intensity observed at other sites in Botswana and Namibia during the late glacial dry period (Robbins, pers. comm.).

A similar cultural discontinuity may be reflected in 'rockfalls', or long-weathering horizons, capping the Middle Stone-Age deposits at several deeply stratified rockshelter sites in the Matopos Hills area of Zimbabwe (C. K. Cooke 1973). Walker (1980, 1986; Vol. 2, Ch. 9) and C. K. Cooke (1978, 1984) have argued that these sterile horizons and the general absence of radiocarbon dates in the 22 000–14 000 BP range suggest abandonment or reduced human occupation in much of Zimbabwe during the LGM. At several sites in the Matopos and elsewhere, backed and microlithic lithic elements, together with typical LSA bone and shell artefacts, are said to occur within the terminal MSA; this transitional industry is termed 'Tshangulan' after the type site, and occurs between *c*. 26 000 BP and 13 000 BP (C. K. Cooke 1984). In the Matopos, the 'Tshangulan' is succeeded by scraper-dominated industries with few or no microblade or geometric elements ('Pomongwe' industry) and then by one or more microlithic LSA industries ('Khami' industry). Both of these latter entities are primarily Holocene in age, as indicated by a date from Nswatugi of 10 265 BP underlying the Pomongwan (Walker 1977). Diatoms associated with this sample may indicate increased precipitation, and are further supportive of a post-glacial-maximum age (Walker 1980).

Both the chronology and composition of industries spanning the MSA–LSA transition and grouped under the term 'Tshangula' have been disputed by Walker (1980). Confusion is due in large part to possible admixture due to human or bioturbation at several key sites, as well as to a somewhat vague definition of the Tshangulan itself. At Pomongwe Cave, for example (C. K. Cooke 1963, Walker 1980), in a long sequence of Bembesi, Charaman, and Bambata (Middle Stone-Age) levels, macrolithic backed tools appear and increase gradually towards the final Bambata. The layer of roof spalls marking the end of the Bambata proper is dated to 35 530 BP, which in turn suggests that most of the Bambata, at least at this site, lies beyond radiocarbon range. (A younger and slightly lower date of 21 700 BP was questioned by both the laboratory and the excavator.) Non-microlithic backed tools, confusingly termed 'Tshangulan' are also present at Nswatugi, in levels predating 41 940 BP (Walker 1980, Volman 1984).

Above the 'rockfall' capping the Bambata levels at Pomongwe, is a transitional 'Tshangulan' or 'Umguzan' industry with backed blades, segments, bone points, and ostrich eggshell beads associated with MSA tools of reduced size. Dates for this industry, based on charcoal samples, place it between about 15 800 and 11 020 BP, and suggest that the cultural hiatus following the Bambata levels may have lasted through the late glacial hypothermal (Walker 1980, 1986; Vol. 2, Ch. 9). In a recent re-excavation of the site by Walker (1986), however, Iron-Age material was found in the 'terminal MSA' assemblage associated with these dates, implying that its transitional character may be due to site disturbance rather than to cultural evolution. Similarly, at the nearby type site of Tshangula, the Tshangulan assemblage (Unit 3) appears affected by stratigraphic disturbance and may combine artefacts 'representative of earlier and later periods' (Walker 1986, p. 2). A radiocarbon date for this unit of 9760 BP is inconsistent with other dates for 'Tshangulan' assemblages. At Shashabugwa, another Matopos site with a comparable 'terminal MSA' industry, a weathering unconformity appeared to separate it from the overlying LSA, suggestive of a much earlier age for the final MSA. Other sites in the Matopos where 'Tshangulan' or transitional MSA–LSA assemblages have been described, but either are not well documented or may result from admixture, include Bambata (Armstrong 1931, Jones 1940, Sampson 1974) and Amadzimba (Cooke & Robinson 1954). In sum, not only are the nature and chronological position of the MSA–LSA transition in the Matopos uncertain, but the existence of any cultural occupation of this area during the glacial maximum appears in some doubt.

Grouping the 'Tshangula' level (layer 4) at Pomongwe with the overlying LSA units, Brain (1981) has argued that the MSA–LSA transition at Pomongwe is accompanied by a possible faunal shift towards greater representation of small or solitary non-herd animals. Quite aside from the stratigraphic problems discussed above, the presence in both Middle and Later Stone-Age assemblages of small or solitary animals such as steenbok, duiker, klipspringer, hyrax, hare, springhare, and tortoise, together with large herd mammals such as zebra, sable, tsessebe, and wildebeest would not appear to support such a conclusion (Brain 1981, Tables 11–13). In addition, minimum numbers of Class I–II bovids hardly change between the two groups of assemblages (MSA = 20, LSA = 18), while a slightly smaller minimum number of Class III–IV bovids and zebras in the Later (N = 13) as opposed to the Middle (N = 19) Stone-Age levels could be easily explained by a change in butchery and transportation patterns. The impression of much greater numbers of small mammals in the LSA as opposed to the MSA levels is primarily due to four- and sevenfold increases in tortoises and hyraxes, respectively, although the percentage contribution of these animals to the diet, even in LSA times, is estimated as less than 8% of the meat by weight. The lack of any dramatic effect of either environmental or cultural change on the bovid–equid faunal remains and inferred human hunting patterns throughout the long Upper Pleistocene and Holocene sequence at Pomongwe is perhaps the most striking aspect of this analysis.

Outside the Matopos area, transitional industries of 'Tshangulan' type have been described from Khami (C. K. Cooke 1957), where a bored stone was recovered in the level, as well as from Redcliff in central Zimbabwe (Brain & Cooke 1967, C. K. Cooke 1978, Klein 1978, Cruz-Uribe 1983). At both sites, the end of the 'Tshangula' appears to correspond to an increase in precipitation reflected in erosional unconformities or increased weathering and cementation of sediments. The Redcliff 'Tshangula' is separated from the underlying Bambata levels by a 'rockfall' and is marked towards the top by a period of increased deposition of large sand grains, originally interpreted (Brain 1969) as indicative of a cooler and wetter interval (low carbonate concentrations reflecting higher rates of transport), but possibly suggesting a period of dryer conditions (more erosion and aeolian transport due to reduced vegetation cover). The absence of typical LSA bone and shell artefacts, and the predominantly MSA character of the assemblage, together with a radiocarbon determination of 25 650 BP and the presence of four extinct species in the faunal assemblage (Cruz-Uribe 1983) imply that the Redcliff 'Tshangula' has little connection to most of the 'Tshangulan' assemblages of the type site and region.

Evidence for a shift in hunting or resource-use patterns at Redcliff between Bambata and 'Tshangula' times, however, parallels that described for Pomongwe (Cruz-Uribe 1983). Small bovids, 'ground game' (hyraxes, springhare, hare, hedgehog, porcupine) and baboons are much more common in the Tshangula than in the underlying Bambata levels, but this may also be due to a much greater representation of carnivores and carnivore activity in the Tshangulan faunal remains.

Further to the northeast, in Mashonaland, several sites including Zombepata (C. K. Cooke 1971) and Duncombe Farm (Hitzeroth 1973, Walker & Wadley 1984) may record an episode of occupation during the late Pleistocene. Although these episodes were originally labelled 'Tshangula', Walker and Wadley (1984, Walker Vol. 2, Ch. 9) have recently disputed the implied connection to the Matopan sequence. In a re-analysis of the material from Duncombe Farm, the absence of true MSA pieces in Level 3, together with strong components of bladelets, bladelet cores, and backed pieces, particularly segments, all suggest affinities with the early Nachikufan industries of Zambia rather than with the 'Tshangula', although the pointed bladelets characteristic of the former (see below) are absent at Duncombe Farm. With its associated date of 18 970 BP, Level 3 provides the only firm evidence for human occupation in Zimbabwe during the glacial maximum itself. As in the industries from northern Botswana and Zambia, microlithic debitage and backed pieces continue through Level 4, approximately 50 cm below the dated level.

At Zombepata, bored stones are present below a 'Tshangula' level dated to 13 000 BP. The association of typical MSA cores and points with LSA elements in the 'Tshangula' level could be due to the same kind of stratigraphic admixture which has so complicated the definition of this industry in the Matopos. Walker (1986) also has suggested the possibility of late Pleistocene occupation at Pfupi rockshelter (Robinson 1952).

As this discussion has demonstrated, any understanding of cultural change during the Late Glacial is complicated by the use of the term 'Tshangula' to cover any industry with backed or small-size artefacts in association with MSA points and scrapers. Walker (1980, p. 23) points out that 'currently this term

['Tshangulan'] is being applied to at least two different industries, and that the more recent of the two in the Matopos is a less formal, scraper-dominated industry.' As both Walker (1980) and Volman (1984) note, this practice has thrown together assemblages in true 'MSA' contexts, which pre-date 40 000 BP and are probably best compared to the Howieson's Poort of South Africa, and 'transitional' assemblages post-dating 20 000 BP.

Without better stratigraphic control and dating of the Zimbabwean sites, it is difficult to characterize the MSA–LSA transition or the human cultural remains surrounding the late glacial hypothermal. At present, the only definite occupation of any Zimbabwean site during the hypothermal itself is at Duncombe Farm. Backing and small-sized artefacts, however, characterize several assemblages that predate the hypothermal by a considerable margin, and the exploitation of small-scale faunal resources may have increased prior to the hypothermal as well. Assemblages just post-dating the hypothermal are associated with bored stones, ostrich eggshell beads, and bone points, as well as with a possible increase in the exploitation of small-scale resources. Finally, recent work has suggested that cultural sequences in Zimbabwe may have differed significantly from north to south, with the northern region participating in the early development of microlithic technology which appears to characterize central Africa. The southern sequence, on the other hand, with (a) the early presence of backing in Middle Stone-Age contexts; (b) absence of formal microlithic tools in the first Later Stone-Age contexts; and (c) terminal Pleistocene emergence of non-microlithic scraper-dominated industries, appears more similar to cultural sequences in South Africa (Walker 1986).

Zambia and Malawi

Middle Stone-Age industries of this area, in the period preceding the LGM, may be divided into two general groups, those characterized by small bifacial and unifacial points and scrapers, similar to the Bambata industry in Zimbabwe, and industries characterized by the larger bifacial lanceolate points, or 'daggers', and core axes generally grouped with the Lupemban industries of central Africa, especially Zambia, Zaire, and Angola (Clark 1970, Phillipson 1976). Dates on the Lupemban industries at Kalambo Falls cluster around 30 000 BP, probably representing minimum ages, and are in accord with similar dates for the Lupemban from sites in Zaire. From the site of Twin Rivers Kopje, 24 km southwest of Lusaka, comes a very different MSA assemblage with a larger number of unifacial and bifacial points, small scrapers, knives, outils écaillés and grindstones, together with a much smaller component of 'Lupemban' types, including core axes, core-scrapers, and bifacial lanceolate points. Dates for this industry, based on travertine samples, range between > 33 200 BP and 22 800 ± 1000 BP (Clark 1971). The possibility that travertine formation might post-date the manufacture of the artefacts, as well as the dating of comparable sites in Zimbabwe and Botswana, suggests that the MSA at this site more probably lies beyond the range of radiocarbon.

At least five excavated sequences from Zambia: Kalambo Falls, Leopard's Hill Cave, Kalemba, Nsalu Cave and Mumbwa Cave contain 'pre-LSA' or 'transitional' industries in which production of microblades and/or small-scale backed pieces was superimposed on a basically Middle Stone-Age discoidal-core technology. Although the latter two sites are completely undated, and only Leopard's Hill has a consistent series of radiocarbon dates for the 'pre-LSA' industry itself, all of these occurrences could well pre-date the LGM.

During or immediately following the LGM at 18 000 BP, assemblages assigned to an early LSA tradition, the Nachikufan I, with numerous small pointed microblades and microblade cores, have been described from Leopard's Hill, Nachikufu shelter, Nsalu shelter, Chifubwa Stream, Mwelu Rocks shelter, and Kalemba. Musonda (1984) has also defined a so-called LSA 'Group I' industry, contemporary with the earliest Nachikufan I but differing in the greater number of formally backed bladelets, from two sites in the Lunsemfwa Basin in central Zambia, Mufulwe and Mwambacimo. While the former is undated, the latter is the only Zambian assemblage which can definitely be assigned to the LGM itself, with an associated radiocarbon date of 18 080 BP at the base.

The Kalambo Falls industry defined locally as 'Rubble component of the Polungu industry' (Clark 1969, 1974) was found in a derived context and cannot be dated precisely. The rubble component is separated from the overlying 'hillslope' component of the same industry by a date of 9550 BP for the surface of Rubble Ia, while the base of Rubble Ic defines the possible chronological boundary between the earliest Polungu industry and the latest 'Lupemban' or Siszya Industry c. 30 500–27 500 BP. The earlier of the two Polungu components differs from the later, Holocene component in its greater representation and variety of medium to large-size Middle Stone-Age tool forms, cores and waste flakes, and a smaller percentage of blades, blade cores, and small discoidal cores. Bifacial retouch is also absent in the later component (Clark 1974). While a bored stone was recovered from the rubble component, geometric microliths and pointed backed bladelets, typical of the Nachikufan I, but not of the latter Nachikufan phases, are rare in both components. Palynological interpretations (van Zinderen Bakker 1969) have indicated a lowered temperature consistent with the late glacial hypothermal (but see above), in samples from clays within Rubble I, immediately overlying the earlier-dated horizon at the base, suggesting that bladelet technology may begin in this area prior to the hypothermal. An age of around 20 000 BP for the earliest Polungu material would be consistent both with the evidence from this site and with dates from the dryer, cooler period of the climatic maximum elsewhere in Central Africa.

At both Leopard's Hill Cave Levels 25–40 (Miller 1969, 1971) and Kalemba Levels H–K (Phillipson 1976), the earliest backed and geometric pieces are associated with industries of 'MSA' character, in which scrapers on flakes predominate, but convex-backed flakes also occur, reaching a frequency of 38% in Level N at Kalemba. These industries, often regarded like the

Tshangula as 'proto–Late Stone Age' (Miller 1969, Klein 1984) or transitional between the Middle and Later Stone Age, are characterized by the first appearance of backed flakes and other pieces as in Levels I and J at Kalemba. At Leopard's Hill, a few backed blades and segments also occur in these horizons. They may be dated to c. 22 000 BP or earlier (Table 6.1) based on radiocarbon determinations. At Leopard's Hill Cave, three dates of 23 600–21 550 BP were obtained on charcoal samples. The problems of bone apatite dates are well illustrated by the Kalemba series (see Collett & Robertshaw 1983). Clearly some of these determinations must be rejected, yet the choice of which to throw out is made in accordance with generally held chronological schemes for the evolution of complex technology in sub-Saharan Africa. These schemes, which suggest a Terminal Pleistocene or Early Holocene date for the advent of microlithic technology and backed microliths, are based on far too few well-dated sequences, most of them located on the periphery of the area, rather than at its centre, nearer to the Zambian sites. The excavator (Phillipson 1976, p. 127) recommends rejection of the earlier determinations (Gx-2768 and Gx-2767) as 'the most economical view' but, clearly, alternative choices might be preferred in the light of new information about the timing of technological advances in central and eastern Africa. A date for these transitional industries in the range of 25 000–40 000 years ago would not be inconsistent with emerging data from Botswana, Tanzania, Kenya, and Zaire.

Following a hiatus in occupation of unknown duration, the succeeding industry at Leopard's Hill Cave (Levels 17–24) and Kalemba, (Levels K–N) termed Nachikufan I, is manufactured from a microlithic, bladelet-based technology, in which the characteristic tool-form is a narrow, pointed curved-backed flake (bladelet). Scrapers are also common, while geometric microliths make their first appearance during this time (Level M at Kalemba). Bored stones (Kalemba Level L) together with grinding and rubbing stones suggest a degree of more intense exploitation of vegetable foods, while bone awls or points suggest an increase in technological complexity. Processed pigments, ochre and haematite, also appear in these levels at Kalemba. Again the available radiocarbon dates are inconsistent, but would indicate that a time span of c. 17 000 BP or slightly earlier, to 13 000 BP or slightly later, could be encompassed by this industry.

An assemblage from Mwambacimo (Level III) in central Zambia, dated to between 18 080 and 9830 BP by radiocarbon on charcoal, is dominated by backed bladelets (31.7% of retouched pieces) and secondarily by segments and other geometrics (23.1%) and by backed flakes (24.8%). Comparable assemblages from the nearby site of Mufulwe, which included two bored stones, are not well-dated (Musonda 1984).

The faunal assemblages from Kalemba and Leopard's Hill Cave have also been interpreted as evidence for increasing economic specialization during the final Pleistocene (Phillipson 1976, Klein 1984). Although the Kalemba assemblage is very small, both Kalemba and Leopard's Hill seem to reflect a concentration on small to medium-sized ungulates, most of which occur in the region at present. Suggestions that the Kalembá Nachikufan I fauna represent a more closed environment and a greater emphasis on small game than in the preceding transitional period are unwarranted in view of the presence of warthog, zebra, and wildebeest in the later horizons. Additionally, as suggested by Klein (1984) for the Leopard's Hill fauna, an apparent emphasis on smaller game may be due to a change in logistical behaviour rather than in hunting practices *per se*, with larger animals butchered at the kill site and smaller animals brought back intact. An analysis of a grouped faunal sample (all LSA levels) from Mufulwe (Gutin & Musonda 1985) suggests that hunting/collecting patterns at this site were dominated by pursuit of small bovids (MNI of Classes I–II = 27, Classes III–IV and zebra = 6) and 'ground game' (MNI of rats, lizards, hares = 6). Since the 'assemblage' may span 20 000 years from the earliest LSA to the Iron Age, the relevance of the analysis for interpreting economic behaviour during or just after the late glacial hypothermal is questionable.

In northern Malawi, a Later Stone-Age industry from the Hora Mountain rockshelter 7 (Robinson & Sandelowsky 1968) described as 'Magosian' (i.e. with Middle Stone-Age elements) documents the appearance of quartz microliths by at least 14 730 BP.

The limited archaeological evidence available from Zambia and Malawi suggests that, as in Botswana, the intensity of occupation may have been reduced between 20 000 and 18 000 BP, although the assemblages from Mwambacimo and nearby sites may reflect occupation in central Zambia during this interval. In addition, the appearance of backing at a much earlier period, together with the evidence for geometric microliths, bored stones, bone tools, and pigment processing in 'Nachikufan I' industries just after 18 000 BP suggest the slow development of technological economic, and social intensification throughout the last 20 000–30 000 years of Pleistocene time, rather than the sudden appearance of 'LSA' adaptations in the Holocene.

East Africa: Tanzania, Kenya, Uganda

While east Africa is certainly better explored archaeologically than most of the tropical African regions to the west and south, few excavated sequences are relevant to the time-period in question. These few include: the sites of Kisese II, Nasera Rock, Mumba, and the Olduvai Gorge Naisiusiu Beds in Tanzania, the site of Munyama Cave in Uganda and, in Kenya, Twilight Cave (GtJi12) from the Naivasha Basin together with five sites from Lukenya Hill.

Kisese II, a painted rockshelter in central Tanzania, contains a series of occupation horizons, in which the artefact assemblages by *outils écaillés* and convex scrapers until the advent of backed microliths, an event which the excavator considers as marking the beginning of the Late Stone Age (Inskeep 1962). Regrettably, the report on the radiocarbon dates from the site (Table 6.1) (Callow *et al.* 1964) does not indicate from which excavation units the charred ostrich eggshell fragments used for dating were obtained, though the

18 190 BP date is considered to relate to the first appearance of backed microliths. Radiocarbon dates on ostrich eggshell are generally considered highly reliable (Haas 1977, Long *et al.* 1983), due to resistance of this material to diagenetic contamination. No analysis of any faunal remains from Kisese II has yet been published.

The artefact assemblage from the Naisiusiu beds at Olduvai (Leakey *et al.* 1972) is rather different in character from that of Kisese II; it contains a significant blade element as well as numerous backed blades and geometric microliths. The assemblage was discovered some 17–23 cm below a small bone scatter, identified predominantly as zebra, from which the radiocarbon dates, based on ostrich eggshell and 'bone gelatin' (collagen), were acquired. Interesting patterns of raw-material usage and procurement have been discerned. Chert obtained from 7 km away was preferred for blade manufacture, while more obsidian was used for geometric microliths and backed blades, and quartz and quartzite were more often employed for other tool forms (Leakey *et al.* 1972). Eight of the obsidian artefacts have been shown by electron microprobe studies to derive from a source in the Sonanchi crater in the Kenyan Rift Valley 255 km from Olduvai (Merrick & Brown 1984).

The deposits within the relevant time-horizon at Nasera rockshelter, for which a somewhat confused set of dates exists, (Table 6.1), commence in layers 7 and 6 with an eponymous quartz industry, the 'Naseran', in which backed pieces and bipolar and other LSA core technologies appear, together with radial cores of MSA type and a few mostly unifacial points, but microliths are absent (Mehlman 1977, pers. comm.). This industry probably pre-dates 20 000 BP, on the basis of the dates from this site and from a comparable level (Lower Bed III) at Mumba (see below).

While the assemblage in layer 5 at Nasera combines artefacts characteristic of both over- and underlying levels and may be the result of mechanical mixing, layer 4 contains an assemblage in quartz and chert characterized by large blades and bipolar core technology, and by microliths and fine backing. Bada (1981) has suggested an age of 20 000 BP for Level 4, based on amino-acid racemization of bone, calibrated with the date from Level 6 (ISGS–425) in which apatite and collagen fractions were more or less in agreement. Radiocarbon ages for Level 4 ranged from 14 780 BP (collagen) to 22 460 BP (apatite). More recently, racemization studies on two samples of ostrich eggshell from Level 4, suggested an antiquity in at least the 20 000–30 000-year range or older, and indicated some degree of stratigraphic admixture in this horizon as well. (Kokis 1988, Brooks *et al.* in press.) The 'considerable antiquity' suggested by Mehlman for the 'Wilton' level at the site (3, lower) may thus extend back into the Terminal Pleistocene, an estimation possibly confirmed by the tentative equation by Hay (Mehlman 1977) of levels 3, 4 and upper 5 with the Naisiusiu beds, while levels 6 and below are correlated with the much earlier Ndutu beds at Olduvai. No clear period of abandonment is evident in the sequence from levels 7 to 3, although a reduction in artefact and faunal element frequency is evident in the lower part of Level 5.

At Mumba-Höhle, in the Lake Eyasi Basin (Mehlman 1979), a pastoral Neolithic horizon (Bed II) with pottery is underlain by almost 2 m of Late Stone-Age cultural horizons (Bed III) in a dense midden of shell, fish, bird, reptile, and mammal bone. Ten intrusive burials may be responsible for some of the ostrich eggshell beads and decorated pottery found in this bed over much of its depth, or the items could be autochthonous. The industry throughout is characterized as Late Stone Age with microliths. The lower part of Bed III, below the burials, is associated with a more reworked midden deposit, characterized by concretions from the dissolution of shell. A radiocarbon date on ostrich eggshell from Lower Bed III at 160 cm below datum, has yielded an age of 26 960 BP (Table 6.1). A piece of eggshell from 180 cm below datum was recently dated by TAMS radiocarbon to 33 200 BP. Amino-acid racemization of 33 ostrich eggshell samples from Bed III and Lower Bed III suggested that all of this material (with the exception of the burials) is late Pleistocene rather than Holocene in age, and that the Lower Bed III series falls in the ranges suggested by the two radiocarbon ages.

Bed IV at Mumba represents a beach deposit associated with a radiocarbon date in *Achatina* shell of 36 900 BP, which may correspond to the higher lake-levels of other east African lakes prior to 25 000 BP. A second midden deposit (Bed V) underlying the beach level, is associated with a transitional industry with backed segments and blade technology along with discoidal cores. Ostrich eggshell beads were absent, but a broken 'palette' and grinder, both with colouring matter adhering were found in the deposit. One of us (Brooks) inspected this material briefly in Tübingen in 1987, and noted a remarkable similarity to Howiesons Poort industries of southern Africa. A radiocarbon sample of *Achatina* shell from the lower part of this horizon yielded an age of 31 070 BP, although the degree of racemization in the four ostrich eggshell samples from this horizon would indicate a considerably older age, in the range of 48 000–56 000 BP (Kokis 1988, Brooks *et al.*, in press). Material in the underlying Bed VI is Middle Stone Age in character with discoidal cores and unifacial and bifacial points and scrapers on quartz. The associated age corresponds to the last interglacial of Europe, *c*. oxygen isotope stage 5a or 6 (Mehlman 1979, 1984, 1987).

The four Tanzanian sites discussed here present a somewhat unified picture. With the possible exception of Nasera, for which the available dates are highly ambiguous, fully microlithic industries with backed geometric forms appear to have been well established in the area prior to the LGM at 18 000 BP. Transitional or 'proto-LSA' industries, with microlithic or blade as well as radial core technologies, some backing but no geometric forms, and colouring material, appear to significantly pre-date this interval, and may be contemporary with similar industries in southern Africa. The best-described fauna, from Mumba (Lehmann 1957), reflects a highly diverse array of large and small herbivores, carnivores, birds, fish, catfish, tortoise, the monitor lizard, and the chimpanzee, the latter in both Level III and Level V. One extinct species, *Menelikia lyrocera* was noted in Level III. The presence of black rhino, bush pig, and chimpanzee may suggest a more heavily vegetated environment than that which presently characterizes the Eyasi Basin. This would be consistent with a pre-LGM age for both levels III and V.

From Kenya, the sequence from Twilight Cave, (Enkapune ya Muto), while not well published as yet, is of particular interest in the light of the picture given by the Tanzanian evidence (Ambrose 1984, pers. comm.). All of the dates available so far are radiocarbon dates on wood charcoal. Here, below the major rockfall zone, an MSA industry in layer 4 is dated to > 26 000 BP, suggesting a possible true age beyond radiocarbon range. The uppermost of the two LSA industries overlying the rockfall is dated to 16 300 ± 270 BP on the basis of small samples, and 35 800 ± 550 BP on a large sample. This LSA lithic industry is characterized by *outils écaillés*, short endscrapers and backed segments, and accompanied by ostrich eggshell beads, while the underlying LSA industry features large backed blades. These earlier LSA horizons are overlain unconformably by 'Eburran' (ex-Kenya Capsian) horizons dating to between 3400 and 6350 BP (Ambrose, pers. comm.).

The origins of the Kenya Capsian industry are unknown, but in recognition of the fact that it bears no resemblance to the Capsian of North Africa, it was recently given its more appropriate regional name after Mt Eburru, on the slopes of which Gamble's Cave and other sites are located (Ambrose *et al.* 1980). Technologically, the Eburran industry is based on the production of long narrow blades, large numbers of which were backed into both geometric and non-geometric microliths. The makers of these tools were fortunate to have locally available sources of obsidian. Other Eburran technological features of note were the use of the microburin technique, also documented in the Holocene age LSA (Kaposwa) industry from Kalambo Falls, and the manufacture of tabular bladelet cores made on large blade segments. These technologies served for the production of assemblages in which backed tools predominate but other categories such as end- and side-scrapers are also important.

As in the case of the Nachikufan of Zambia, several chronological phases of the Eburran industry have been defined on the basis of tool-type frequences, size and shape variation in backed microliths, and later, the presence of pottery and domestic stock (Ambrose 1984). The earliest phases I and II, span the period between 12 000 and 10 300 BP, preceding a major rise of Lake Nakuru to *c.* 180 m above present levels. Following a hiatus of about 2000 years when lake-levels were high, Eburran settlement resumed at Gamble's Cave and other sites.

The Eburran is preceded by several local industries in the central rift region to which it shows little if any resemblance. These include not only the early LSA assemblages from Twilight Cave but also an assemblage from Nderit Drift characterized by an abundance of micropercoirs and dating to about 12 700 BP (Ambrose *et al.* 1980). Early LSA assemblages have been reported from several sites at Lukenya Hill on the edge of the grasslands east of the rift valley and some 30 km southeast of Nairobi (Gramly & Rightmire 1973, Gramly 1976, Miller 1979, Ambrose 1984, Nelson & Kimengich 1984). At both GvJm 22 and GvJm 46, assemblages characterized by backed blades, *outils écaillés*, and distinctive fan-shaped endscrapers have been dated to between 17 000 and 20 000 BP on both apatite and collagen fractions of bone, and a third LSA assemblage dating to 17 000 BP is reported from GvJm 16 (Merrick 1975). The distinctive endscrapers are also found in the Naisiusiu beds at Olduvai as well as in the early LSA assemblages from Twilight Cave, although backed microliths similar to those from the early Tanzanian sites are present only in the upper levels at GvJm 46.

Faunal remains are well preserved at both GvJm 22 and GvJm 46. In both assemblages, plains game, particularly zebra, hartebeest and wildebeest, predominate, although remains of some species, such as impala and bushbuck, which prefer more closed environments, were also found. An environment similar to that surrounding Lukenya Hill at present is indicated. A fragmentary human cranium from the early LSA level at GvJm 22 shows Negroid affinities and does not support theories of early Khoisan or Caucasoid populations in East Africa (Gramly & Rightmire 1973, Schepartz 1987). While the Kenyan evidence is at present less well documented than the Tanzanian evidence, it is consistent with the possible development of Late Stone-Age microlithic industries prior to the LGM.

The single excavated sequence from Uganda, Munyama Cave on Buvuma Island in Lake Victoria (van Noten 1971) also confirms this picture. This site contained a sequence of Late Stone-Age deposits yielding a microlithic industry manufactured on vein quartz. Very small backed bladelets are the predominant tool form, together with numerous endscrapers, core scrapers, borers, a few crude segments and triangles, and *outils écaillés*. Two radiocarbon dates on charcoal from the lowest spits indicate an age of *c*. 15 000 BP, suggesting the early development of Late Stone-Age technology in Uganda during or just after the LGM.

Mention might be made here of the site of Magosi in northeastern Uganda, the type site of the 'Magosian' industry, originally regarded as transitional between Middle Stone Age and microlithic Later Stone Age. New excavations at Magosi, however, revealed that the artefacts derived from at least two separate archaeological occurrences, and a review of the literature suggested that other transitional assemblages grouped under the term 'Magosian' were also from dubious contexts. Although the term 'Magosian' has been abandoned (Cole 1967), the existence in the later Pleistocene of transitional Middle Stone-Age industries with either backing or microlithic technology has been well established by careful excavation at many of the sites discussed in this summary.

The Horn of Africa

Until the past decade, research on the LSA of the Horn generally lagged behind the rest of eastern Africa, despite the firm foundations that had been laid by Desmond Clark in Somalia during World War II (Clark 1954). Even now, it is only for Lake Besaka, a small alkaline lake situated at the junction of the Ethiopian Rift and Afar triangle 200 km east of Addis Ababa, that a detailed cultural and environmental sequence for the late Pleistocene and Holocene has been established. The results of other researches in central and eastern Ethiopia can be tentatively linked to this sequence. In Somalia, a resurgence of interest has led to new work in the northeast and at the site complex at Buur Heybe (Bur Eibe), where recent excavations at the sites of Gogoshiis Qabe and Guli Waabayo are providing important data (Brandt 1986).

At Lake Ziway in Ethiopia an exposed section near the Bulbula River contains an occupation horizon embedded within a palaeosol, for which there is a radiocarbon date on charcoal of about 27 000 BP (Gasse & Street 1978, Gasse et al. 1980). The artefact assemblage belongs to a blade industry with non-geometric microliths and scrapers (Brandt 1986). This would seem to be the earliest well-dated LSA site in the Horn. The occupation dates to around the onset of the late Pleistocene wet phase, which lasted until 22 000 BP and is thought to have resulted from cooler temperatures and slightly greater precipitation than those of the present (Perrot & Street-Perrot 1982).

Excavations at several sites around Lake Besaka, combined with palaeo-environmental research (Williams et al. 1981), have resulted in the recognition of an Ethiopian Blade Tool Tradition subdivided into five temporal phases (Clark & Williams 1978, Brandt 1980, 1982). The first phase dates to the late Pleistocene, between about 22 000 and 19 000 BP, when the now-saline lake was deep and fresh. The assemblage, in which almost all artefacts are made in obsidian, is dominated by relatively long, thin backed blades, a variety of scraper types and burins; there are no geometric microliths. Five ostrich eggshell beads may be the earliest evidence in the Horn of personal ornaments. A small collection of faunal remains includes warthog, hippo, a variety of bovids, birds and reptiles, as well as two species of fish, including catfish (Dechant & Crader 1982).

Although there appears to be a hiatus in occupation at Lake Besaka between 18 000 and 12 000 BP, correlating with a cold and arid climatic episode, a stone tool assemblage belonging in the late Pleistocene phase from the K'one (formerly Garibaldi) Caldera Complex, 30 km west of the lake, has been dated to approximately 15 000 BP (Clark & Williams 1978). A similar date on charcoal is associated with a very small assemblage of artefacts recovered in test excavations at Laga Oda rockshelter (Clark & Prince 1978, Clark & Williams 1978).

The succeeding 'Earliest Holocene' phase at Lake Besaka is thought to date at about 12 000 BP and shows an overall reduction in artefact size from the previous phase. The assemblages contain high frequencies of scrapers and microliths, the latter predominantly in the form of curved-backed blades and truncated pieces. Burins are well represented but there are no microburins and very few geometric microliths.

Several other Ethiopian sites have assemblages which may fit into the Lake

Besaka cultural sequence. Sites at Lake Ziway and Aladi Springs (Clark & Williams 1978, Humphreys 1978) have microlithic assemblages characterized by long backed-blades, which date between about 10 000 and 11 000 BP and hence belong in the 'Earliest Holocene' phase. The undated site of Kella near Melka-Kunture, containing assemblages in which geometric microliths are absent (Hivernel-Guerre 1970), may also be linked to this phase.

Similarities with the Lake Besaka sequence can also be discerned from the results of excavations at Gobedra rockshelter near Aksum (Phillipson 1977a). Although stone tools are rare in the lower levels of this site, for which there is a date of about 10 000 BP, there are a few long retouched blades and irregular scrapers. The remainder of the sequence has yielded a microlithic industry in which geometrics and backed flakes predominate.

Moving east into northern Somalia we find blade and burin assemblages, with occasional small disc cores and points but very few geometric microliths, which have been grouped together as the Hargeisan industry (Clark 1954, pp. 218–25). The transitional character of this industry was recently confirmed by excavations at Midhishi 2, where a radiocarbon date on charcoal of 18 790 ± 340 BP is associated with both typical MSA tools, manufactured by Levallois and disc-core techniques, and microliths, endscrapers and blade cores. However, as the assemblage comes from a stratified cave site, there remains the possibility of stratigraphic mixing (Gresham 1984, Brandt 1986). The Hargeisan, which is believed to be a local development, is succeeded by a microlithic industry, to which the name 'Somaliland Wilton' has been applied (Clark 1954, pp. 260–90). Recent excavations at the painted shelter of Karin Heegan have resulted in the first radiocarbon dates – about 2000 BP – for this industry, with which at this site are associated a few potsherds (Brandt 1986).

On the southern plateau and coastal plain of Somalia between the Webi Shebelli and Juba rivers have been discovered assemblages with distinctive bifacial and unifacial, lanceolate and foliate pressure-flaked points, together with microlithic tools, particularly curved-back blades. The term 'Doian' or 'Eibian' has been applied to these assemblages. The Somaliland Wilton and the Doian/Eibian have been regarded as regional variants representing local divergence within a single culture (Clark 1954, p. 158). The Doian/Eibian is best known from early excavations at Buur Heybe, some 200 km northwest of Mogadishu. New excavations have recently been commenced at Gogoshiis Qabe (formerly known as Gure Makeke), one of the many rockshelters on this granite inselberg. Underlying the Doian/Eibian levels at this site is an assemblage with unifacial and bifacial points, as well as microliths and other tools manufactured by both Levallois and blade-core techniques, which Clark (1954) labelled 'Magosian'. The excavator suggests a possible age of 30 000– 20 000 BP for this material, with the overlying Doian/Eibian dated to the Terminal Pleistocene on lithostratigraphic evidence and radiocarbon dates for the succeeding occupations (Brandt 1986).

In summary, the evidence from the Horn seems to suggest a local transition from the MSA to the LSA, with blade industries including microliths occurring in highland Ethiopia prior to the hypothermal. However, fully fledged LSA industries would appear to date somewhat later in Somalia. Future research in the Horn is of particular interest because of the potential it holds for contrasting the differing climatic effects and human responses to the hypothermal in highland Ethiopia and lowland Somalia.

It has been suggested that the origins of the LSA in this part of Africa might ultimately be traced to the Nachikufan I assemblages of Zambia (Phillipson 1977b, p. 33). Subsequent publication of the dates for the beginnings of the Lake Besaka sequence have, however, negated this hypothesis and revealed that the LSA of the Horn is probably at least as old as it is anywhere else in eastern Africa; a local origin seems the most likely explanation. Similarities between the Hargeisan, the blade industries of Ethiopia, and the assemblages known until recently as the Kenya Capsian have been noted, though with some reservations, by several writers (Phillipson 1977b, p. 32, Clark & Williams 1978, Brandt 1980, p. 243). How far these similarities represent similar responses to particular tool requirements by peoples at a similar technological stage with access to very fine-grained raw materials, or how far they might result from culture contact is an open question, particularly in view of our ignorance of the Terminal Pleistocene prehistory of much of eastern Africa. However, technological and typological features of the Kenya Capsian (now known as the Eburran industry) set it distinctly apart from the industries of the Horn: first, the microburin technique is an important feature of the Eburran (Ambrose et al. 1980), yet it is unknown in Somalia and makes its first appearance in Ethiopia only with the mid-Holocene Besaka industry; secondly, geometric microliths occur in all phases of the Kenya Capsian, but are extremely rare or absent from the early microlithic assemblages of the Horn.

Central Africa: Rwanda, Burundi, Zaire, Angola, Central African Republic, Gabon, Congo, and Cameroon

In Rwanda and Burundi, no industries can be referred with confidence to the time-interval reviewed here. Transitional industries with Middle Palaeolithic (Lupemban) bifacial 'daggers' and scrapers in association with small bifacial points and/or crescents occur in stratified open-air contexts above core axe industries at Nyarunazi in Burundi, and at the Campion site in Rwanda, but no age estimates are available. A similarly undated 'Magosian' assemblage with backed blades is known from the Rutonde site, near Kigali (Nenquin 1967).

In contrast, recent work in Zaire, although still very widely scattered over more than two million km^2, has demonstrated the presence of advanced technology (microlithic) and economic adaptations prior to the LGM. One such site is Matupi Cave in the Mt Hoyo massif on the eastern edge of the Ituri forest which was one of three main forest refugia postulated for the late Pleistocene dry phase. A deeply stratified series of 210 cm of deposits here shows no clear hiatus from the base, dated by radiocarbon to between 32 000 and > 40 700 BP based on charcoal samples, to the end of the Stone-Age series at about 2000 BP (van Noten 1977, 1982).

All the Stone-Age levels contain small bipolar cores and splintered pieces (*pièces esquillées*) together with a few small bladelets, all made almost exclusively on vein quartz (van Noten 1977). Geometric microliths are uncommon in all levels, although segments do occur as low as 170–175 cm below the surface, underneath horizons dated to 22 100 and 21 630 BP. Although relatively poor in overall artefact density, the uppermost horizons (2000–12 000 BP) contain a few ostrich eggshell beads and bone-point fragments, as well as ground haematite. The densest concentration of artefacts in the middle levels (65–140 cm, 12 000–21 000 BP) was associated with numerous charcoal concentrations, as well as with a fragment of a decorated bored stone, two stone drills, and ground haematite. Haematite also occurs in the lower levels (140–185 cm, 21 000–32 000 BP), together with many worked fragments of rock crystal. The lowest levels (below 185 cm and > 32 000 BP) were relatively poor in cultural material, although still fully microlithic in technology. It should be pointed out that samples of retouched stone artefacts are very small throughout; the entire combined stone assemblage from all levels numbers only 434 retouched and 390 utilized pieces.

Analysis of the pollen from Matupi, rich in Gramineae and Chenopodiaceae, together with spores of ferns characteristic of forest environments, have led Roche (1975) to suggest that the savanna zone extended as far as Matupi during the later Pleistocene, but that forest, or at least gallery-forest, was also an important component of the local environment. The faunal analysis also suggests the proximity of savanna habitats, possibly in a forest–savanna mosaic. Difficulties in interpreting pollen diagrams from tropical forest habitats, however, together with the possibility of human transport of faunal elements, lead us to consider these conclusions with some degree of caution.

About 100 km south of Matupi, the open-air site of Ishango (de Heinzelin de Braucourt 1957, 1961) is located on an ancient beach at 10–12 m above present water levels, at the point where the present Semliki River exits from Lake Rutanzige (ex-Edward). Below a series of Iron Age and 'Mesolithic' horizons, the latter with both microblades and segments, a rather amorphous non-microlithic quartz industry of small dimensions was associated with bone harpoons and abundant remains of both fish and mammals, as well as with fragmentary human skeletal material with affinities to modern peoples of East Africa (Twiesselmann 1958, Schepartz 1987). Bone harpoons with two rows of barbs, unknown or extremely rare at other sites, were the dominant form in the two lower of the three 'Ishangian' horizons.

Early efforts to derive an age for the 'Ishangian' based on radiocarbon determinations on mollusc shell were abandoned, particularly when shell from the modern beach below the site yielded an age of 3000 BP (de Heinzelin de Braucourt 1957). An Early Holocene age was suggested on stratigraphic and comparative cultural grounds. Recent re-excavation of the site to obtain samples for dating, however, together with a restudy of the faunal remains by Peters (1989), may indicate that the original age estimates were not as inaccurate as previously supposed. In particular, a piece of ostrich eggshell, generally regarded as highly resistant to contamination and diagenetic change (Haas 1977, Long *et al.* 1983, Brooks *et al.* in press), associated with the main double-row harpoon level (Niveau Fossilifere Principal) has been dated to *c.* 25 000 BP by both radiocarbon, using the AMS accelerator technique, and amino-acid racemization of eggshell protein (Brooks & Smith 1987, Brooks *et al.* in press). The large mammalian body sizes suggested by the faunal elements, are also more consistent with a Pleistocene age than with a date in the Holocene. The presumably lower lake-levels of the late glacial hypothermal may be reflected both in the unconformity between the 'Ishangian' and the later Mesolithic of the Holocene, and in the major extinction of the fish fauna in the lake, which followed the Ishangian.

Excavation at a second Ishangian site about 2 km downstream, also dated by radiocarbon on shell to between 20 000 and 23 000 BP, has indicated further economic specialization, as the representation of lacustrine fauna is quite different, with an emphasis on freshwater crabs and catfish. While in all probability the Ishangian was just prior to the 18 000 BP focus of this volume, these sites in the Semliki Valley demonstrate the early development of technological and economic specializations once thought to be restricted to the Holocene in Africa.

More than 1250 km further south and west, in the Kamoa Valley near Kolwezi and the Zambian border in Shaba Province, Cahen (1975) excavated a long sequence of industries with no associated fauna or radiometric dates, except in the uppermost, Holocene horizons, which were dated to between 6025 and 1840 BP on charcoal. In the 'redistributed ochreous sand I', in sediments suggesting an arid interval, a transitional 'Lupembo-Tshitolian' industry, with a mixture of small Lupemban bifacial points, short core axes and discoidal cores, together with more evolved blade and bladelet cores, was accorded an estimated age of 12 000 to 15 000 BP, based on sedimentation rates as well as on pollen profiles that suggested increasing humidity towards the top of the unit (see above, Moeyersons 1975, Roche 1975).

On the west side of the forest basin, a series of transitional industries assigned to the upper Lupemban and Lupembo–Tshitolian were described from the upper levels of the 'redistributed sand III' in Lunda Province, northeast Angola, in association with grindstones, and increasing numbers of blades throughout, as well as a sequence of transverse and then tanged arrowheads (Clark 1963, 1968). A suggested age of 15 000–11 000 BP was derived from several radiocarbon dates on charcoal. In addition, a date of 12 970 ± 250 BP, also on charcoal, for the lower phase of the succeeding Tshitolian industry in the 'redistributed Sands IV' confirms the impression that transverse arrowheads and microblade technology developed in this area during the later Pleistocene. The stratigraphic contexts of the Lunda transitional materials are unclear, however, owing to collection procedures and distribution of materials through 6–8 m of deposits.

At Gombe Point, on the Kinshasa Plain, recent excavations resulted in the dating of the middle- to upper-Lupemban or Lupembo-Tshitolian equivalent there, the 'Djokocian', to between 15 000 and 8000 BP, in the lower part of a deposit of 'Kalahari' sands. These dates are consistent with an earlier series of dates for the Middle and Upper Lupemban in the Kinshasa Plain of 15 080 and 12 230 BP (van Moorsel 1968). The sands represent an interval of arid conditions, reduced vegetation cover and aeolian transport from the south, termed the 'Leopoldvillian', which is thought to have begun at about 20 000 BP, on the basis of radiocarbon dates on charcoal. Refitting of cores and debitage by Cahen and Moeyersons (1977), however, showed that objects in Kalahari sands may move vertically up to 1 m from their original position, and cast doubt on the stratigraphic integrity of this and other sites, as well as on the association of charcoal samples with industries.

In material from the recent excavations, the Djokocian is characterized by leaf-shaped, tanged, bifacial and unifacial points, and long daggers, as well as by blades and blade cores in combination with Levallois flakes and cores. To complicate matters, the recent excavation revealed numerous small tranchet arrowheads and a few backed pieces in the underlying Sangoan/Lower Lupemban industry, the 'Kalinian', dated at > 30 000 BP, although bipolar cores and outils écaillés occur only in the overlying microlithic Tshitolian or 'Ndolian' industry. This latter industry is associated with the palaeosol at the top of the sands attributed to the more humid 'Kibangian' interval following the Leopoldvillian, and is dated to the Holocene by radiocarbon.

From the recent evidence, one can certainly conclude that doubts over the stratigraphic integrity of the Kinshasa Plain assemblages make it impossible even to describe the succession of industries, let alone to define a chronology. Yet the tranchet arrowheads in the earliest levels are not distinguished in their patina from the crude 'Sangoan' core aces and picks in the same assemblage. If the existence of tranchet arrowheads and backed blades in the earliest levels is not an artefact of later admixture, then the western region of sub-Saharan Africa, like the east and south, may have been characterized by the development of advanced lithic technologies prior to the LGM, as well as by a gradual replacement of large discoidal and Levallois flake cores by smaller bipolar and microblade ones.

Perhaps the most interesting new evidence from Zaire derives from recent explorations in the Lac Tumba area, the 'cuvette central' or central basin of the Zaire River, an area once considered to have retained its forest cover throughout the Pleistocene. Recent surveys here by J. Preuss (University of Hamburg) and Kanimba Misago (Institut des Musées Nationaux, Kinshasa), have resulted in a series of surface collections of small quartz and quartzite artefacts of uncertain age, but post-dating a pedogenetically transformed sand dating to between 37 640 and 24 860 BP. The artefacts are thus probably younger than 25 000 BP, and, in the case of riverbank assemblages from the Ruiki and other drainages just northeast of Lac Tumba, may be associated with radiocarbon dates on the riverbank sediments of 19 920 and 17 735 BP. Since axes, pottery and other Neolithic hallmarks are absent from these assemblages, while small leaf-shaped points are common, they may represent an occupation of the tropical forest prior to the development of agriculture, possibly during the Terminal Pleistocene in association with an extension of savanna habitats into the central forest 'refugium'.

In Gabon, the Congo, and the Central African Republic, no excavated stratified sites definitely attributed to the late glacial hypothermal have been reported in the literature, although a recent reference to two Middle Stone-Age occurrences in the Congo Republic dated to $c.\,20\,000$ and $c.\,18\,000$ BP may revise this lacuna in the near future (de Maret 1985, p. 130). Nor is there any evidence in Gabon or the Congo, to date, of occupation prior to the Lupemban. In Cameroon, however, at the open-air site of Mayo Louti in the north, a final Lupemban industry with flake-blades and Levallois debitage underlies two radiocarbon dates on calcretes of 15 000 BP, and one much younger date, suggesting a possible case of stratigraphic admixture (Marliac 1973, 1974). The gravel containing the artefacts may be derived from or may predate the 'Douroumain' interval of dry conditions marking the Late Glacial in the area.

West Africa, south of 10° north: Nigeria to Guinee

Although Lupemban surface assemblages have been reported from several sites in this region, and Allsworth-Jones has documented a cluster of Middle-Stone-Age assemblages on the Jos plateau of Nigeria (Allsworth-Jones 1979, 1986), excavated material in definite association with radiocarbon dates from the late glacial hypothermal are rare. Confusingly, the few radiocarbon dates from MSA sites in this region have yielded ages in the Holocene. One possible site is at Odo Ogun near the present forest–savanna boundary $c.\,200$ km north of Lagos in western Nigeria, where Burke et al. (1969, 1971) reported a flake industry in association with a pediment gravel representing an arid interval in the later Pleistocene and presumed to date to 18 000 BP.

Summary and discussion

It should be only too clear from this review that our knowledge of tropical Africa during the LGM is woefully inadequate. Yet much of the new data, however widely scattered and inadequately published, suggests a very different picture from that prevailing in general summaries of world prehistory at this date. Furthermore, the picture is at least sufficient to begin to suggest answers to the three questions posed at the outset of this chapter.

(a) What was the nature of late Pleistocene environmental change in sub-Saharan tropical Africa, in comparison to events in the rest of the Old World?

Evidence from a large number of lake cores, together with a smaller number of terrestrial sediment and pollen studies, suggest that during the period from *c*. 20 000 to *c*. 14 000 BP, most regions of tropical Africa experienced a period of arid conditions, reflected in reduced vegetation cover, increased deposition of aeolian sands, lowered shorelines, formation of calcretes, and absence of speleotherm formation in caves. Dates associated with these conditions, while not always reliable, may suggest that the timing of the arid interval varied, with the onset of aridity closer to 20 000 BP in West Africa, and the end of the arid period as late as 13 000 BP in the east. In addition, local conditions may affect the expression of aridity in the particular sediments studied: a deep lake with many inlets and outlets may be less affected than a shallow lake in a relatively closed basin. Compression of altitudinal vegetation belts due to lowered temperatures worldwide, together with increased savanna penetration of forested zones, may have created favourable environments for human exploitation outside the desert regions, particularly where steep vertical gradients provided access to several different environmental zones within a short distance. The general aridity of late glacial times in tropical Africa compares closely to the expansion of the Sahara during the same interval, as well as to the hyperaridity documented over much of the Middle East and Australia around 18 000 BP (see Bar-Yosef, Vol. 2, Ch. 3, Jones, Vol. 2, Ch. 14).

(b)   What is the evidence for the development of specialized economic and technological behaviours in late glacial times, in comparison to other areas of the Old World?

Just prior to the late glacial hypothermal, in the interval between 30 000 and 20 000 BP, human occupation has been documented throughout tropical sub-Saharan Africa, with the possible exception of the forest refugium around the mouth of the Zaire River. Particularly in the eastern central part of this area, in eastern Zaire, Zambia, Zimbabwe, and Tanzania, these occupants were already experimenting with microlithic technology (Matupi, Mumba-Höhle, Kalemba), as well as with backing of segments and small blades (Leopard's Hill Cave, Pomongwe, Tshangula, Depression Cave). The first cylindrical bone points also occur in the area at this time. Both microlithic technology and backing were superimposed on a technological base which was essentially focused on flake production and was Middle Stone Age in character.

Faunal remains suggest that a large number of different game animals, large and small, were taken, probably using a variety of techniques including ambush-hunting (particularly for zebra, warthog, and kudu), and trapping (particularly for hare, birds, and small antelope). Microlithic technology may have made possible new ways of exploiting game (Phillipson 1976, 1980), but the evidence from the few studied faunal assemblages spanning the adoption of microliths is equivocal at best. Early reliance on lacustrine resources, however, is well documented during this interval at the Zairian site of Ishango (now Ishango 11) as well as at the nearby site of Ishango 14. Other new food sources which may have been associated with the technological shift prior to 20 000 BP include snails, whose remains comprise much of the deposit in Lower Bed III at Mumba-Höhle, and gathered foods, whose more intensive exploitation with weighted digging sticks may be reflected in the first appearance of bored stones possibly during or just prior to the hypothermal at Khami and Leopard's Hill Cave.

While some areas, particularly in the desert regions (Gi, Depression Cave), experienced an apparent reduction in occupation intensity during the hypothermal just before and after 18000 BP, at sites in the central area, such as Mumba-Höhle and Matupi, the evidence for long-term abandonment of the site during the hypothermal is absent. At such sites, the slow increase in adoption of microlithic and backing technology continues, together with continued exploitation of small-scale resources, such as snails, tortoises, and hyraxes, as well as of large-game animals. The African evidence indicates that the 'broad-spectrum revolution' suggested by Flannery (1969) begins in the African tropics well before 20000 BP, together with technological developments often thought of as mesolithic. As to what might have motivated such a development, well before the late glacial aridity or final Pleistocene extinctions on the continent, we can only suggest that further work is needed on the uses of various different toolkits, as well as on the nature of late Pleistocene faunas and floras, before an answer can be given (see Robertshaw 1988). Human population saturation at a hunting-and-gathering level of technology is certainly also a possibility, since the period just prior to the development of microliths witnessed the expansion of peoples with Middle Stone-Age technologies into most, if not all, African habitats.

We would also like to add a comment on the estimation of population pressure or even of regional abandonment from archaeological site data. In a recent paper, Brooks & Yellen (1987) have argued from ethnographic evidence that hunter-gatherer settlements of several weeks or even months duration may be archaeologically invisible, if environmental constraints or technoeconomic strategies do not favour reoccupation. Conversely, increasing densities of debris scatters, and greater numbers of visible sites may not correlate with increased populations, but rather with changing strategies of subsistence of settlement duration and reoccupation. People may thus 'appear' suddenly in the archaeological record when, in fact, they have been present in the region for millennia.

(c)   Was the tropical forest occupied prior to the development of agriculture?

Among the more intriguing conclusions of this review is the demonstration that in at least two areas once thought to represent Pleistocene forest refugia, hunter-gatherers were present during the late glacial hypothermal at or around 18 000 BP. In both cases, however, the picture of unbroken forest succession in the vicinity of the archaeological occurrence is contradicted, in one instance (Matupi) by the presence of savanna mammals and in the other (Equateur Province, Zaire) by the presence of sandy deposits underlying present-day forest soils. No evidence of late Pleistocene occupation is currently available from the western forest refugium in Gabon. We can only conclude from the available evidence that, while the tropical forest region may have been occupied during the late Pleistocene, the tropical forest itself may have incorporated enough savanna microhabitats to provide plenty of carbohydrate resources for forest hunters. Although outside the temporal scope of this chapter, we should also note that evidence of Holocene hunter–gatherer settlement in forested regions is available from several sites, most notably from Iwo Eleru in Nigeria, although there is some question at this site about the timing of forest regeneration following the end of the Pleistocene (Shaw 1978).

Although the evidence for early development of microlithic technologies and specialized economies prior to or in the context of late glacial arid conditions seems to be consistent throughout much of the area under study, this reconstruction of late glacial settlement technologies and subsistence patterns in tropical Africa has been based on very meagre evidence, and could be radically changed by the excavation of a single site from even the best-known region discussed here.

References

Allsworth-Jones, P. 1979. The Middle Stone Age industry from Zenabi, northern Nigeria. In *Proceedings of the 8th Panafrican Congress of Prehistory and Quaternary Studies, Nairobi, September 1977*, R. E. Leakey & B. A. Ogot (eds), 244–7. Nairobi: The International Louis Leakey Memorial Institute for African Prehistory.

Allsworth-Jones, P. 1986. Middle Stone Age and Middle Palaeolithic: the evidence from Nigeria and Cameroun. In *Stone Age prehistory: studies in memory of Charles McBurney*, G. N. Bailey & P. Callow (eds), 153–68. Cambridge: Cambridge University Press.

Ambrose, S. H. 1984. Holocene environments and human adaptations in the Central Rift Valley, Kenya. Unpublished PhD dissertation, University of California, Berkeley, California.

Ambrose, S. H., F. Hivernel & C. M. Nelson, 1980. The taxonomic status of the Kenya Capsian. In *Proceedings of the 8th Panafrican Congress of Prehistory and Quaternary Studies, Nairobi, September, 1977*, R. E. F. Leakey & B. A. Ogot (eds), 248–52. Nairobi: TILLMIAP.

Armstrong, A. L. 1931. Rhodesian archaeological expedition (1929): excavations in Bambata cave and researches on prehistoric sites in southern Rhodesia. *Journal of the Royal Anthropological Institute of Great Britain and Ireland* 61, 239–76.

Avery, G. 1984. Micromammalian population dynamics and environmental change: the last 18,000 years in the southern Cape. In *Later Cainozoic Palaeoclimates of the Southern Hemisphere*, J. C. Vogel (ed.), 361–9. Rotterdam: A. A. Balkema.

Bada, J. L. 1981. Racemization of amino acids in fossil bones and teeth from the Olduvai Gorge region, Tanzania, East Africa. *Earth and Planetary Science Letters* 15, 223–31.

Bailey, R. & N. Peacock, 1988. Efe pygmies of northeast Zaire: subsistence strategies in the Ituri forest. In *Coping with uncertainty in the food supply*, I. de Garine & G. Harrison, (eds), 88–117. Oxford: Clarendon Press.

Beadle, L. C. 1981. *The inland waters of tropical Africa*, 2nd edn. New York: Longman.

Brain, C. K. 1969. New evidence for climatic change during Middle and Late Stone Age times in Rhodesia. *South African Archaeological Bulletin* **24**, 127–43.

Brain, C. K. 1974. The use of microfaunal remains as habitat indicators in the Namib. *South African Archaeological Society. Goodwin Series* **2**, 55–60.

Brain, C. K. 1981. *The hunters or the hunted? An introduction to African cave taphonomy.* Chicago: Chicago University Press.

Brain, C. K. & C. K. Cooke, 1967. A preliminary account of the Redcliff Stone Age site in Rhodesia. *South African Archaeological Bulletin* **21**, 171–82.

Brandt, S. A. 1980. Archaeological investigations at Lake Besaka, Ethiopia. In *Proceedings of the 8th Panafrican Congress of Prehistory and Quaternary Studies, Nairobi, September, 1977,* R. E. F. Leakey & B. A. Ogot (eds), 239–43. Nairobi: TILLMIAP.

Brandt, S. A. 1982. A Late Quaternary cultural/environmental sequence from Lake Besaka, southern Afar, Ethiopia. PhD thesis, University of California, Berkeley. Ann Arbor: University Microfilms.

Brandt, S. A. 1986. The Upper Pleistocene and early Holocene prehistory of the Horn of Africa. *African Archaeological Review* **4**, 41–82.

Brooks, A. S. & C. S. Smith, 1987. Ishango revisited: new age determinations and cultural interpretations. *African Archaeological Review* **5**, 65–78.

Brooks, A. S. & J. E. Yellen, 1987. The Preservation of activity areas in the archaeological record: ethnoarchaeological and archaeological work in northwest Ngamiland, Botswana. In *Method and theory for activity area research: an ethnoarchaeological approach,* S. Kent (ed.), 63–106. New York: Columbia University Press.

Brooks, A. S., P. E. Hare & J. Kokis, 1985. Amino acid racemization in ostrich eggshell: implications for dating and microstratigraphy in the Middle and Upper Pleistocene of Africa. Paper presented at the Carnegie Institution of Washington Conference on Biomineralization and the Fossil Record, Airlie, VA, 14–17 April, 1985.

Brooks, A. S., P. E. Hare, J. E. Kokis, G. Miller, R. Ernst & F. Wendorf in press. Chronometric dating of African sites by amino acid racemization of ostrich eggshell proteins.

Burke, K., A. B. Durotoye, & A. J. Whiteman, 1971. A dry phase south of the Sahara 20,000 years ago. *West African Journal of Archaeology* **1**, 1–8.

Burke, K., A. B. Durotoye, J. Reingold & T. Shaw, 1969. Late pleistocene and holocene deposits at Odo Ogun, southwestern Nigeria. *Journal of Mining Geology* **4**(142), 116.

Butzer, K. W. 1971. *Recent history of an Ethiopian delta.* University of Chicago Department of Geography Research Papers No. 136.

Butzer, K. W. 1984. Late Quaternary environments in South Africa. In *Later Cainozoic palaeoclimates of the southern hemisphere,* J. C. Vogel (ed.), 235–64. Rotterdam: A. A. Balkema.

Butzer, K. W., G. L. Isaac, J. L. Richardson, & C. K. Washburn-Kamau, 1972. Radiocarbon dating of east African lake levels. *Science* **175**, 1069–76.

Cahen, D. 1975. *Le Site Archéologique de la Kamoa (Region du Shaba, République du Zaire). De l'Age de Pierre Ancien à l'Age de Fer.* Tervuren: Annales du Musée Royale de l'Afrique Centrale, Série in 8⁰, Sciences Humaines n. 84.

Cahen, D. 1976. Nouvelles fouilles à la Pointe de Gombe (ex-Pointe de Kalina), Kinshasa, Zaire. *L'Anthropologie* **80**, 573–602.

Cahen, D. & J. Moeyersons, 1972. Le site préhistorique de la Kamoa, Katanga, Zaire. *Palaeoecology of Africa and the Surrounding Islands* **6**, 237–8.

Cahen, D. & J. Moeyersons, 1977. Surface movements of stone artifacts and their implication for the prehistory of Central Africa. *Nature* **266**, 812–15.

Callow, W. J., M. J. Baker & D. H. Pritchard, 1964. National Physical Laboratory radiocarbon measurements II. *Radiocarbon* **6**, 25–30.

Cerling, T. E. 1984. The stable isotope composition of soil carbonate and its relationship to climate. *Earth and Planetary Science Letter* **71**, 229–40.

Cerling, T. E. & R. L. Hay, 1986. An isotopic study of paleosol carbonates from Olduvai Gorge. *Quaternary Research* **25**, 63–78.

Clark, J. D. 1954. *The Prehistoric Cultures of the Horn of Africa*. Cambridge: Cambridge University Press.

Clark, J. D. 1963. *Prehistoric cultures of northeast Angola and their significance in Tropical Africa*. Lisboa: Companhia de Diamantes de Angola.

Clark, J. D. 1967. *Atlas of African prehistory*. Chicago: University of Chicago Press.

Clark, J. D. 1968. *Further palaeo-anthropological studies in northern Lunda*. Lisboa: Companhia de Diamantes de Angola.

Clark, J. D. 1969. *Kalambo falls prehistoric site. Volume I: The geology, palaeo-ecology and detailed stratigraphy of the excavations* (with contributions by other specialists). Cambridge: Cambridge University Press.

Clark, J. D. 1970. *The prehistory of Africa*. New York: Praeger.

Clark, J. D. 1971. Human behavioral differences in southern Africa during the later Pleistocene. *American Anthropologist* **73**(5), 1211–36.

Clark, J. D. 1974. *Kalambo Falls prehistoric site II: The later prehistoric cultures*. Cambridge: Cambridge University Press.

Clark, J. D. & G. R. Prince, 1978. Use-wear on Later Stone Age microliths from Laga Oda, Harraghi, Ethiopia, and possible functional interpretations. *Azania* **13**, 101–10.

Clark, J. D. & M. A. J. Williams, 1978. Recent archaeological research in southeastern Ethiopia (1974–1975): some preliminary results. *Annals d'Ethiopie* **11**, 19–44.

Clark, J. D. & E. M. van Zinderen Bakker, 1964. Prehistoric culture and Pleistocene vegetation at Kalambo Falls, Northern Rhodesia. *Nature* **201**, 971–5.

Coetzee, J. A. 1967. Pollen analytical studies in east and southern Africa. *Palaeoecology of Africa and the Surrounding Islands* **3**, 1–146.

COHMAP members, 1988. Climatic changes of the last 18,000 years: observations and model simulations. *Science* **241**, 1043–52.

Cole, G. H. 1967. A re-investigation of Magosi and the Magosian. *Quaternaria* **9**, 153–68.

Collett, D. & P. Robertshaw, 1983. Problems in the interpretation of radiocarbon dates: the Pastoral Neolithic of east Africa. *African Archaeological Review* **1**, 57–74.

Cooke, C. K. 1957. The waterworks site at Khami, Southern Rhodesia: stone age and protohistoric. *Occasional Papers of the National Museum, Southern Rhodesia* **3**(21a), 1–60.

Cooke, C. K. 1963. Report on excavations at Pomongwe and Tshangula caves, Matopos Hills, Southern Rhodesia. *South African Archaeological Bulletin* **18**, 73–151.

Cooke, C. K. 1971. Excavations at Zombepata Cave, Sipolilo District, Mashonaland, Rhodesia. *South African Archaeological Bulletin* **26**, 104–26.

Cooke, C. K. 1973. The Middle Stone Age in Rhodesia and South Africa. *Arnoldia (Rhod.)* **6**(20), 1–4.

Cooke, C. K. 1978. The Redcliff Stone Age Site, Rhodesia. *Occasional Papers of the National Museums of Rhodesia. Series A. Human Sciences* **4**(2), 43–73.

Cooke, C. K. 1979. Excavations at Diana's Vow Rock Shelter, Makoni District, Zimbabwe, Rhodesia. *Occasional Papers of the National Museum of Rhodesia. Series A. Human Sciences* **4**(4), 115–48.

Cooke, C. K. 1984. The industries of the Upper Pleistocene in Zimbabwe. *Zimbabweia* **1**, 23–7.

Cooke, C. K. & K. R. Robinson, 1954. Excavations at Amadzimba Cave located in the Matopos Hills, Southern Rhodesia. *Occasional Papers of the National Museum of Southern Rhodesia II* **19**, 699–728.

Cooke, H. J. 1975. The palaeoclimatic significance of caves and adjacent land forms in western Ngamiland, Botswana. *Geographical Journal* **141**, 430–44.

Cooke, H. J. 1978. The palaeogeography of the middle Kalahari of northern Botswana and adjacent areas. In *Proceedings of the Symposium on the Okavango Delta and its Future Utilization*, 21–8. 30 August to 3 September, 1976. Gaborone, Botswana, Gaborone: The Botswana Society.

Cooke, H. J. 1984. The evidence from northern Botswana of Late Quaternary climatic change. In *Later Cainozoic palaeoclimates of the southern hemisphere*, J. C. Vogel (ed.), 265–78. Rotterdam: A. A. Balkema.

Cruz-Uribe, K. 1983. The mammalian fauna from Redcliff Cave, Zimbabwe. *South African Archaeological Bulletin* **38**, 7–16.

Deacon, J., N. Lancaster & L. Scott, 1984. Evidence for Later Quaternary climatic change in southern Africa. Summary of the proceedings of the SASQUA Workshop held in Johannesburg. September, 1983. In *Later Cainozoic palaeoclimates of the southern hemisphere*, J. C. Vogel (ed.), 391–404. Rotterdam: A. A. Balkema.

Dechant, D. & D. Crader, 1982. The faunal remains from Lake Besaka. In A Late Quaternary cultural/environmental sequence from Lake Besaka, Southern Afar, Ethiopia, Appendix A, (S. A. Brandt), 332–82. PhD thesis, University of California, Berkeley.

Ebert, J. & R. K. Hitchcock, 1978. Ancient Lake Makgadikgadi, Botswana: mapping, measurement and palaeoclimatic significance. *Palaeoecology of Africa and the Surrounding Islands* **10/11**, 47–57.

Fiedler, L. & J. Preuss, 1985. Stone tools from the inner Zaire basin, (Region de l'Equateur, Zaire). *African Archaeological Review* **3**, 179–87.

Flannery, K. V. 1969. Origin and ecological effects of early domestication in Iran and the Near East. In *The domestication and exploitation of plants and animals*, P. J. Ucko & G. W. Dimbleby (eds), 73–100. Chicago: Aldine Publishing.

Gasse, F. 1980. Late Quaternary changes in lake-levels and diatom assemblages on the south-eastern margin of the Sahara. *Palaeoecology of Africa and the Surrounding Islands* **12**, 333–50.

Gasse, F. & F. A. Street, 1978. Late Quaternary lake-level fluctuations and environments of the northern Rift Valley and Afar regions (Ethiopia and Djibouti). *Palaeogeography, Palaeoclimatology, Palaeoecology* **24**, 279–325.

Gasse, F., R. Rognon & F. A. Street, 1980. Quaternary history of the Afar and Ethiopian Rift lakes. In *The Sahara and the Nile* M. A. J. Williams & H. Faure (eds), 361–400. Rotterdam: A. A. Balkema.

Gramly, R. M. 1976. Upper Pleistocene archaeological occurrences at site GvJm/22, Lukenya Hill, Kenya. *Man* **3**, 319–44.

Gramly, R. M. & G. P. Rightmire, 1973. A fragmentary cranium and dated Later Stone Age assemblage from Lukenya Hill, Kenya. *Man* **8**, 571–9.

Gresham, T. H. 1984. An investigation of an Upper Pleistocene archaeological site in northern Somalia. M. A. thesis, University of Georgia, Athens, USA.

Grove, A. T. 1969. Landforms and climatic change in the Kalahari and Ngamiland. *Geographical Journal* **135**, 191–212.

Gutin, J. A. & F. B. Musonda, 1985. Faunal remains from Mufulwe rock shelter, Zambia, and their implications. *South African Archaeological Bulletin* **40**, 11–16.

Haas, H. 1977. Radiocarbon dating of charcoal and ostrich egg shells from Mushabi and Lagama sites. In *Prehistoric investigations in Gebel Maghara, Northern Sinai*, O. Bar-Yosef & J. L. Phillips (eds), 261–4. Jerusalem: Hebrew University Press.

Haberyan, K. A. 1987. Fossil diatoms and the palaeolimnology of Lake Rukwa, Tanzania. *Freshwater Biology* **17**, 429–36.

Haberyan, K. A. & R. E. Hecky, 1987. The late Pleistocene and Holocene stratigraphy and palaeolimnology of Lakes Kivu and Tanganyika. *Palaeogeography, Palaeoclimatology, Palaeoecology* **61**, 169–97.

Hamilton, A. C. 1982. *Environmental History of East Africa: a Study of the Quaternary.* London: Academic Press.

Harvey, T. J. 1976. The palaeolimnology of Lake Mobutu Sese Seko, Uganda-Zaire: the last 28000 years. Unpublished PhD dissertation, Duke University, Durham, North Carolina.

Hastenrath, S. & J. E. Kutzbach, 1983. Palaeoclimatic estimates from water and energy budgets of east African lakes. *Quaternary Research* **19**, 141–53.

Headland, T. N. 1987. The wild yam question; How well could independent hunter–gatherers live in a tropical rain forest ecosystem? *Human Ecology* **15**(4), 463–91.

Hecky, R. E. & E. T. Degens, 1973. Late Pleistocene–Holocene chemical stratigraphy and palaeolimnology of the Rift Valley lakes of Central Africa. *Technical Report, Woods Hole Oceanographic Institute*, Woods Hole, MA.

Heine, K. 1982. The main stages of the Late Quaternary evolution of the Kalahari region, southern Africa. *Palaeoecology of Africa and the surrounding islands* **15**, 53–76.

Heine, K. & M. A. Geyh, 1984. Radiocarbon dating of speleotherms from the Rossing Cave, Namib desert, and palaeoclimatic implications. In *Late Cainozoic palaeoclimates of the southern hemisphere*, J. C. Vogel (ed.), 465–70. Rotterdam: A. A. Balkema.

Heinzelin de Braucourt, J. de 1957. *Les Fouilles d'Ishango*. Exploration du Parc National Albert. Fasc. 2. Bruxelles: Institut des Parcs Nationaux du Congo Belge.

Heinzelin de Braucourt, J. de 1961. Ishango. *Scientific American* **206**, 105–16.

Helgren, D. H. & A. S. Brooks, 1983. Geoarchaeology at Gi, a Middle and Later Stone Age site in the Northwest Kalahari. *Journal of Archaeological Science* **10**, 181–97.

Hitzeroth, L. 1973. Results of a stone age excavation from Duncombe Farm Shelter, Concession, 1970. *Rhodesian Prehistory* **10**, 14–18.

Hivernel-Guerre, F. 1970. Introduction à l'étude du "Late Stone Age" de Kella (Melka Kontoure). *Documents pour Servir a l'Histoire de la Civilization Ethiopienne* **2**, 39–48.

Holdship, S. A. 1976. The Palaeolimology of Lake Manyara, Tanzania: a diatom analysis of a 56 meter sediment core. Unpublished PhD dissertation, Duke University, Durham, North Carolina.

Humphreys, G. K. 1978. A preliminary report of some Late Stone Age occurrences in the Lake Ziway area of the central Ethiopian Rift Valley. *Annales d'Ethiopie* **1**, 45–66.

Inskeep, R. R. 1962. The age of the Kondoa rock paintings in the light of recent excavations at Kisese II rock shelter. In *Actes du 4ᵉ Congres Panafricain de Prehistoire, Leopoldville, 1959*, G. Mortelmans & J. Nenquin (eds), 246–56. Tervuren: Musée Royale de l'Afrique Centrale.

Jones, N. 1940. Bambata Cave: a reorientation. *Occasional Papers of the Rhodesian Museum* **1**(12), 11–28.

Kendall, R. L. 1969. An ecological history of the Lake Victoria basin. *Ecological Monographs* **39**, 121–76.

Klein, R. G. 1978. Preliminary analysis of the mammalian fauna from the Redcliff Stone Age Cave site, Rhodesia. *Occasional Papers of the National Museums of Rhodesia. Series A. Human Sciences* **4**, 74–80.

Klein, R. G. 1980. Environmental and ecological implications of large mammals from Upper Pleistocene and Holocene sites in southern Africa. *Annals of the South African Museum* **81**, 223–83.

Klein, R. G. 1984. Later Stone Age faunal samples from Heuningneskrans Shelter

(Transvaal) and Leopard's Hill Cave (Zambia). *South African Archaeological Bulletin* **39**, 109–16.

Kokis, J. E. 1988. Protein diagenesis dating of ostrich (*Struthio camelus*) eggshell: an Upper Pleistocene dating technique. Unpublished M.A. thesis, The George Washington University, Washington, DC.

Labeyrie, J., J. C. Duplessy, G. Delibrias, & R. Letolle, 1967. Etude des temperatures des climats anciens par la mésure de O^{18}, de C^{13} et de $\dot{C}^{14}$ dans les concretions des cavernes. In *Radioactive dating and methods of low-level counting*, 153–60. Vienna: IAEA.

Leakey, M. D., R. L. Hay, D. L. Thurber, R. Protsch & R. Berger 1972. Stratigraphy, archaeology and age of the Ndutu and Naisiusiu Beds, Olduvai Gorge, Tanzania. *World Archaeology* **3**, 328–41.

Lee, R. B. 1979. *The !Kung San: men, women and work in a foraging society*. Cambridge: Cambridge University Press.

Lehmann, U. 1957. Eine jungpleistozäne Wirbeltierfauna aus Östafrika. *Mitteilungen Staatsinstitut von Hamburg* **26**, 100–40.

Livingstone, D. A. 1965. Sedimentation and the history of water level change in Lake Tanganyika. *Limnology & Oceanography* **10**, 607–10.

Livingstone, D. A. 1967. Postglacial vegetation of the Ruwenzori mountains in Equatorial Africa. *Ecological Monographs* **37**, 25–52.

Livingstone, D. A. 1971. A 22,000-year pollen record from the plateau of Zambia. *Limnology and Oceanography* **16**, 349–56.

Livingstone, D. A. 1975. Late Quaternary climatic change in Africa. *Annual Review of Ecology and Systematics* **6**, 249–80.

Long, A., R. B. Hendershott & P. S. Martin 1983. Radiocarbon dating of fossil eggshell. *Radiocarbon* **25**, 533–9.

Maret, P. de 1985. Recent archaeological research and dates from central Africa. *Journal of African History* **26**, 129–48.

Marliac, A. 1973. Prospection archéologique au Cameroun. *Cahiers ORSTOM, Series Sciences Humaines* **10**, 47–114.

Marliac, A. 1974. Prospection archéologique au Cameroun septentrional. *West African Journal of Archaeology* **4**, 83–97.

Mehlman, M. J. 1977. Excavations at Nasera Rock, Tanzania. *Azania* **12**, 111–18.

Mehlman, M. J. 1979. Mumba-Höhle revisited: the relevance of a forgotten excavation to some current issues in East African prehistory. *World Archaeology* **11**, 80–94.

Mehlman, M. J. 1984. Archaic *Homo sapiens* at Lake Eyasi, Tanzania: recent misrepresentations. *Journal of Human Evolution* **13**, 487–501.

Mehlman, M. J. 1987. Provenience, age and associations of archaic *Homo sapiens* crania from Lake Eyasi, Tanzania. *Journal of Archaeological Science* **14**, 133–62.

Merrick, H. V. 1975. Change in later Pleistocene lithic industries in eastern Africa. Unpublished PhD dissertation, University of California, Berkeley, California.

Merrick, H. V. & F. H. Brown 1984. Obsidian sources and patterns of source utilization in Kenya and northern Tanzania: some initial findings. *African Archaeological Review* **2**, 129–52.

Miller, S. F. 1969. The Nachikufan Industries of the Zambian Later Stone Age. Unpublished PhD dissertation, University of California, Berkeley, California.

Miller, S. F. 1971. The age of Nachikufan industries in Zambia. *South African Archaeological Bulletin* **26**, 143–6.

Miller, S. F. 1979. Lukenya Hill, GvJm46, excavation report. *Nyame Akuma* **14**, 31–4.

Moeyersons, J. 1975. Evolution paléogéographique du site de la Kamoa. In *Le Site Archéologique de la Kamoa (Region du Shaba, République du Zaire)*. De l'Age de Pierre

Ancien a l'Age de Fer, D. Cahen (ed.). 18–46. Tervuren: Annales du Musée Royale de l'Afrique Centrale. Série in 8⁰, Sciences Humaines no. 84.

Moeyersons, J. & E. Roche, 1977–1978. Evolution palaeogéographique et phytosociologique en Afrique centrale durant le Pleistocene supérieur. Interpretations des données géomorphologiques, botaniques, et palynologiques. *Etudes d'Histoire Africaine* **IX–X** 37–48.

Moeyersons, J. & E. Roche, 1982. Past and present environments. In *The archaeology of Central Africa*, F. van Noten (ed.), 15–26. Graf: Akademische Drück- und Verlagsanstalt.

Moorsel, H. van 1968. *Atlas de Préhistoire de la Plaine de Kinshasa*. Kinshasa: Publication de l'Université Louvanium.

Musonda, F. B. 1984. Late Pleistocene and Holocene microlithic industries from the Lusemfwa Basin, Zambia. *South African Archaeological Bulletin* **39**, 24–36.

Nelson, C. M. & J. Kimengich 1984. Early phases of pastoral adaptation in the central highlands of Kenya. In *Origin and development of food-producing cultures in northeastern Africa*, L. Krzyzaniak & M. Kobusiewicz (eds), 481–7. Poznan: Polish Academy of Sciences.

Nenquin, J. 1967. *Contribution to the study of the prehistoric cultures of Rwanda and Burundi*. Tervuren: Annales du Musée Royale de l'Afrique Centrale, Sciences Humaines, no. 59.

Noten, F. van 1971. Excavations at Munyama Cave. *Antiquity* **45**, 56–8.

Noten, F. van 1977. Excavations at Matupi Cave. *Antiquity* **51**, 35–40.

Noten, F. van 1982. *The archaeology of Central Africa*. Graf: Akademische Drück- und Verlagsanstalt.

Osmaston, H. A. 1965. The past and present climate and vegetation of Ruwenzori and its neighborhood. DPhil thesis, Oxford University.

Perrot, R. A. & F. A. Street-Perrot, 1982. New evidence for a Late Pleistocene wet phase in northern intertropical Africa. *Palaeoecology of Africa* **14**, 57–75.

Peters, J. 1989. Late Pleistocene hunter-gatherers at Ishango (eastern Zaire); the faunal evidence. *Revue de Paléobiologie* **8**(1).

Phillipson, D. W. 1976. *The prehistory of eastern Zambia*. Nairobi: British Institute in Eastern Africa Memoir no. 6.

Phillipson, D. W. 1977a. The excavation of Gobedra rock-shelter, Axum: an early occurrence of cultivated finger millet in northern Ethiopia. *Azania* **12**, 53–82.

Phillipson, D. W. 1977b. *The later prehistory of eastern and southern Africa*. London: Heinemann.

Phillipson, D. W. 1980. Some speculations on the beginnings of backed-microlith manufacture. In *Proceedings of the 8th Panafrican Congress of Prehistory and Quaternary Studies, Nairobi, September 1977*, R. E. Leakey & B. Ogot (eds), 229–30. Nairobi: TILLMIAP.

Phillipson, D. W. 1986. *African archaeology*. Cambridge: Cambridge University Press.

Preuss, J. G. J. 1986. Jungpleistozäne klimaanderungen im Kongo-Zaire-Becken. *Geowissenschaften in Unserer Seit* **4**(6), 177–87.

Renaut, R. W. & R. B. Owen 1980. Late Quaternary fluvio-lacustrine sedimentation and lake levels in the Baringo Basin, northern Kenya Rift Valley. *Recherches Geologiques en Afrique* **5**, 130–3

Richardson, J. L. & R. A. Dussinger 1986. Paleolimnology of mid-elevation lakes in the Kenya Rift Valley. *Hydrobiologia* **147**, 167–74.

Richardson, J. L. & A. E. Richardson, 1972. History of an African Rift lake and its climatic implications. *Ecological Monographs* **42**, 499–534.

Robbins, L. H. & A. C. Campbell, in press. The Depression rock shelter site. *Botswana Notes and Records*, Vol. 18.

Robertshaw, P. 1988. Environment and culture in the late Quaternary of eastern Africa: a critique of some correlations. In *Prehistoric cultures and environments of the Late Quaternary of Africa*, J. R. F. Bower & D. Lubell (eds), 115–26. Oxford: BAR, International Series 405.

Robinson, K. R. 1952. Excavations in two rock shelters near the Rusawi river, central Mashonaland. *South African Archaeological Bulletin* **7**(27), 108–29.

Robinson, K. R. & B. H. Sandelowsky, 1968. The Iron Age of northern Malawi: recent work. *Azania* **3**, 107–46.

Roche, E. 1975. Analyse palynologique du site archéologique de la Kamoa. In *Le Site Archéologique de la Kamoa (Region du Shaba, République du Zaire). De l'age de la Pierre ancien a l'Age du Fer*, D. Cahen (ed.), 331–7. Annales du Musée Royale de l'Afrique Centrale. Série in 8⁰, Sciences Humaines no. 84.

Rust, U. 1984. Geomorphic evidence of Quaternary environmental changes in Etosha, South West Africa/Namibia. In *Late Cainozoic palaeoclimates of the southern hemisphere*, J. C. Vogel (ed.), 279–86. Rotterdam: A. A. Balkema.

Rust, U., H. H. Schmidt & K. R. Dietz 1984. Palaeoenvironments of the present day arid south western Africa 30 000–5000 BP: results and problems. *Palaeoecology of Africa and the surrounding Islands* **16**, 109–48.

Sampson, C. G. 1974. *The Stone Age archaeology of southern Africa*. New York: Academic Press.

Sandelowsky, B. 1983. Archaeology in Namibia. *American Scientist* **71**, 606–15.

Schepartz, L. 1987. From hunters to herders: subsistence pattern and morphological change in eastern Africa. Unpublished PhD dissertation, University of Michigan, Ann Arbor, MI.

Scholz, C. A. & B. R. Rosendahl, 1988. Low lake stands in Lakes Malawi and Tanganyika, East Africa, delineated with multifold seismic data. *Science* **240**, 1645–8.

Schrire, C. (ed.) 1984. *Past and present in hunter-gatherer studies*. New York: Academic Press.

Servant, M. & S. Servant-Vildary, 1980. L'environment quaternaire du bassin du Tchad. In *The Sahara and the Nile*, M. A. J. Williams & H. Faure (eds), 133–62. Rotterdam: A. A. Balkema.

Servant, M., S. Servant & G. Delibrias 1969. Géologie du Quaternaire. Chronologie du Quaternaire recent des basses regions du Tchad. *Comptes Rendus des Seances l'Academie des Sciences* **269** 1603–6.

Shackleton, N. C. 1982. Stratigraphy and chronology of the Klasies River Mouth deposits: oxygen isotope evidence. In *The Middle Stone Age at Klasies River Mouth in South Africa*, R. Singer & J. J. Wymer (eds), 194–9. Chicago: University of Chicago Press.

Shaw, T. 1978. *Nigeria: its archaeology and early history*. London: Thames and Hudson.

Silberbauer, G. B. 1981. *Hunter and habitat in the central Kalahari Desert*. Cambridge: Cambridge University Press.

Sowunmi, M. A. 1986. The effect of the last glacial maximum on the environment in equatorial Africa: palynological evidence. Preprint of paper prepared for the World Archaeology Congress, Southampton, England, September.

Stager, J. C. 1984. The diatom record of Lake Victoria (East Africa): the last 17,000 years. In *Proceedings of the 7ᵗʰ Diatom symposium, Philadelphia, 22–27 August 1982*, D. G. Mann (ed.), 455–76. Koenigstein: Otto Koeltz Science Publishers.

Street, F. A. & A. T. Grove 1976. Environmental and climatic implications of late Quaternary lake-level fluctuations in Africa. *Nature* **261**, 385–90.

Talbot, M. R., D. A. Livingstone, P. G. Palmer, J. Maley, J. M. Melack, G. Delibrias,

& S. Gulliksen 1984. Preliminary results from sediment cores from Lake Bosumtwi, Ghana. *Palaeoecology of Africa and the Surrounding Islands* **16**, 173–92.

Tiercelin, J. J., R. W. Renaut, G. Delibrias, J. LeFournier & S. Bieda. 1981. Late Pleistocene and Holocene lake level fluctuations in the Lake Bogoria basin, northern Kenya rift valley. *Palaeoecology of Africa and the Surrounding Islands* **13**, 105–20.

Twiesselmann, F. 1958. *Les Ossements Humains, Gîte Mesolithique d'Ishango*. Exploration du Parc National Albert. Fasc 5. Brussels: Institute des Parcs Nationaux du Congo Belge.

Vogel, J. C. (ed.) 1984. *Later Cainozoic palaeoclimates of the southern hemisphere*. Rotterdam: A. A. Balkema.

Volman, T. P. 1984. Early prehistory of southern Africa. In *Southern African prehistory and palaeoenvironments*, R. G. Klein, (ed.), 169–220. Rotterdam: A. A. Balkema.

Walker, N. J. 1977. Nswatugi. *Southern African Association of Archaeologists Newsletter* **10**.

Walker, N. J. 1980. Later Stone Age research in the Matopos. *South African Archaeological Bulletin* **35**, 19–24.

Walker, N. J. & L. Wadley. 1984. Evidence for an early microlithic industry at Duncombe Farm in Zimbabwe. *Cookeia* **1** (1), 4–13.

Wendt, W. E. 1972. Preliminary report on an archaeological research program in South West Africa. *Cimbebasia B* **2**(1), 1–61.

Wendt, W. E. 1974. 'Art mobilier' aus der Apollo 11-Grotte in Südwest Afrika: die ältesten datierten Kunstwerke Afrikas. *Acta Prehistorica Archaeologica* **5**, 1–42.

Wendt, W. E. 1976. 'Art mobilier' from the Apollo 11 cave, South West Africa: Africa's oldest dated works of art. *South African Archaeological Bulletin* **31**, 5–11.

Williams, M. A. J., F. M. Williams & P. M. Bishop, 1981. Late Quaternary history of Lake Besaka, Ethiopia. *Palaeoecology of Africa* **13**, 93–104.

Williams, M. A. J., P. M. Bishop, F. M. Dakin & R. Gillespie 1977. Late Quaternary lake levels in southern Afar and the adjacent Ethiopian Rift. *Nature* **267**, 690–3.

Yellen, J. E., A. S. Brooks, R. Stuckenrath & R. Welbourne 1987. A terminal Pleistocene assemblage from Drotsky's Cave, western Ngamiland, Botswana. *Botswana Notes and Records* **19**, 1–6.

Zinderen Bakker, E. M. van 1967. Upper Pleistocene and Holocene stratigraphy and ecology on the basis of vegetation changes in sub-Saharan Africa. In *Background to human evolution in Africa*, W. W. Bishop & J. D. Clark (eds), 125–46. Chicago: University of Chicago Press.

Zinderen Bakker, E. M. van 1969. The Pleistocene vegetation and climate of the basin. In *Kalambo Falls prehistoric site*, Vol. I, J. D. Clark (ed.), 57–84. Cambridge: Cambridge University Press.

Zinderen Bakker, E. M. van 1984a. Aridity along the Namibian Coast. *Palaeoecology of Africa and the Surrounding Islands* **16**, 149–60.

Zinderen Bakker, E. M. van 1984b. A Late- and Post-glacial pollen record from the Namib Desert. *Palaeoecology of Africa and the Surrounding Islands* **16**, 421–8.

7 Changes in the archaeological record in South Africa at 18 000 BP

JANETTE DEACON

Introduction

One of the major preoccupations of Palaeolithic archaeologists has been the question of causality, and in particular the extent to which climatic and associated environmental changes influenced the technology, economy, and social organization of prehistoric people. As part of this paradigm, the South African evidence for the scale and timing of changes at the Last Glacial Maximum (LGM) was gathered over the past few decades primarily to document the temporal and geographical limits of stone artefact industries and to find environmental correlates. The data, summarized below, show no simple correlation between environmental and technological change. Human demographic patterns and the structure of plant and animal communities, on the other hand, suggest that harsher climates of glacial cycles reduced population levels and species diversity relative to interglacial times to the extent that LGM environments have no modern analogue. The current challenge is to trace social changes and to identify in the archaeological record the relations of production characteristic of the modern San in the expectation that we should be able to recognize when the modern system of distributing food and material was initiated and what its correlates may be (Lewis–Williams 1984, Wadley 1988). This chapter examines the timing and nature of environmental, technological, economic, and demographic shifts to highlight the contrasting modes of glacial and interglacial times and to test whether changes in the forces and relations of production coincided with or were independent of environmental change around the time of the LGM.

Modern environments and the archaeological record

South Africa, including southern Africa from the latitude of the Limpopo River at 22°S to the southern tip of the African continent at about 34°S, is a southern hemisphere region of the Old World that was not glaciated during the Pleistocene. Today it has moderate to warm mean annual temperatures ranging from about 23.3°C in the northwestern Cape to about 11.5°C in the

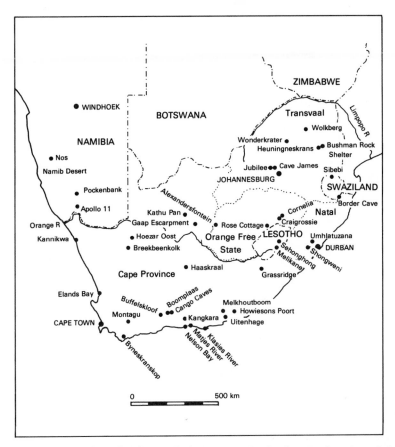

Figure 7.1 Map of South Africa and adjoining territories showing location of places mentioned in the text and in Table 7.1.

highlands of Lesotho. The 400 mm isohyet divides the subcontinent into a drier western half and a moister eastern half. In the southwest where 70–80% of the rain falls in winter, mean annual rainfall ranges from less than 100 mm to more than 1000 mm. In the all-year rainfall region along the south Cape coast it ranges from about 200 mm to more than 1200 mm, and in the eastern half of the country, where more than 80% of the rain falls in summer, mean annual rainfall ranges from 400 mm in the west to over 1200 mm along the escarpment mountains in the east. Low rainfall in the interior is exacerbated by evaporation. Mean annual pan evaporation ranges from 3000 to 4000 mm in the centre and northwest to 1500–2500 mm in the eastern half (Schulze 1984). In the eastern half, daily rainfall exceeds 10 mm on 20–30 days, whereas in the west there are typically fewer than ten such days (Schulze 1984, Tyson 1986). A general decrease in rainfall would therefore increase the risk for hunter-gatherers in the dry interior, whereas higher rainfall would allow higher population densities in what are today relatively arid regions.

Table 7.1 Generalized summary of radiocarbon-dated occurrences of technological, economic, and temperature changes at sites in South Africa from c. 40 000 to c. 10 000 BP

Date ×1000 years BP	Final MSA	Early LSA	Robberg-type assemblages	Oakhurst/Albany assemblages	Decorated & decorative items	Polished bone tools	Formal burial	Large grazing fauna	Small browsing fauna	Temperature estimate from Cango speleothem
10			Heuningneskrans Byneskranskop Shongweni	Widespread after 12 000 BP	OES and marine shell beads common	Polished bone tools common	Matjes River		Boomplaas Elands Bay Nelson Bay	no data but ?15°C
14			Kangkara Elands Bay Sehonghong Melkoutboom		Boomplaas: decorated OES flasks, tortoise-shell bowls, OES beads	Elands Bay Nelson Bay Boomplaas		Boomplaas Elands Bay Nelson Bay Melkoutboom Heuningneskrans		13°C
18		Apollo 11, Nos Pockenbank Buffelskloof Heuningneskrans Elands Bay Boomplaas Shongweni Rose Cottage	Boomplaas Nelson Bay Sehonghong Melikane		A few OES beads at Boomplaas, Nelson Bay, Heuningneskrans	Nelson Bay		Boomplaas Nelson Bay Elands Bay		11°
22						Boomplaas		Boomplaas Heuningneskrans		12°C
26	Apollo 11 Umhlatuzana	Rose Cottage			paintings on rock slabs at Apollo 11			Boomplaas		12.7°
30	Boomplass	Rose Cottage Heuningneskrans Cave James								13°
34	Grassridge Pockenbank									no data
38		Border Cave			A few OES beads at Border Cave	Border Cave		Border Cave		
greater than 40	Border Cave Rose Cottage					Klasies River greater than 60 000 BP	?Border Cave greater than 40 000 BP			

OES, ostrich eggshell; present-day temperature at Cango is 16.4°C.

References: Apollo 11, Nos, Pockenbank: Wendt (1972, 1976); Umhlatuzana: Vogel & Kaplan (pers. comm.); Boomplaas: H. J. Deacon (1979), J. Deacon (1984a); Grassridge: Opperman (1987); Border Cave, Rose Cottage, Heuningneskrans: Beaumont & Vogel (1972), Beaumont (1978, 1981); Buffelskloof: Opperman (1978); Elands Bay: Parkington (1987); Shongweni: Davies (1975); Cave James: Wadley (1988); Byneskranskop: Schweitzer & Wilson (1982); Kangkara, Nelson Bay: J. Deacon (1984a); Sehonghong, Melikane: Carter (1978); Melkhoutboom: H. J. Deacon (1976); Klasies River: Singer & Wymer (1982); Matjes River: Louw (1960); Cango speleothem temperatures: Vogel (1983), J. Deacon & Lancaster (1988, Fig. 6.11).

The number of excavated sites with dated occupation horizons at the LGM is limited to Apollo 11, Nos, and Pockenbank in Namibia; Nelson Bay Cave, Buffelskloof, and Boomplaas Cave in the southern Cape; Elands Bay Cave in the southwestern Cape; Shongweni in Natal; Rose Cottage Cave in the Orange Free State; Heuningneskrans in the Transvaal; and Sehonghong and Melikane in Lesotho (Fig. 7.1, Table 7.1). A number of other sites have radiocarbon-dated deposits on either side of event 2.2, but none dated to the LGM proper. Sites such as Bushman Rock Shelter, Sibebi, Howiesons Poort, Montagu, and Klasies River have radiocarbon dates in the LGM time bracket, but for various reasons (mostly because they are associated with Middle Stone-Age artefact assemblages and also include infinite dates) these are not considered to be reliable estimates of the age of the deposits. Of all of these, only Boomplaas, Nelson Bay, Melikane, Heuningneskrans and Elands Bay have LGM artefact assemblages accompanied by faunal remains, and only Apollo 11, Sehonghong, Boomplaas and Heuningneskrans have a relatively continuous occupation from the lead down to and out of the LGM within oxygen isotope stage 2, i.e. from c. 32 000 to c. 12 000 BP.

The palaeoclimatic record

The LGM is taken as event 2.2 in the high resolution chronostratigraphy calculated from southwestern Indian Ocean core RC11-120 (Martinson et al. 1987). The age estimates range from 17 850 ± 1370 to 23 930 ± 4790 BP. This is essentially the coldest part of the last glacial cycle and is a climatic event that is clearly discernible in deep-sea cores throughout the world (CLIMAP 1976, Ruddiman & Duplessy 1985).

The terrestrial record for temperature change over the LGM in South Africa includes three temperature curves based on isotope analyses of samples derived ultimately from rainwater precipitated from the Indian Ocean. Fossil water samples from the Uitenhage aquifer in the eastern Cape (Vogel 1983, Heaton et al. 1986) show a maximum depression of c. 5°C between about 22 000 and 18 000 BP. Oxygen isotope measurements on a speleothem from the Cango Caves in the southern Cape show a similar scale of temperature depression (5.5°C) between about 18 000 and 16 000 BP (Heaton 1981, Vogel 1983, J. Deacon & Lancaster 1988). By contrast, two oxygen isotope samples from stalagmites in the Wolkberg Caves in the Transvaal dated to 29 600 and 19 800 BP suggest a temperature drop of between 8°C and 9.5°C when compared with the most recent samples dating to the late Holocene (Talma et al. 1974). All three indicate a similar timing of the maximum temperature depression of the LGM that, not surprisingly, is comparable with that observed in deep-sea core samples from the surrounding oceans (Vincent 1972, Morley & Hays 1979, Prell et al. 1979, Martin 1981, Howard & Prell 1984, Martinson et al. 1987). Additional estimates of relative temperature changes have been calculated from biological samples that give community composition and variations in growth patterns of individual species in microfauna, pollen, and charcoal samples at Boomplaas Cave (H. J. Deacon 1979, Avery 1982, H. J. Deacon *et al.* 1984, Scholtz 1986, Thackeray 1987) and carbon isotope analyses of zebra teeth at Melikane (Vogel 1983). These measures show the maximum temperature depression in the sequence to have been between 22 000 and 17 000 BP and indicate a clear contrast between glacial and interglacial conditions. Although the scale of change suggests that the LGM was more than 5°C cooler than the present (and indeed than most of the Holocene), the difference between temperatures at *c.* 32 000 BP and *c.* 18 000 BP is of the order of only 1–2°C, but is about 3–4°C between *c.* 18 000 and *c.* 14 000–12 000 BP (Vogel 1983, Thackeray 1987, Fig. 3, J. Deacon & Lancaster 1988, Table 1).

With regard to precipitation at the LGM, the time of maximum cold coincided with the driest conditions, but higher rainfall than at present was widespread during the lead down to and out of the LGM, i.e. between *c.* 40 000 and 22 000 BP and again between *c.* 16 000 and 12 000 BP (J. Deacon & Lancaster 1988). In the Namib Desert to the northwest, lake and groundwater levels fell at the LGM and the driest conditions occurred around 19 000–18 000 BP (Heine 1978, Teller & Lancaster 1985) coinciding with drier conditions in the semi desert Karoo to the south at Haaskraal (Partridge & Dalbey 1986) and Kathu Pan (Beaumont *et al.* 1984, J. Deacon & Lancaster 1988). In the all-year rainfall region, evidence for LGM rainfall conditions comes from pollen and charcoal analyses at Boomplaas that show a plant community of low diversity that has no modern analogue (H. J. Deacon *et al.* 1984). The species composition indicates few trees and a high percentage of composites in an area that has woodland vegetation today. Xylem analysis of the charcoal (Scholtz 1986) shows narrow vessels and spindly growth, which are characteristic of dry and windy conditions. The community composition of the microfauna also suggests that the climate was exceptionally dry both at Boomplaas at *c.* 22 000–18 000 BP and at Nelson Bay Cave at *c.* 18 000 BP (Avery 1982, H. J. Deacon *et al.* 1984, J. Deacon & Lancaster 1988). Thereafter, however, charcoal, pollen, and microfauna indicate that the wettest conditions of the last 70 000 years prevailed between 14 000 and 12 000 BP, with woodland vegetation developing in the Cango valley.

To the east of the summer-rainfall region, drier conditions are inferred from pollen analyses at Cornelia and Craigrossie between *c.* 20 000 and 12 000 BP (Scott 1986) and the period of maximum cold is accompanied by an impoverished vegetation indicative of dry conditions at Wonderkrater in the Transvaal (Scott 1982, Scott & Thackeray 1987). However, there are several reports of higher precipitation at the LGM in the western part of the summer-rainfall region at Alexandersfontein Pan (Butzer 1984a, 1984b) and on the Gaap Escarpment (Butzer *et al.* 1978), and even further west at Breekbeenkolk, Hoezar Oost and Kannikwa (Beaumont 1986). All these estimates are based on tufa and lake or pan levels and carbonates have supplied organic material for dating.

In the winter-rainfall region to the southwest, Butzer (1979) has suggested dry and windy conditions from sediment analyses at Elands Bay Cave, and this is supported by the size of mole-rats that also indicate drier conditions than at present, in the time-range *c.* 20 000–11 000 BP (Klein 1984). The development of palaeosols that alternate with dunes in the vicinity of Cape Town and date to the LGM is considered by Butzer (1984b, p. 239) to indicate dune stability relating to the lower sea-level rather than a genuinely moist climate as assumed by Cockcroft *et al.* (1987).

Apart from temperature and precipitation changes, the LGM is also characterized by a lower sea-level, and radiocarbon dating of littoral shells from the sea bed off the present coast suggests that the maximum regression may have been as much as 130 m below present sea-level. The shape of the continental shelf around the subcontinent indicates that at the southern tip of Africa the coastline was over 100 km south of its present position 18 000 years ago, but in the east along the Natal coast and in the west where the continental shelf is narrow, the coastline was not so much far away from its present position as well below it (Dingle & Rogers 1972a, 1972b, Vogel & Visser 1981, J. Deacon & Lancaster 1988). LGM sea-surface temperature estimates off the South African coast range from no change to 5°C cooler (Vincent 1972, CLIMAP 1976, Morley & Hays 1979, Prell *et al.* 1979, Martin 1981, Howard & Prell 1984).

In summary, these palaeoclimatic data are for the most part in agreement that temperatures at the time of maximum cold in South Africa (20 000–16 000 BP) were 5°C, and possibly as much as 9.5°C, cooler than at present. The time of maximum cold coincides with a generally dry spell, but when temperatures were 1–3°C higher than at the LGM both prior to and immediately after the period of maximum cold, there is good evidence for higher precipitation than at present. Faunal and floral communities reflect the harsher conditions by being less diverse at the LGM. The fact that these biological communities have no modern analogue intimates in turn that modern climatic patterns may be inappropriate analogues for modelling LGM climate and weather patterns as has been attempted by Tyson (1986) and Cockcroft *et al.* (1987) (J. Deacon & Lancaster 1988).

The artefact record

With final Middle Stone-Age assemblages dating in the 40 000 to 25 000-year range, the LGM in South Africa coincides broadly with the earliest manifestations of the Later Stone Age. When Goodwin & Van Riet Lowe (1929) published the first authoritative description of southern African Stone-Age industries, they were impressed by the difference in stone artefact technology between assemblages they labelled as Middle Stone Age (MSA) with large flake blades, triangular flakes with facetted platforms, and Levallois-type cores, and those of the Later Stone Age (LSA) generally with a microlithic techology and non-lithic items similar to those used during the ethnographic present

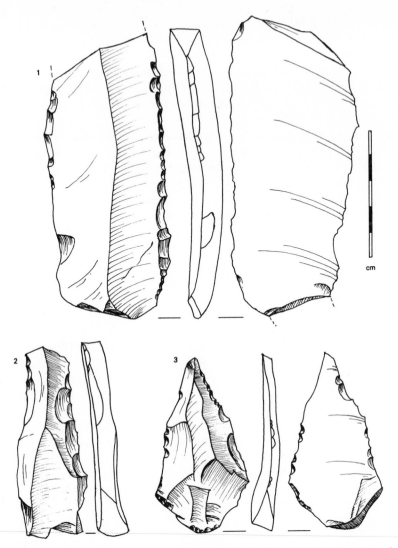

Figure 7.2 Stone artefacts typical of the final stage of the Middle Stone Age from Boomplaas dated to *c*. 32 000 BP. 1, truncated retouched blade; 2, retouched blade; 3, unifacial point.

(J. Deacon 1984b). The change is broadly similar to that from the Middle to the Upper Palaeolithic/Mesolithic in Europe. As more sites were investigated, it appeared as though there were transitional industries that combined attributes from both MSA and LSA, and these were grouped into the Second Intermediate (Clark 1959). However, the Second Intermediate concept was based on poorly dated assemblages that included material from disturbed contexts, and the term was dropped (Bishop & Clark 1967, Sampson 1974). In South Africa it was represented by the Howiesons Poort, which has been

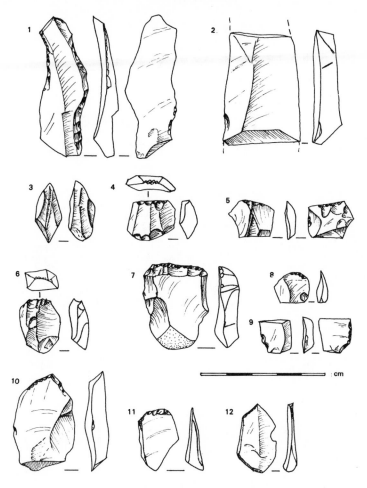

Figure 7.3 Stone artefacts from the early Later Stone Age and early Robberg industry at Boomplaas, 1–5, undated but between *c.* 30 000 and *c.* 22 000 BP; 6–12, dated to *c.* 21 000 BP. 1, retouched flake blade; 2, truncated blade; 3, bladelet core; 4–6, *pièces esquillées*; 7, scraper; 8–12, utilized flakes.

shown at several sites to be the penultimate rather than the final stage of the Middle Stone Age and dates beyond the range of radiocarbon dating (Beaumont & Vogel 1972, Beaumont *et al.* 1978, Singer & Wymer 1982, Volman 1984).

The South African stone artefact sequence, as understood at present, has the Howiesons Poort dating to beyond 60 000 BP, overlain by a final MSA with some unifacial points and large flake blades (Fig. 7.2). This is followed by assemblages grouped informally within the Early LSA (ELSA) (Beaumont & Vogel 1972) in which bipolar flaking, particularly on vein quartz, produces large numbers of *pièces esquillées* and very few formally retouched tools (Fig. 7.3). Beaumont (1978) has reported a few ostrich eggshell beads and a polished

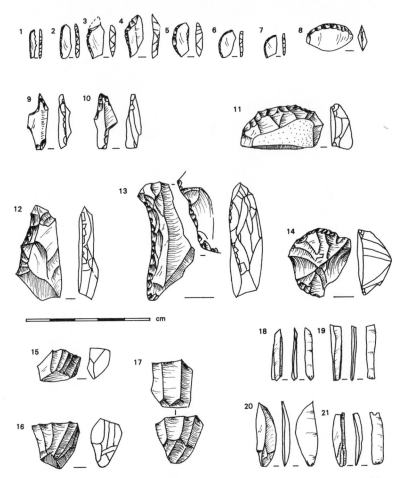

Figure 7.4   Stone artefacts from the Robberg industry at Boomplaas dated between
c. 17 800 and 12 000 BP. 1–7, backed microliths; 8, 11, 14, scrapers; 9, 10, borers; 12, 13,
adzes; 15–17, bladelet cores; 18–21, untrimmed bladelets.

bone point with this industry at Border Cave, dating to *c.* 38 000 BP. Although
the dating of the transition between the MSA and ELSA is inconsistent at
different sites (ranging between *c.* 38 000 and *c.* 25 000 BP) and the two seem to
overlap, at no site does MSA technology occur after the ELSA or LSA has
appeared in a sequence (Table 7.1). The scale of change between assemblages
grouped into the MSA and those in the LSA is a fundamental technological
shift that is recognizable in all classes of stone artefacts from cores and
untrimmed flakes to formally retouched tools and non-lithic artefacts.

Overlying the ELSA at several sites is the Later Stone-Age Robberg
industry, characterized by the production of microbladelets from standardized
single-platform bladelet cores using fine-grained raw materials such as silcrete,
chalcedony, chert, and crystal quartz (Fig. 7.4). There are a few formal tools

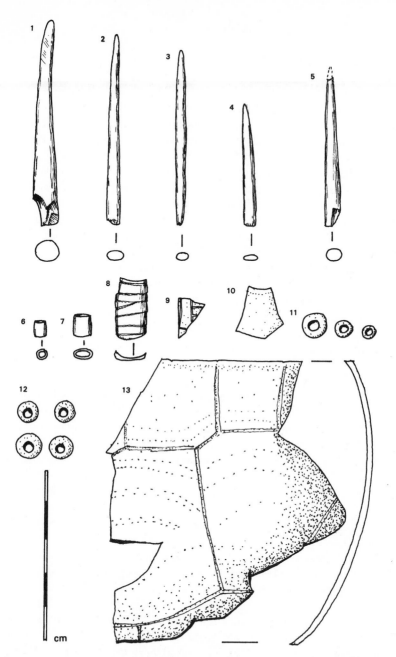

Figure 7.5 Non-lithic artefacts from the Robberg industry. 1–4; polished bone points from Boomplass *c*. 21 000 BP; 5, polished bone point from Nelson Bay *c*. 16 700 BP; 6, polished bone bead from Boomplaas *c*. 17 800 BP; 7, 8, polished and grooved bone beads from Boomplaas *c*. 14 000 BP; 9, decorated fragment and 10, aperture fragment of ostrich eggshell water flask from Boomplaas *c*. 14 000 BP; 11, ostrich eggshell beads from Boomplaas, dated *c*. 14 000 BP; 12, ostrich eggshell beads from Nelson Bay dated *c*. 18 500 BP; 13, fragment of tortoiseshell bowl from Boomplaas dated *c*. 14 000 BP.

(0.1% of the total assemblage), which include typical Later Stone-Age scrapers and backed bladelets, but no typical MSA forms. Amongst the non-lithic component there are a few ostrich eggshell beads and a bone bead, as well as several polished bone tools from the earliest Robberg, between 21 000 and 18 000 BP, at Nelson Bay Cave and Boomplaas (Fig. 7.5). None of these items occur regularly with Middle Stone-Age assemblages, and their appearance is seen as definitive of the Later Stone Age (J. Deacon 1984a, 1984b). Robberg-type bladelet assemblages are present between 21 000 and 16 000 BP in the southern Cape at Boomplaas and Nelson Bay Cave (J. Deacon 1984a) and in Lesotho at Sehonghong and Melikane (Carter 1978, Mitchell, Vol. 2, Ch. 8). Between 14 000 and 12 000 BP they are more common and occur at Elands Bay Cave, Byneskranskop, Kangkara, Boomplaas, Nelson Bay Cave, and Melkhoutboom and possibly also at Shongweni and Umhlatuzana. These later assemblages include not only ostrich eggshell beads and polished bone tools, but fragments of decorated ostrich eggshell water-flasks and a tortoiseshell bowl as well (Table 7.1, Fig. 7.5, J. Deacon 1984b).

Heuningneskrans in the Transvaal with radiocarbon and amino-acid dates from c. 31 000 to c. 9000 BP (Beaumont 1981) has typical Robberg-type cores and bladelets in chert in levels dating between c. 14 000 and c. 12 000 BP, but an amorphous ELSA quartz industry with pièces esquillées between c. 32 000 and c, 19 800 BP.

At Nos, Apollo 11, and Pockenbank in Namibia the LGM industry is macrolithic, again with few or no formal tools. More remarkably, several small slabs of rock, not from the walls of the cave, were found in the Apollo 11 deposits and represent the oldest dated works of art in southern Africa (Wendt 1976). The excavator considers that they were associated with a MSA blade industry and charcoal dated by a number of radiocarbon assays to between 27 500 and 25 500 BP (Wendt 1976, p. 7), but there are in addition radiocarbon dates of c. 19 000 BP associated with a macrolithic LSA assemblage immediately overlying the slabs that may date them more accurately. This is unequivocal evidence for art at the LGM or earlier.

When climatic and technological sequences are compared (Table 7.1) there is no clear correlation between the scale and timing of changes in the two sets of data. The ELSA grades into the Robberg after 22 000 BP and the Robberg is replaced by the Oakhurst or Albany industries after 12 000 BP, so despite very considerable variations in temperature and rainfall between 30 000–25 000 and 12 000 BP, environmental changes did not affect basic flaking methods or the range of formal tools. There is a marked increase in frequency of decorative items and polished bone tools after 14 000 BP, and particularly between 12 000 and 10 000 BP (J. Deacon 1984a, 1984b), that contrasts with their patchy distribution and relative scarcity before this time.

Economy

The number of radiocarbon-dated occupation horizons has been taken as a rough guide to population numbers in the past in southern Africa (H. J. Deacon 1972, J. Deacon 1974, 1984a, 1984b, H. J. Deacon & Thackeray 1984). The general pattern throughout Africa (J. Deacon & Lancaster 1988, Fig. 8.1) is that within the past 40 000 years, when the radiocarbon method is reliable, there are relatively few sites that date to the Last Glacial and LGM, and numbers pick up only after $c.$ 12 000 BP. When sites only are compared (i.e. not only dated ones), the southern Cape pattern (which may not be representative of the whole country) shows relatively high numbers of sites that date to the last and present Interglacials, with much lower frequencies in the intervening glacial cycle. These two distribution patterns suggest either that the Stone-Age population of South Africa was higher in interglacial than in glacial times, and/or that the effect of smaller and larger group sizes in interglacials and glacials respectively led to higher and lower numbers of living sites. In either case, the low archaeological visibility of sites is a feature of the entire Last Glacial (oxygen isotope stages 4, 3, and 2) and is not restricted to the LGM.

At all the southern and southwestern Cape LGM sites, Robberg assemblages are associated with remains of large gregarious migratory grazers, contrasting with the faunal remains from Holocene assemblages that are dominated by small, solitary, non-gregarious browsers. This contrast is not as clear in regions where grassland predominates in the interior of South Africa today, but even away from the southern Cape there is a general focus on smaller antelope in the Holocene and larger migratory game in the Last Glacial and LGM. The change starts at around 10 000 BP and is generally complete by the mid-Holocene (Klein 1972a, 1972b, 1980, 1984), so is not contemporary with the shift from Middle to Later Stone-Age technology. The shift away from grazers appears to have been the result of a combination of environmental change that placed the large grazers (some now extinct) under stress, and the possibility that people became more efficient hunters (Klein 1984). Apart from the end-Pleistocene shift, there is no obvious change in human hunting patterns during the time-period of oxygen isotope stage 2, nor is there an appreciable difference in the fauna at end-MSA and earliest-LSA sites.

The implication of this change in hunting pattern is that it may correlate with group size and organization. The hunting of larger migratory antelope is usually linked with large-group organization, low population density, and a general absence of fixed territorial boundaries; whereas small non-gregarious browsers are most commonly hunted by people in small territorial groups with a higher population density (H. J. Deacon 1976, p. 163). Although comparisons between faunal remains and artefacts show no consistent correlation (J. Deacon 1978, 1984a), and technological innovations such as microlithic backed bladelets appear in the archaeological record well before the major change in faunal remains, there is a gross difference between glacial and interglacial demography that reflects changes in group size and organization.

Social correlates

The significance of the polished bone points, painted slabs, decorated ostrich eggshell, beads, and tortoiseshell bowls is that collectively they signal the appearance of items still made and used in the ethnographic present by San in southern Africa, and (with one or two exceptions) they are all unique to the Later Stone Age. The exceptions are a single bone point recovered from a Middle Stone-Age level at Klasies River (Singer & Wymer 1982), a conus shell found associated with skeletal remains of a child at Border Cave (Beaumont *et al.* 1978), and the possibility that the painted slabs and a few pieces of engraved ostrich eggshell at Apollo 11 are associated with Middle rather than Later Stone-Age artefacts (Wendt 1972, p. 33, 1976, p. 7). Individually, however, these items may not have the same implications for modern behaviour as they do when they occur more frequently.

Lewis-Williams (1984) has argued that the presence and nature of art in the time-bracket 27 000 to 19 000 BP at Apollo 11 demonstrates the existence of trance activity and its ritual concomitants (including kinship) and that therefore the form of the relations of production and ideology at that time was essentially the same as in the ethnographic present. The question that arises is whether there was any change in the relations and mode of production between the terminal MSA and early LSA, or within the LSA. The difficulty in answering this question is exacerbated because the archaeological record is scanty at the best of times, and the vast majority of MSA sites have only stone artefacts and, occasionally, faunal remains. Furthermore, it is maintained that changes in the forces of production (technology and food-getting strategies) are not in themselves sufficient to trigger complete systemic change (Godelier 1978, Lewis-Williams 1984) so that changes in technology will not necessarily signal changes in the relations of production. The need is to identify correlates of the relations of production in the archaeological record.

Amongst present-day San, marriage and associated *hxaro* or gift exchange function as a means of reducing the risk of economic stress by providing alternate residences and access to complementary food resources of marriage partners' families in times of need (Wiessner 1984). Wadley (1988) suggests that arrows and ostrich eggshell beads have been the most widely used *hxaro* items, and reasons that their presence in the archaeological record signals the existence of *hxaro* practices. The existence of kinship networks is thought to be detectable in

(a)   the occurrence of *hxaro* items;
(b)   the presence of both aggregation and dispersal living sites that show social organization related to kinship and the finding of marriage partners; and
(c)   the occurrence of ritual art.

In looking for the presence of modern ethnographic relations of production, Wadley (1988) suggests that they may have originated during the Howiesons Poort phase of the Middle Stone Age (at least 60 000 BP) because of the occurrence of large backed segments assumed to have been used for projectile points, the bone point at Klasies River, and the few engraved fragments of ostrich eggshell at the same level as Howiesons Poort artefacts in Apollo 11 Cave. However, there is no indication of these items occurring between the Howiesons Poort at > 60 000 and the earliest LSA, a time-gap of 25 000 years or more. If segments, polished bone points, and decorated ostrich eggshell are indeed a reliable correlate of *hxaro* and the San form of kinship and marriage, then their regular occurrence in the archaeological record may be a more reliable signal of significant change in the relations of production.

A second possible archaeological correlate for kinship is the presence or absence of contemporary aggregation and dispersal sites. Wadley (1988) has shown these to be identifiable in the Holocene, but the identification of aggregation sites is based partly on the presence of *hxaro* items so the correlates are not independent, and where known exchange items are rare other indicators will need to be found. Aggregation may, for example, be reflected simply in a high incidence of artefacts and faunal remains per bucket of deposit. In the long sequence from Boomplaas, 'aggregation' is evident, using this index, only in units post-dating 14 200 BP, when *hxaro* items are also more common. Wadley (1988) has suggested that people of the ELSA may not have dispersed and aggregated as did the San because the hunting of large migratory game suggests group sizes were larger and kinship and marriage were therefore possible within, rather than between, groups, obviating the necessity for *hxaro*. However, *hxaro* items appear regularly in the archaeological record – and indeed become relatively common – some 4000 years before the major change in hunting pattern at *c*. 10 000 BP. Either the relations of production changed before the shift in hunting pattern, or the significance of beads and other items changed some time after they were introduced.

Some conclusions

What we call Middle Stone-Age technology was phased out some time after 40 000 and before 25 000 BP (i.e. before the LGM) and was replaced by the ELSA and the Robberg and related industries, or by a macrolithic industry. The dating of the first appearance of various technological innovations associated with the Later Stone Age shows that they did not all appear at once as a 'package' in the archaeological record, nor are there tools that are specific to LGM. Thus, there does not appear to be a toolkit or toolmaking technique that could be seen as a LGM adaptation, nor is there a unique LGM economy. The LGM is just part of the glacial mode of large-game hunting, large group size, and lower population levels. Unlike the change from Middle to Upper Palaeolithic in Europe, the technological shift from Middle to Later Stone Age in South Africa was not apparently accompanied by a change in the physical attributes and mental capabilities of the toolmakers, although it must be noted that no human skeletal material from this period of the Last Glacial has been found.

There is, however, a major distinction between glacial and interglacial environments, related hunting patterns, and human demography that was initiated with post-glacial warming after $c.$ 12000 BP. Technological changes, on the other hand, occurred at irregular intervals, apparently independently of environmental factors. This means that we cannot infer changes in environment and economy from changes in an artefact sequence, and it gives general support to the historical materialist stance that changes in technology (the forces of production) do not necessarily coincide with and do not precipitate a change in the relations of production (ideology and the related systems of kinship and distribution of food and material) (Godelier 1978, Lewis–Williams 1984). To identify a change in the relations of production we need to know the meaning of particular artefacts above and beyond their utilitarian value.

The appearance of art and decorative items at about the time of the earliest Later Stone-Age assemblages hints at ideological similarities with the modern San. What we do not know is whether these late Pleistocene painted slabs, ostrich eggshell beads, and decorated flasks, polished bone points, and backed stone tools were used to cement kinship relationships in the same way as in the ethnographic present. Whereas the painted slabs are strongly indicative of the work of shamans (Lewis–Williams 1984), one could argue that the mere presence of beads and other decorative items does not necessarily imply that they were used in exchange in the same way as *hxaro* items today, and their low frequency may suggest that they were not. If we work backwards from the ethnographic present to search for a significant change in ideology, as Lewis–Williams (1984) has suggested it is necessary to do if we are to identify a change in relations of production, then the combination of regular formal burial, high frequencies of *hxaro* items, high archaeological visibility of sites, and a change in hunting pattern after $c.$ 12000 BP would seem to be a more convincing indication of modern relations of production than the irregular occurrence of various decorated and decorative items associated with a different economy and demographic pattern during the Last Glacial. The relations of production of people during glacial times in South Africa may thus have been different from those in interglacial times. In the same way that modern analogues are probably inappropriate for modelling glacial climates and environments because the 'mix' of elements is so different, the kinship and belief systems of modern San may have less in common with those of late Pleistocene hunter-gatherers than we would like to suppose.

Acknowledgements

Financial support from the Council for Scientific and Industrial Research, the Human Sciences Research Council and the University of Stellenbosch is gratefully acknowledged. I thank H. J. Deacon and Anne Thackeray for useful comments during preparation of this paper.

References

Avery, D. M. 1982. Micromammals as palaeoenvironmental indicators and an interpretation of the late Quaternary in the southern Cape Province, South Africa. *Annals of the South African Museum* **85**, 183–374.

Beaumont, P. B. 1978. Border Cave. Unpublished MA thesis, University of Cape Town.

Beaumont, P. B. 1981. The Heuningneskrans shelter. In *Guide to archaeological sites in the northern and eastern Transvaal*, E. A. Voigt (ed.), 133–45. Pretoria: Transvaal Museum.

Beaumont, P. B. 1986. Where did all the young men go during O^{18} stage 2? *Palaeoecology in Africa* **17**, 79–86.

Beaumont, P. B. & J. C. Vogel, 1972. On a new radiocarbon chronology for Africa south of the Equator. *African Studies* **31**, 66–89, 155–82.

Beaumont, P. B., H. De Villiers, & J. C. Vogel, 1978. Modern man in sub-Saharan Africa prior to 49 000 years BP: a review and evaluation with particular reference to Border Cave. *South African Journal of Science* **74**, 409–19.

Beaumont, P. B., E. M. Van Zinderen Bakker, & J. C. Vogel, 1984. Environmental changes since 32 000 BP at Kathu Pan, northern Cape. In *Late Cainozoic palaeoclimates of the southern hemisphere*, J. C. Vogel (ed.), 329–38. Rotterdam: A. A. Balkema.

Bishop, W. & J. D. Clark, (eds) 1967. *Background to evolution in Africa*. Chicago: University of Chicago Press.

Butzer, K. W. 1979. Geomorphology and geo-archaeology at Elandsbaai, western Cape, South Africa. *Catena* **6**, 157–66.

Butzer, K. W. 1984a. Late Quaternary palaeoenvironments in South Africa. In *Southern African palaeoenvironments and prehistory* R. G. Klein (ed.), 1–64. Rotterdam: A. A. Balkema.

Butzer, K. W. 1984b. Late Quaternary enviroments in South Africa. In *Late Cainozoic palaeoclimates of the southern hemisphere*, J. C. Vogel (ed.), 235–64. Rotterdam: A. A. Balkema.

Butzer, K. W., R. Stuckenrath, A. J. Bruzewicz, & D. M. Helgren, 1978. Late Cenozoic palaeoclimates of the Gaap Escarpment, Kalahari margin, South Africa. *Quarternary Research 10*, 310–39.

Carter, P. L. 1978. The prehistory of eastern Lesotho. Unpublished PhD thesis, University of Cambridge.

Clark, J. D. 1959. *The prehistory of southern Africa*. Harmondsworth: Penguin.

CLIMAP Project Members 1976. The surface of the Ice-Age earth. *Science* **191**, 1131–7.

Cockcroft, M. J., M. J. Wilkinson, & P. D. Tyson, 1987. The application of a present-day climatic model to the Late Quaternary in southern Africa. *Climatic Change 10*, 161–91.

Davies, O. 1975. Excavation at Shongweni South Cave. *Annals of the Natal Museum.* **22**, 627–62.

Deacon, H. J. 1972. A review of the post-Pleistocene in South Africa. *South African Archaeological Society Goodwin Series* **1**, 26–45.

Deacon, H. J. 1976. *Where hunters gathered: a study of Holocene Stone Age people in the eastern Cape*. Claremont: South African Archaeological Society.

Deacon, H. J. 1979. Excavations at Boomplaas Cave – a sequence through the Upper Pleistocene and Holocene in South Africa. *World Archaeology* **10**, 241–57.

Deacon, H. J. & J. F. Thackeray, 1984. Late Quaternary environmental changes and implications from the archaeological record in southern Africa. In *Late Cainozoic palaeoclimates of the southern hemisphere*, J. C. Vogel (ed.), 375–90. Rotterdam: A. A. Balkema.

Deacon, H. J., J. Deacon, A. Scholtz, J. F. Thackeray, J. S. Brink, & J. C. Vogel 1984. Correlation of palaeoenvironmental data from the Late Pleistocene and Holocene deposits at Boomplaas cave, southern Cape. In *Late Cainozoic palaeoclimates of the southern hemisphere*, J. C. Vogel (ed.), 339–52. Rotterdam: A. A. Balkema.

Deacon, J. 1974. Patterning in the radiocarbon dates for the Wilton/Smithfield complex in southern Africa. *South African Archaeological Bulletin* **29**, 3–18.

Deacon, J. 1978. Changing patterns in the late Pleistocene/early Holocene prehistory of southern Africa as seen from the Nelson Bay Cave stone artifact sequence. *Quaternary Research* **10**, 84–111.

Deacon, J. 1984a. *The Later Stone Age of southernmost Africa*. Oxford: British Archaeological Reports International Series 213.

Deacon, J. 1984b. Later Stone Age people and their descendants in southern Africa. In *Southern African palaeoenvironments and prehistory*, R. G. Klein (ed.), 221–328. Rotterdam: A. A. Balkema.

Deacon, J. & N. Lancaster 1988. *Late Quaternary palaeoenvironments of southern Africa*. Oxford: Oxford University Press.

Dingle, R. V. & J. Rogers 1972a. Pleistocene palaeogeography of the Agulhas Bank. *Transactions of the Royal Society of South Africa* **40**, 155–65.

Dingle, R. V. & J. Rogers 1972b. Effects of sea-level changes on the Pleistocene palaeoecology of the Agulhas Bank. *Palaeoecology in Africa* **6**, 55–8.

Godelier, M. 1978. Infrastructures, societies, and history. *Current Anthropology* **19**, 763–71.

Goodwin, A. J. H. & C. Van Riet Lowe 1929. The Stone Age cultures of South Africa. *Annals of the South African Museum* **27**, 1–289.

Heaton, T. H. E. 1981. Dissolved gases: some applications to groundwater research. *Transactions of the Geological Society of South Africa* **84**, 91–7.

Heaton, T. H. E., A. S. Talma & J. C. Vogel 1986. Dissolved gas paleotemperatures and oxygen-18 variations derived from groundwater near Uitenhage, South Africa. *Quaternary Research* **25**, 79–88.

Heine, K. 1978. Radiocarbon chronology of Late Quaternary lakes in the Kalahari, southern Africa. *Catena* **5**, 145–9.

Howard, W. R. & W. L. Prell 1984. A comparison of radiolarian and foraminiferal paleoecology in the southern Indian Ocean: new evidence for the interhemispheric timing of climatic change. *Quaternary Research* **21**, 244–63.

Klein, R. G. 1972a. Preliminary report on the July through September 1970 excavations at Nelson Bay Cave, Plettenberg Bay (Cape Province, South Africa). *Palaeoecology of Africa* **6**, 177–208.

Klein, R. G. 1972b. The Late Quaternary mammalian fauna of Nelson's Bay Cave (Cape Province, South Africa): its implications for megafaunal extinctions and environmental and cultural change. *Quaternary Research* **2**, 135–42.

Klein, R. G. 1980. Environmental and ecological implications of large mammals from Upper Pleistocene and Holocene sites in southern Africa. *Annals of the South African Museum* **81**, 223–83.

Klein, R. G. 1984. The large mammals of southern Africa: Late Pliocene to Recent. In *Southern African prehistory and paleoenvironments*, R. G. Klein (ed.) 107–46. Rotterdam: A. A. Balkema.

Lewis-Williams, J. D. 1984. Ideological continuities in prehistoric southern Africa: the evidence of rock art. In *Past and present in hunter–gatherer studies*, C. Schrire (ed.), 225–51. Orlando: Academic Press.

Louw, J. T. 1960. Prehistory of the Matjes River shelter. *Memoir of the National Museum, Bloemfontein* **1**, 1–143.

Martin, A. K. 1981. Evolution of the Agulhas Current and its palaeo-ecological implication. *South African Journal of Science* **77**, 547–54.

Martinson, D. G., N. G. Psias, J. D. Hays, J. Imbrie, T. C. Moore & N. J. Shackleton 1987. Age dating and the orbital theory of the ice ages: development of a high-resolution 0–300,000-year chronostratigraphy. *Quaternary Research* **27**, 1–29.

Morley, J. J. & J. D. Hays 1979. Comparison of glacial and interglacial oceanographic conditions in the South Atlantic from variations in calcium carbonate and radioalarian distribution. *Quaternary Research* **12**, 396–408.

Opperman, H. 1978. Excavations in Buffelskloof rock shelter near Calitzdorp, southern Cape. *South African Archaeological Bulletin* **33**, 8–38.

Opperman, H. 1987. *The Later Stone Age of the Drakensberg Range and its foothills.* Oxford: British Archaeological Reports International Series 339.

Parkington, J. 1987. A critique of the consensus view of Howiesons Poort assemblages. Precirculated paper for Workshop: The origins and dispersal of modern humans, behavioural and biological perspectives, Cambridge, March 1987.

Partridge, T. C. & T. S. Dalbey 1986. Geoarchaeology of the Haaskraal Pan: a preliminary palaeoenvironmental model. *Palaeoecology of Africa* **17**, 69–78.

Prell, W. L., W. H. Hutson & D. F. Williams 1979. The subtropical convergence and late Quaternary circulation in the southern Indian Ocean. *Marine Micropalaeontology* **4**, 225–34.

Ruddiman, W. F. & J. C. Duplessy 1985. Conference on the Last Deglaciation: timing and mechanism. *Quaternary Research* **23**, 1–17.

Sampson, C.G. 1974. *The Stone Age archaeology of southern Africa.* New York: Academic Press.

Scholtz, A. 1986. Palynological and palaeobotanical studies in the southern Cape. Unpublished MA thesis, University of Stellenbosch.

Schulze, B. R. 1984. *Climate of South Africa, Part 8. General survey WB28*, 5th edn. Pretoria: South African Weather Bureau.

Schweitzer, F. & M. L. Wilson 1982. Byneskranskop 1: a late Quaternary living site in the southern Cape Province, South Africa. *Annals of the South African Museum* **88**, 1–203.

Scott, L. 1982. A Late Quaternary pollen record from the Transvaal Bushveld, South Africa. *Quaternary Research* **17**, 339–70.

Scott, L. 1986. Pollen analysis and palaeoenvironmental interpretation of Late Quaternary sediment exposures in the eastern Orange Free State, South Africa. *Palaeoecology of Africa* **17**, 113–22.

Scott, L. & J. F. Thackeray 1987. Multivariate analysis of late Pleistocene and Holocene pollen spectra from Wonderkrater, Transvaal, South Africa. *South African Journal of Science* **83**, 93–8.

Singer, R, & J. Wymer 1982. *The Middle Stone Age at Klasies River Mouth in South Africa.* Chicago: University of Chicago Press.

Talma, A. S., J. C. Vogel & T. C. Partridge 1974. Isotopic contents of some Transvaal speleothems and their palaeoclimatic significance. *South African Journal of Science* **70**, 135–40.

Teller, J. T. & N. Lancaster 1985. History of sediments at Khommabes, central Namib desert. *Madoqua* **14**, 267–78.

Thackeray, J. F. 1987. Late Quaternary environmental changes inferred from small mammalian fauna, southern Africa. *Climatic Change* **10**, 285–305.

Tyson, P. D. 1986. *Climatic change and variability in southern Africa.* Cape Town: Oxford University Press.

Vincent, E. 1972. Climatic change at the Pleistocene–Holocene boundary in the southwestern Indian Ocean. *Palaeoecology of Africa* **6**, 45–54.

Vogel, J. C. 1983. Isotopic evidence for past climates and vegetation of South Africa. *Bothalia* **14**, 391–4.

Vogel, J. C. & E. Visser 1981. Pretoria radiocarbon dates II. *Radiocarbon* **23**, 43–80.

Volman, T. P. 1984. Early prehistory of southern Africa. In *Southern African prehistory and paleoenvironments*, R. G. Klein (ed.) 169–220. Rotterdam: A. A. Balkema.

Wadley, L. 1988. *A social and ecological interpretation of the Later Stone Age in the southern Transvaal.* Oxford: British Archaeological Reports International Series S380.

Wendt, W. E. 1972. Preliminary report on an archaeological research programme in South West Africa. *Cimbebasia* **B** 2(1), 1–61.

Wendt, W. E. 1976. Art mobilier from the Apollo 11 cave, South West Africa: Africa's oldest dated works of art. *South African Archaeological Bulletin* **31**, 5–11.

Wiessner, P. 1984. Considering the behavioural basis for style: a case study among the Kalahari San. *Journal of Anthropological Archaeology.* **3**, 190–234.

8 A palaeoecological model for archaeological site distribution in southern Africa during the Upper Pleniglacial and Late Glacial

PETER MITCHELL

Introduction

Lee's (1963) pioneering article on the likely distribution of prehistoric populations in Southern Africa under varying environmental conditions started an interest among the region's archaeologists in understanding long-term trends in human palaeodemography. Recent detailed discussion by H. Deacon & Thackeray (1984) has concentrated on changes in the size and distribution of hunter–gatherer populations in Africa south of the Limpopo over the last 125 000 years. Using shifts in the occurrence and number of dated archaeological sites as a measure of these variables, they have interpreted them in terms of variations in resource productivity ultimately deriving from climatic changes during the most recent Interglacial–Glacial–Interglacial cycle. The same approach has been used to provide more detailed information on a regional scale (Sampson 1985, Beaumont 1986). In this chapter attention is focused, not on a particular region, but on a particular period, with the aim of explaining the localized distribution of archaeological occupations dating to, at, or near the Last Glacial Maximum (LGM).

The assemblages found in southern Africa during the period represent the earliest occurrences attributable to the Later Stone Age (LSA). All the occurrences referred to here are characterized by a microlithic technology (hence their designation as 'early microlithic'), often stressing the production of unretouched bladelets and core-reduced pieces (*pièces esquillées, outils écaillés*), but with a marked lack of formal tools. They may also include small numbers of items, such as beads, ostrich eggshell water containers and bone points, which are almost entirely absent from earlier assemblages and which can be directly paralleled in the material culture of the San hunter–gatherers of the ethnographic present. A more detailed description of these Early LSA or early microlithic assemblages is given by J. Deacon (1984a), and the evidence is reviewed on a site by site basis by Mitchell (1988).

The nature and reliability of the evidence

During the period 25 000 to 16 000 BP human occupation of South Africa seems to have been limited both quantitatively and spatially (Table 8.1). The definite geographical localization of these sites, along the rim of the interior plateau in the south-western and southern Cape Province, the Drakensberg Mountains of Lesotho, and the eastern Transvaal, Natal, and Swaziland is shown in Figure 8.1. No sites occur in the interior of South Africa, with the single exception of Rose Cottage Cave. The same pattern is noticeable in the period following the LGM from 16 000 to 12 000 BP (table 8.2, Fig. 8.2), although the number of dated occupations increases considerably. The only indication of an expansion in the area of settlement is given by dates from the two sites of Dikbosch I and Wonderwerk, both in the northern Cape Province, but in neither case does LSA occupation extend back beyond 13 500 BP (Humphreys & Thackeray 1983).

Table 8.1 Archaeological assemblages from southern Africa dating to the Upper Pleniglacial 25 000–16 000 BP

Site	Date (BP)
BPA Boomplaas	21 220 ± 195
	21 110 ± 420
	21 070 ± 180
	17 830 ± 180
BUF Buffelskloof	22 800 ± 850
	22 575 ± 270
EBC Elands Bay Cave	20 180 ± 220
HK Heuningneskrans	24 630 ± 300
	23 900 ± 800
	21 100 ± 300
	20 500 ± 160
MEL Melikane	20 000 ± 170
NBC Nelson Bay Cave	18 660 ± 110
	18 100 ± 550
	16 700 ± 240
SEH Sehonghong	20 900 ± 270
	20 240 ± 230
	19 860 ± 220
	17 820 ± 270
SHO Shongweni	22 990 ± 310
SIB Sibebe Shelter	22 850 ± 160

Rose Cottage (RCC) is included in Figure 8.1 because, on typological grounds, it appears to be contemporary with the early microlithic assemblage from Sehonghong, the earliest date for which is 17 820 ± 270 BP.

Table 8.2 Archaeological assemblages from southern Africa dating to the Late Glacial 16 000–12 000 BP

Site	Date (BP)
BPA Boomplaas	$14\,220 \pm 240$
	$13\,210 \pm 55$
	$12\,480 \pm 130$
	$12\,060 \pm 105$
BY Byneskranskop	$12\,730 \pm 185$
DIK Dikbosch	$13\,770 \pm 130$
	$13\,510 \pm 120$
	$13\,240 \pm 125$
	$12\,450 \pm 100$
EBC Elands Bay Cave	$12\,450 \pm 280$
HK Heuningneskrans	$13\,100 \pm 110$
	$12\,590 \pm 130$
KRA Kangkara	$12\,550 \pm 110$
	$12\,330 \pm 130$
MHB Melkhoutboom	$15\,400 \pm 120$
SEH Sehonghong	$13\,200 \pm 150$
	$13\,000 \pm 140$
	$12\,800 \pm 250$
	$12\,250 \pm 300$
	$12\,200 \pm 250$
SHO Shongweni	$14\,760 \pm 130$
SIP Siphiso Shelter	$13\,000$
WK Wonderwerk	$12\,380 \pm 95$
	$12\,160 \pm 115$
	$12\,130 \pm 110$

Reasons are advanced in Mitchell (1988) for suggesting that the early microlithic assemblage from Bushman Rock Shelter (BRS), Ravenscraig (RAV) and Rose Cottage Cave (RCC) may date to this period. They are therefore included in Figure 8.2.

It would be incorrect to imply that the interior of South Africa was *not* inhabited by human populations at the LGM. Following H. Deacon & Thackeray (1984), we can, however, suggest that the spatiotemporal distribution of radiocarbon dates reflects the density of population over the subcontinent. If it can be shown that this distribution is not a function of the localization of archaeological research, then it challenges us to seek an alternative explanation.

Figure 8.3, adapted from Parkington (1984), illustrates the location of research programmes carried out in LSA archaeology over the past 20 years. It is true that there is a correlation between the relatively large number of sites in the southern Cape and the extensive fieldwork carried out there by H. and J. Deacon (H. Deacon 1976, H. Deacon & Brooker 1976, J. Deacon 1984b), Klein (1974) and Schweitzer (Schweitzer & Wilson 1982), and continued by Binneman (1985) and Hall (1985). But it is equally true that other comparatively well-researched areas, such as the northern Cape (Humphreys &

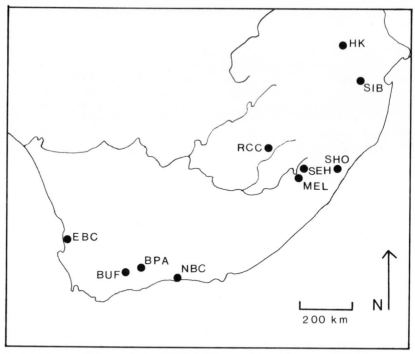

Figure 8.1 Distribution of archaeological sites in southern Africa dating to the Upper Pleniglacial, 25 000–16 000 BP. Site names are given in full in Table 8.1. Note: Rose Cottage Cave (RCC) appears in both Figure 8.1 and Figure 8.2 because its Pre-Wilton assemblage is, on typological grounds, contemporary with the early micro-lithic assemblage from Sehonghong (Mitchell 1988).

Thackeray 1983) and the Middle Orange River and Seacow valleys (Sampson 1972, 1985), have failed to provide evidence of human occupation during the Upper Pleniglacial.

Caves, which might have acted as repeated foci of settlement and which could have preserved extensive sequences of occupation, are rare in such areas compared with the Cape Fold Mountain Belt and the Drakensberg. Most sites in these regions consequently take the form of surface assemblages and generally consist only of lithic artefacts which are undateable by radiometric means. Moreover, many early microlithic surface sites may represent only a limited range of activities and/or a transient occupation, and a lithic component restricted to flakes, bladelets, and perhaps cores, is likely to be difficult to distinguish from later Holocene assemblages. Springs, pans, and similar features could, however, be expected to have repeatedly acted as foci of occupation and thus to have seen the build-up of a larger, more representative, and hence more readily classifiable assemblage. Nevertheless, the absence of early microlithic assemblages from such extensively well-surveyed areas as the Seacow Valley (Sampson 1985) is striking.

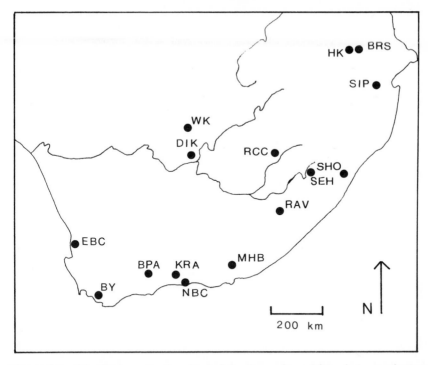

Figure 8.2   Distribution of archaeological sites in southern Africa dating to the Late Glacial 16 000–12 000 BP. Site names are given in full in Table 8.2. Note: Rose Cottage (RCC) appears in both Figure 8.1 and Figure 8.2 because its Pre-Wilton assemblage is, on typological grounds, contemporary with the early microlithic assemblage from Sehonghong (Mitchell 1988).

An alternative possibility would be that while early microlithic LSA assemblages were restricted to a rim around the interior plateau, the plateau itself was occupied by people employing a wholly different lithic tradition. Thus Parkington (1984, p. 128–9) has suggested that the Lockshoek industry of the Middle Orange River Valley (Sampson 1974, p. 270–4) may be a contemporary inland variant of the Robberg industry, arguing that differences between the two are largely the result of raw material availability. In this model the microlithic nature of the Robberg is interpreted as reflecting expedient use of formerly little-used raw materials such as quartz due to a local absence of the hornfels, which was widely available in the interior. Naturally backed knives are interpreted as the typological indicators of this relation. The model suggests that sites in the southern and south-western Cape represent only occasional forays into the Cape Fold Mountain Belt by groups concentrated in the interior.

This model rests upon the assumption that the interior experienced a wetter palaeoclimate and was therefore preferred for human settlement. I shall show below that there are grounds for questioning this premise. Other grounds can

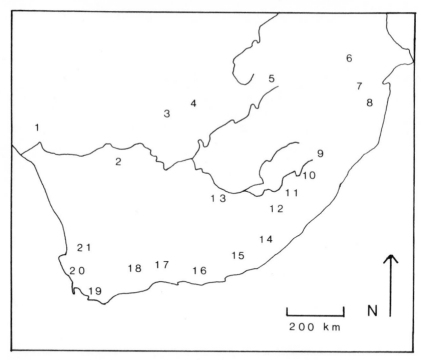

Figure 8.3   Distribution of recent LSA research in southern Africa (after Parkington 1984). 1, Wendt; 2, Smith; 3, Beaumont, Thackeray and Thackeray; 4, Humphreys; 5, Wadley; 6, Beaumont and Plug; 7, Beaumont; 8, Price-Williams; 9, Mazel; 10, Carter; 11, Parkington and Poggenpoel; 12, Opperman; 13, Sampson; 14, Robertshaw and S. Hall; 15, Deacon, Deacon and Brooker; 16, Deacon, Deacon, Inskeep, Klein and Binneman; 17, Deacon, Deacon and Brooker; 18, Opperman; 19, Avery, Schweitzer, Wilson and M. Hall; 20, Smith; 21, Parkington and Poggenpoel.

also be cited for discounting Parkington's model. Foremost among these is the fact that the Lockshoek industry is itself undated (although re-excavation of the Blydefontein Shelter promises to remedy this problem, Bousman 1985). Secondly, his view tends to ignore the microlithic component of the Robberg industry, which surely denotes a very different kind of stoneworking and toolmaking tradition from that associated with the macrolithic Lockshoek. This may be particularly significant as such a component could easily have been produced from the crypto-crystalline materials which occur in the Orange River gravels, or even from hornfels, and yet there is no sign of it in Lockshoek assemblages. The recently analysed early microlithic occurrence from the site of Sehonghong in eastern Lesotho (Mitchell 1987) is of key importance here since it is demonstrably very similar to the Robberg assemblages of the southern Cape, and yet, while occurring in an area in which hornfels is plentiful, includes only a single naturally backed knife. Sehonghong therefore contradicts any suggestion that the Lockshoek and Robberg assemblages should be seen as contemporary products of a single population, the differences between which depend on differences in raw material availability between the Cape Fold Mountain Belt and the interior plateau.

Another interpretation would be that there is a chronological relation between early microlithic assemblages, where naturally backed knives are few, and Terminal Pleistocene/Early Holocene ones, where they are more common. Comparisons on this basis suggest that the Lockshoek represents one version of the terminal Pleistocene/Early Holocene Oakhurst complex (Sampson 1974).

The alternative approach I favour here builds on the ample documentation in the ethnographic record of a consistent relation between the density and distribution of hunter–gatherer populations on the one hand, and the availability, predictability, and reliability of subsistence resources on the other (e.g. Lee & DeVore 1968). Since this is well established, it seems reasonable to attempt an explanation of the distribution of these sites in ecological terms.

The Last Glacial Maximum palaeoenvironment and the distribution of archaeological sites

Palaeoenvironmental evidence for southern Africa during the Upper Pleniglacial has recently been reviewed and discussed by J. Deacon et al. (1984). Local southern African data support more general global circulation models that this represents a maximum cold period within the last 125 000 years. A temperature depression of 4–5°C, is confirmed by oxygen-isotope studies from Uitenhage and the Cango Caves (Vogel 1983), although temperatures may have been up to 9°C lower in parts of the interior (Talma et al. 1974).

Both global and local evidence shows that Upper Pleniglacial precipitation patterns differed considerably from those of the present. J. Deacon (1984b, p. 35) has shown how a temperature depression of 6°C could have decreased the amount of precipitable water by 30–50% along the southern Cape coast as a result of cooler ocean temperatures, a weakening of the Agulhas Current (Prell et al. 1979) and the exposure of the continental shelf. Charcoal, microfaunal, and pollen data from the site of Boomplaas all confirm this by documenting markedly arid conditions at the LGM (H. Deacon et al. 1984).

In the interior of southern Africa observations from a number of sites suggest that drier conditions prevailed over Lesotho, Natal, and parts of the Transvaal (Harper 1969, Butzer et al. 1978, Avery 1982, Scott 1982). Geomorphological evidence and other general circulation models indicate, however, that rainfall may have increased over the south-western (Butzer 1984) and northern cape (Butzer et al. 1973, 1978). Both the interpretation and the tightness of the dating of this evidence can be questioned, particularly in the case of the northern Cape where Butzer (1984) has recently suggested that data from Kathu Vlei indicate precipitation was less than in the Holocene. Acceptance of a wetter LGM climate in the northern Cape will depend upon consistent and well-dated evidence from a range of palaeoclimatic indicators, biological as well as geological.

One further factor which requires comment is changes in sea-level which, at the LGM *c.* 18 000 BP, may have been as much as 120 or 130 m below that of the present (Dingle & Rogers 1972). In the southern Cape it is particularly interesting to find that the ridge-and-vale pattern of the rocks underneath the area so exposed would have encouraged the formation of lagoons (Birch 1979) and these could, combined with the proximity of the coast, have offered a variety of food-resources unobtainable inland.

It is not yet possible to attempt detailed reconstructions of the palaeoecological systems of southern Africa at the LGM, but maps of present-day temperature and rainfall patterns can offer a starting point in trying to relate the palaeoenvironmental evidence to the archaeological evidence. Even where quantitative estimates are not possible, as in the case of precipitation, the combination of palaeoclimatic data with an understanding of the general principles governing the modern climate should permit the identification of relatively wetter and drier, or colder and warmer, regions. This will be used to model regional differences in resource productivity.

Figure 8.4 illustrates the distribution of sites dating to the Upper Pleniglacial and Late Glacial in relation to the present temperature regime of South Africa. From this it can be seen that sites tend to concentrate in colder areas, with mean annual temperatures ranging at present from 18° to 12°C. Temperature variation on a regional scale is largely controlled by two factors, altitude and latitude (Wellington 1955, p. 219), neither of which can be expected to have been significantly different from the present. The same relative pattern of colder and warmer areas may therefore be inferred for the Pleistocene. The archaeological data indicates that human population density was greatest in the colder parts of southern Africa. This seems counter-intuitive, as extensive cold can be expected, and is known, to have had a deleterious effect on the density, distribution, and diversity of animal and plant populations (H. Deacon & Thackeray 1984). What it probably signifies, therefore, is that other factors were more important in regulating population density.

One such factor is likely to have been the availability of water. This is the principal limiting factor for plant growth, and hence for plant and animal biomass, in southern Africa today (Tainton 1981), and may be expected to have been so during the Upper Pleistocene, even allowing for the effects of generally lower temperatures, increased frost frequency and intensity, and increased wind strengths. The distribution of archaeological sites dating to the Upper Pleniglacial and Late Glacial in relation to present mean annual precipitation is shown in Figure 8.5. A gross correlation can be discerned between site distribution and those areas that today experience moderate to high rainfall. The problem is how can this pattern be transformed in qualitative terms to approximate that of the LGM?

It is apparent that during the Upper Pleniglacial rainfall decreased over the southern Cape, Natal, and parts of the Transvaal, and indeed probably did so

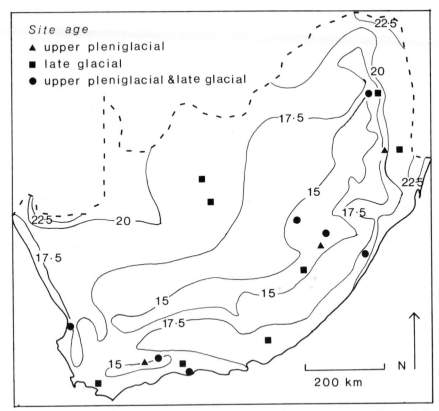

Figure 8.4 Distribution of archaeological sites in southern Africa dating to the Upper Pleniglacial and Late Glacial in relation to present mean annual surface temperature (°C).

over most of South Africa's interior, while the southwestern and northern Cape possibly, but by no means certainly, experienced increased precipitation. In the present winter-rainfall area, precipitation is associated with the easterly movement of cyclones and anticyclones originating in the south Atlantic Ocean (Wellington 1955, p. 259). Orographic effects and the proximity of the Cape Fold Mountain Belt to the sea result in it being concentrated on the mountains backing the coast and the coastal forelands, while 'leeward of the mountain ranges the rain shadow is accompanied by semi-aridity and xerophyllous vegetation' (Wellington 1955; p. 240). In the summer-rainfall region, where precipitation derives mainly from the inflow of oceanic air-streams from east coast highs, orographic effects (caused here by the Drakensberg Mountains) and distance from the Indian Ocean combine to render Natal, Swaziland, eastern Lesotho, and the eastern Transvaal the wettest parts of southern Africa (Wellington 1955). Allowing that most, or possibly all, of southern Africa experienced a drier climate during the Upper Pleniglacial than today, it was still the case that orographic effects and distance

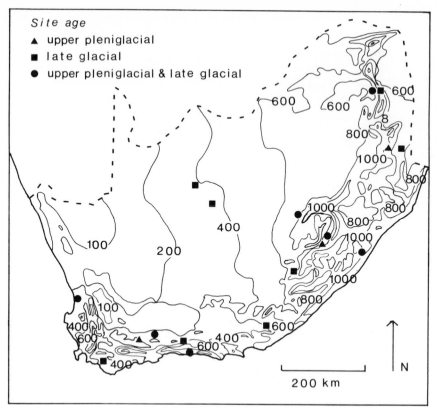

Figure 8.5 Distribution of archaeological sites in southern Africa dating to the Upper Pleniglacial and Late Glacial in relation to present mean annual precipitation (mm).

from the sea probably resulted in Natal and areas on the windward sides of the Drakensberg and the Cape Fold Belt being, in relative terms, the wettest parts of the country.

A tentative ecological model of Last Glacial Maximum site distribution

Rainfall and temperature, together with other factors not discussed here, such as humidity, wind velocity, and evaporation rate, provide the climatic framework which structure the resources exploited by a hunter–gathering population. Although the availability of shelter and of inorganic raw materials, particularly isotropically fracturing stone, are of some importance in determining the choice of particular settlement loci, it is the productivity of animal and plant resources, coupled with the availability of fresh water, that principally influence the density and location of population on the larger scale (Jochim 1976).

Direct measures of palaeoproductivity are not obtainable, but estimates can be made from correlations observed among contemporary data. Thus, Whittaker (1970, p. 82) demonstrates that a nearly linear positive correlation exists between mean annual precipitation and net primary productivity in areas receiving up to 800 mm of rain a year, although differences in vegetation type may modify the relationship (Thackeray 1977). Similarly, Coe *et al.* (1976) have found a statistically significant positive correlation between herbivore biomass and mean annual precipitation in areas receiving up to 700 mm of rain per year; it is possible that this correlation may remain valid in areas obtaining up to 1400 mm of precipitation per annum (cited in Thackeray 1977). As a first generalization, it may therefore be suggested that the relatively wetter regions, in which sites dating to the Upper Pleniglacial occur, were also the most ecologically productive parts of southern Africa at that time.

Studies of rainfall reliability and drought occurrence have shown that the wettest parts of southern Africa tend to be those which suffer least from drought (Wellington 1955; p. 255) and that rainfall predictability is strongly positively correlated with mean annual precipitation (Harris 1980). The overall effect will have been to increase animal and plant productivity and thus enhance further the security of hunter–gatherer populations in areas receiving higher precipitation compared with those receiving less.

Figure 8.5 also shows that, even within those areas likely to have been relatively wettest at the LGM, some regions, e.g. the eastern half of the Orange Free State and the Transvaal west of the Drakensberg Mountains, are apparently devoid of archaeological sites and may therefore have supported either a smaller human population or none at all. In explaining this, attention should be paid to a further factor already commented upon by J. Deacon (1984a, p. 322), namely 'that the distribution of sites of this time range in the Cape ecozone and the eastern half of southern Africa suggests that regions of moderate topographic variability ... were preferred.' The apparent concentration of sites in areas with greater variability in relief, even within the wetter parts of southern Africa, suggests that topographic diversity itself offered some advantages for the maintenance of human populations under LGM conditions.

The limits imposed by the prevailing level of technology on the transport of persons, food, and raw material control the size of a group's annual territory. Hayden (1981, p. 382), in an overview of hunter–gatherer ecology, suggests that as a result of such factors 'the maximum range utilized by hunter–gatherers having no transportation aids is probably in the neighbourhood of 2500 km^2.'

This figure is broadly consistent with others provided for pedestrian hunter–gatherers by Foley (1978) and by individual ethnographic studies (Tanaka 1980, Silberbauer 1981). The necessary implication of this estimate of regional size is that where resources are insufficiently plentiful, reliable, or predictable then permanent occupation of an area is unlikely by hunter–gatherers who lack such transportation aids as horses, sleds, or canoes, and/or who lack the technology to store food over long periods of time.

In discussing the density of Holocene populations in South Africa, Humphreys (1979) has drawn attention to the 'unstructured' nature of environments in South Africa's interior, and has suggested that this would have resulted in a marginal region for human settlement under particularly severe conditions, such as those of the Upper Pleniglacial, because it lacked 'the diversity and concentration of reliable resources to maintain communities within defined home ranges through the seasonal round' (H. Deacon & Thackeray 1984, p. 385). Hunter–gatherer adaptations should be considered over a timespan of at least several decades (Lee 1979) and access to the variety of resources required to support a population under rare but extremely adverse conditions is thus of greater importance than their short-term abundance in areas that are marginal over the longer term. It may be suggested that the unstructured environments of the interior plateau were insufficiently varied to offer the diversity of resources which could have provided a secure basis for long-term, large-scale human population maintenance.

Increased topographic diversity, on the other hand, could be expected to have favoured a greater diversity of habitats, and hence of exploitable resources, and to have concentrated this diversity within a comparatively small area. Harpending & Davis (1977) have shown that the size of a group's subsistence territory will vary inversely with environmental diversity. A tentative indication of interregional differences in ecological diversity may be given if we consider the distribution of veld-types in southern Africa as described by Acocks (1975). Variety in the number of veld-types occurring within areas of the same size in different parts of the country is due to variation in climate, topography, and lithology. In so far as climatic variations are governed by altitude and latitude, these factors are likely to have been little changed under the very different conditions of the Upper Pleistocene. Areas showing great variation in the number of veld-types present today may therefore also have been more diverse in the past. For example, areas in the environs of Heuningneskrans in the eastern Transvaal and of Boomplaas in the southern Cape are more diverse than those in the northern Cape or the middle Orange River Valley.

The highveld of the interior plateau is believed to have been covered by grassland environments during the late Upper Pleistocene (van Zinderen Bakker 1982) and this may be a further reason in explaining the sparse occupation of the region by hunter–gatherer groups. The reason for this is that grass-dominated plant communities, although associated with a high animal biomass, are 'unsuitable for direct human consumption' (Foley 1982).

Ethnographic data derived from studies of modern San show that 'in energy returns hunting is a less rewarding activity than gathering' (Lee 1979, p. 205) and worldwide tropical, subtropical, and temperate hunter–gatherers have been observed to depend more upon foraged foods, mainly plants but also small ground game and shellfish, than on hunting (Lee 1968). The reason for this is that while foraging is a relatively high-yield and low-risk activity (since these resources are immobile, more predictable in ocurrence and generally easier and safer to exploit), hunting is a relatively low–yield but high–risk activity in southern African savannas. The significance of this is that an abundance of large game within an area, particularly of migratory or nomadic species, may by itself have been insufficient to have rendered an area suitable for maintaining a human population. The existence of more stationary and reliable resources, such as plant foods, ground game, and shellfish, would then have been critical.

It can also be suggested that the additional resources offered by proximity to the coast and coastal lagoons may have acted as a further focus of denser human populations. Human exploitation of shellfish is attested in MSA deposits at Klasies River Mouth in layers probably dating back beyond 125 000 BP (Singer & Wymer 1982), and there is no reason why this resource should not also have been used during the Last Glacial, even though evidence will have been lost by the post–glacial rise in sea–level. As indicated by their use in other parts of the world (Bailey 1975), shellfish may have been a supplement at any season or a staple when other high–return resources were temporarily unavailable.

The model developed here tries to show that the distribution of human populations in southern Africa during the Upper Pleniglacial can be understood in terms of the effects which precipitation and topographic diversity are likely to have had on the availability, reliability, and productivity of subsistence resources. Sites are concentrated in those areas which were probably relatively wetter even under LGM conditions, and within these an emphasis on areas marked by considerable variability in relief and ecology can be discerned. It is in these areas that resource productivity and diversity are likely to have been highest.

The distribution of archaeological sites in South Africa during the Late Glacial and Post-glacial

Details of the palaeoenvironmental evidence for the period 16 000 to 12 000 BP have been given by J. Deacon et al (1984). Temperatures seem to have risen rapidly only c.10 000 BP, and thus after the disappearance of the early microlithic assemblages with which we are principally concerned here. A substantial increase in rainfall compared with the Upper Pleniglacial seems to have occurred in many parts of southern Africa during this period, although it is unclear how far this may have been due to changes in the relative positions of summer- and winter-rainfall regions.

An increase in ecological productivity would be expected to have occurred as a result of this increase in precipitation, given that aridity is the main limiting factor for animal and plant biomass in South Africa (Tainton 1981), and is indicated by data from Boomplaas in the southern Cape. Diversity indices for charcoals, small mammals, and pollens all increase at this time (H. Deacon et al.

1984). The increase in the number of radiocarbon dates for this same period compared with those known for the Upper Pleniglacial suggests that there may have been a concomitant increase in the level of the human population. Although the situation is complicated by the possibility that changes in subsistence–settlement strategy may have rendered archaeological sites more visible, and by readjustments in demographic arrangements as the exposed continental shelf was drowned by the post-glacial rise in global sea-levels, it seems that population remained, during most of the Late Glacial, largely restricted to the same areas as those in which it seems to have been highest during the Upper Pleniglacial (Figures 8.4 and 8.5). Perhaps only when these areas reached a level of saturation did the population expand significantly into the now better-watered and increasingly productive areas of the interior plateau. Archaeologically, this may be seen in the dates from Dikbosch I and Wonderwerk, confirming human occupation in the northern Cape by *c.* 13 500 BP (Humphreys & Thackeray 1983).

We may also note that there seems to be a relatively small number of sites dated to the period 18 000–13 000 BP, compared not only with the succeeding millennia but also with the earlier part of the Upper Pleniglacial. Despite this, there is a continuity in technological traditions across the intervening period at both Boomplaas and Sehonghong (Mitchell 1988). This patterning can be explained in terms of the ecological pressures likely to have been created by the hyperaridity of the LGM, *if* these pressures intensified quite markedly around 18 000 BP. The resulting 'crash' in population numbers might well have taken several millennia to overcome.

The mid-Holocene seems to have been another period of acute stress for southern African hunter–gatherers, with the interior of both the Transvaal and the Orange Free State largely devoid of occupation between 9000 and 4500 BP, and areas such as the southern Cape once more acting as refugia with dense human settlement (J. Deacon 1984a, p. 322). Further back in time, the periodicity of cold and warm, wet and dry phases throughout the Pleistocene suggests that regional pulses of occupation and non-occupation can be expected to have also affected Early and Middle Stone-Age populations (H. Deacon & Thackeray 1984, Beaumont 1986). A still unresearched question is the extent to which such discontinuities in population distribution may have influenced the physico-genetic differentiation of Khoisan populations from a broader, ancestral African base.

References

Acocks, J. P. H. 1975. *Veld types of South Africa*. South African Botanical Survey memoir 35.

Avery, D. M. 1982. The micromammalian evidence from Border Cave, Kwazulu, South Africa. *Journal of Archaeological Science* **9**, 187–204.

Bailey, G. N. 1975. The role of shell-middens in prehistoric economies. Unpublished PhD Thesis, University of Cambridge.

Beaumont, P. B. 1986. Where did all the young men go in oxygen–isotope stage 2? *Palaeoecology of Africa* **17**, 79–86.

Binneman, J. N. F. 1985. Research along the south-eastern Cape coast. In *Guide to archaeological sites in the eastern and north-eastern Cape*, J. N. F. Binneman & S. L. Hall (eds), 117–34. Grahamstown: Southern African Association of Archaeologists.

Birch, G. 1979. Nearshore Quaternary sedimentation off the south coast of South Africa. *Marine Geoscience report, University of Cape Town* **11**, 127–46.

Bousman, B. 1985. Excavations at Blydefontein Shelter. Unpublished paper delivered at the Southern African Association of Archaeologists Conference, Grahamstown, September.

Butzer, K. W. 1984. Late Quaternary environments in South Africa. In *Late Cainozoic palaeoclimates of the southern hemisphere*, J. C. Vogel (ed.), 235–64. Rotterdam: A. A. Balkema.

Butzer, K. W., G. J. Fock, R. Stuckenrath & A. Zilch 1973. Palaeohydrology of a late Pleistocene lake, Alexandersfontein, Kimberley South Africa. *Nature* **243**, 328–30.

Butzer, K. W., R. Stuckenrath, A. J. Bruzewicz & D. M. Helgren 1978. Late Cenozoic paleoclimates of the Gaap escarpment, Kalahari margin, South Africa. *Quaternary Research* **10**, 310–39.

Coe, M. D., D. H. Cummings & J. Phillipson 1976. Biomass and productivity of African large herbivores in relation to rainfall and primary production. *Oecologia* **22**, 341–54.

Deacon, H. J. 1976. *Where hunters gathered: a study of Holocene Stone Age people in the eastern Cape*. Claremont: South African Archaeological Society Monograph 1.

Deacon, H. J. & M. Brooker 1976. The Holocene and Upper Pleistocene sequence in the southern Cape. *Annals of the South African Museum* **71**, 203–14.

Deacon, H. J. & J. F. Thackeray 1984. Late Quaternary environmental changes and implications from the archaeological record in southern Africa. In *Late Cainozoic palaeoclimates of the southern hemisphere*, J. C. Vogel; (ed.), 375–90. Rotterdam: A. A. Balkema.

Deacon, H. J., J. Deacon, A. Scholtz, J. F. Thackeray, J. S. Brink & J. C. Vogel 1984. Correlations of palaeoenvironmental data from the Late Pleistocene and Holocene deposits at Boomplaas Cave, southern Cape. In *Late Cainozoic palaeoclimates of the southern hemisphere*, J. C. Vogel (ed.), 339–51. Rotterdam: A. A. Balkema.

Deacon, J. 1984a. The Later Stone Age. In *Southern African prehistory and palaeoenvironments*, R. G. Klein (ed.), 221–328. Rotterdam: A. A. Balkema.

Deacon, J. 1984b. *The Later Stone Age of southernmost Africa*. Cambridge Monographs in African archaeology 12, British Archaeological Reports International Series, 213.

Deacon, J., N. Lancaster & L. Scott 1984. Evidence for Late Quaternary climatic change in southern Africa. In *Late Cainozoic palaeoclimates of the southern hemisphere*, J. C. Vogel (ed.), 391–404. Rotterdam: A. A. Balkema.

Dingle, V. R. & J. Rogers 1972. Pleistoene palaeogeography of the Agulhas bank. *Transactions of the Royal Society of South Africa* **40**, 155–65.

Foley, R. 1978. Incorporating sampling into initial research design: some aspects of spatial archaeological. In *Sampling in contemporary British archaeology*, J. F. Cherry, C. Gamble & S. Shennan (eds), 49–66. British Archaeological Reports 50.

Foley, R. 1982. A reconsideration of the role of predation on large mammals in tropical hunter–gatherer adaptation. *Man* **17**, 393–402.

Hall, S. L. 1985. Edgehill and Welgeluk. In *Guide to archaeological sites in the eastern and north-eastern Cape*, 1–38. Grahamstown: Southern African Association of Archaeologists.

Harpending, H. & H. Davis 1977. Some implications for hunter–gatherer ecology derived from the spatial structure of resources. *World Archaeology* **8**, 275–86.

Harper, G. 1969. Periglacial evidence in southern Africa during the Pleistocene epoch. *Palaeoecology of Africa* **4**, 71–101.

Harris, D. R. 1980. Tropical savanna environments: definition, distribution, diversity and development. In *Human ecology in savanna environments*, D. R. Harris (ed.), 31–9. New York: Academic Press.

Hayden, B. 1981. Subsistence and ecological adaptations of modern hunter–gatherers. In *Omnivorous primates – gathering and hunting in human evolution*, R. S. Harding & G. Teleki (eds), 344–421. New York: Columbia University Press.

Humphreys, A. J. B. 1979. The Holocene sequence in the Northern Cape and its position in the prehistory of South Africa. Unpublished PhD Thesis, University of Cape Town.

Humphreys, A. J. B. & A. I. Thackeray 1983. *Ghaep and Gariep*. Claremont: South African Archaeological Society Monograph 2.

Jochim, M. A. 1976. *Hunter–gatherer subsistence and settlement: a predictive model*. New York: Academic Press.

Klein, R. G. 1974. Environment and subsistence of prehistoric man in the southern Cape Province, South Africa. *World Archaeology* **5**, 249–84.

Lee, R. B. 1963. The population ecology of prehistoric man in the early Upper Pleistocene of southern Africa. *Proceedings of the Prehistoric Society*, 235–57

Lee, R. B. 1968. What hunters do for a living or, how to make out on scare resources. In *Man the hunter*, R. B. Lee & I. DeVore (eds), 30–48. Chicago: Aldine.

Lee, R. B. 1979. *The !Kung San: men, women and work in a foraging society*. Cambridge: Cambridge University Press.

Lee, R. B. & I. DeVore (eds) 1968, *Man the hunter*. Chicago: Aldine.

Mitchell, P. J. 1987. The Sehonghong bladelet industry in the context of the Southern African Later Stone Age. Unpublished D. Phil. Thesis, University of Oxford.

Mitchell, P. J. 1988. *The early microlithic assemblages of Southern Africa*. British Archaeological Reports International Series, 538.

Parkington, J. E. 1984. Changing views of the Later Stone Age of South Africa. *Advances in World Archaeology* **3**, 89–142.

Prell, W. L., W. H. Hutson & D. F. Williams 1979. The subtropical convergence and late Quaternary circulation in the southern Indian Ocean. *Marine Micropalaeontology* **4**, 225–34.

Sampson, C. G. 1972. The Stone Age industries of the Orange River Scheme and South Africa. *Memoirs of the National Museum at Bloemfontein* **6**, 1–283.

Sampson, C. G. 1974. *The Stone Age archaeology of southern Africa*. New York: Academic Press.

Sampson, C. G. 1985. Atlas of Stone Age settlement in the Seacow Valley. *Memoirs of the National Museum at Bloemfontein* **20**, 1–116.

Schweitzer, F. R. & M. L. Wilson 1982. Byneskranskop 1: a late Quaternary living site in the southern Cape Province, South Africa. *Annals of the South African Museum* **88**, 1–203.

Scott, L. 1982. A late Quaternary pollen record from the Transvaal bushveld. *Quaternary Research* **17**, 339–70.

Silberbauer, G. 1981. *Hunter and habitat in the central Kalahari*. Cambridge: Cambridge University Press.

Singer, R. & J. Wymer 1982. *Klasies River Mouth*. Chicago: University of Chicago Press.

Tainton, N. 1981. Introduction to the concepts of development, production and stability of plant communities. In *Veld and pasture management in South Africa*, N. Tainton (ed.), 1–56. Pietermaritzburg: Shuter and Shooter.

Talma, A. S., J. C. Vogel & T. C. Partridge 1974. Isotopic contents of some Transvaal speleothems and their palaeoclimatic significance. *South African Journal of Science* **70**, 135–40.

Tanaka, J. 1980. *The San hunter–gatherers of the Kalahari – a study in ecological anthropology*. Tokyo: University of Tokyo Press.

Thackeray, J. F. 1977. Environmental change and terminal Pleistocene extinctions. Unpublished M.Sc. Thesis, University of Cape Town.

Wellington, J. H. 1955. *Southern Africa: a geographical study*. Cambridge: Cambridge University Press.

Whittaker, R. H. 1970. *Communities and ecosystems*. New York: Macmillan.

Zinderen Bakker, E. M. van 1982. African palaeoclimates 18 000 years BP. *Palaeoecology of Africa* **15**, 77–99.

Vogel, J. C. 1983. Isotopic evidence for past climates and vegetation of South Africa. *Bothalia* **14**, 391–4.

9 *Zimbabwe at 18 000 BP*

NICK J. WALKER

Introduction

Zimbabwe is a reasonably well-defined geographic region, bounded to the north by the Zambesi River, to the east by the eastern highlands, to the south by the Limpopo and Shashi rivers and to the west by the Kalahari sandveld. In area the country extends over 390 000 km² and lies mainly between 300 and 1500 m above sea-level. Rainfall is largely determined by the position of the Intertropical Convergence Zone (ITCZ), which is at its southern limit over Zimbabwe in summer, and this is when the country receives most of its rain (Hattle 1971). Precipitation in most areas ranges between 400 and 1000 mm per annum, but the influence of the ITCZ is weakest in the southern regions. Southern Zimbabwe is therefore drought-prone, receiving on average less than 400 mm a year (Lineham 1965). Mean annual temperatures range from about 15° to 27°C (Torrance 1965), and generally the central plateau and eastern mountains are cooler than the lower-lying Zambesi and Limpopo valleys.

Little research has been carried out on Quaternary palaeoclimates within Zimbabwe since the collapse of the Pluvial Hypothesis in the 1960s, but it is possible to postulate a model of climatic history on the basis of recent research in neighbouring territories. This suggests that during glacial periods the ITCZ did not extend as far south as it does today (Nicholson & Flohn 1980). Certainly, northern Botswana was more arid at the Last Glacial Maximum (LGM) than it is at present (Heine 1978, Street & Grove 1979, Lancaster 1981). It can therefore be argued that Zimbabwe in general, and the southern regions in particular, were probably also considerably drier during glacials. Overall temperatures were likely to have been depressed by about 6°C at these times (Morley & Hays 1979, Deacon 1982).

Research on faunal remains indicates that central Zimbabwe experienced appreciable vegetation changes in the past, with the present savanna woodland being replaced on occasion by more open country. Klein (1978) and Cruz-Uribe (1983) have suggested that these periods of increased grassland equated with glacial periods and would have been wetter and cooler. However, exotic species such as springbok, which are present in these faunas, are representative of drier conditions, and this is in keeping with the palaeoclimatic reconstruction of a more arid glacial climate.

Archaeological research

Stone-Age research has been concentrated on central Matabeleland in south-western Zimbabwe. Even though other areas have received increased attention in the past 20 years it remains the case that the generalized cultural history for Zimbabwe is based largely on work in the Matopos and Bulawayo area (e.g. Armstrong 1931, Jones 1949, Cooke 1957, 1963, Cooke et al. 1966; Table 9.1)

In the Matopos, ten Stone-Age sites have been excavated since 1950, and recent work has shown that the Later Stone Age can be traced back here to just over 13 000 BP (Walker 1980a, in prep.). The period immediately before this is poorly understood. Cooke (1969b, 1984) believes that the Tshangula industry dates from about 26 000 BP to about 13 000 BP, and that it occurs throughout Zimbabwe. According to his model, it is characterized by a developed Middle Stone-Age (MSA) technology with the addition of microlithic tools and bone and shell artefacts more typical of the Late Stone Age (LSA) (Cooke 1963, 1969a, 1984, Cooke & Garlake 1968). However, it would seem that the label 'Tshangula' is being used as a blanket term for all assemblages that either date, or are expected to date, to the Terminal Pleistocene and lie chronologically between 'more typical' MSA (i e. Bambata industries) and more acceptable LSA industries (Walker 1980a; see Volman 1984 and Deacon 1982 for definitions of MSA and LSA, respectively).

The only claimed Terminal Pleistocene assemblages from excavation in the Matopos and those that have yielded radiocarbon dates are, unfortunately, mixed. Unit 3 at the site after which the Tshangula industry is called appears to have artefacts typologically more representative of both earlier and later

Table 9.1 The cultural history of the Terminal Pleistocene and Holocene in Zimbabwe

Approx. Years BP	Central Matabeleland	Mashonaland
	Ceramic Matopan	
2100	- - - - - - - - - - - - -	Final LSA
	Amadzimba	
4800	- - - - - - - - - - - - -	
	Nswatugi	
9400	- - - - - - - - - - - - -	
	Pomongwe	Developing LSA
11 000	- - - - - - - - - - - - -	
13 000	Maleme	
20 000	Uninhabited?	Early LSA
		- - - - - - - - - - - - -
	Late MSA (Tshangula)	
35 000	- -	
	Upper Bambata	

periods (Walker in prep.). During the excavation, Cooke (notebooks, 1963) recorded disturbance, poorly defined stratigraphy and shallow units, and was uncertain as to the status of the assemblage. The date of *c.* 9760 BP (Pta 2473) for the unit bears this out.

Pomongwe Cave (Cooke 1963), a key reference site for the Tshangula industry, has comparable problems caused from disturbance. In recent excavations, the relevant levels have been found to include an early LSA industry, which dates from about 13 000 to 11 000 BP (Walker in prep.) and is provisionally called the Maleme industry. It overlies a late MSA industry at Pomongwe Cave (the lower part of the Tshangula industry), but in my recent excavation, adjacent to Cooke's key third trench, I encountered Holocene-aged artefacts, as well as 19th-century pottery and modern cow dung (Walker in prep.). All these items had been introduced subsequently by dung beetles and springhares. This casts doubt on the associated radiocarbon dates of between *c.* 16 000 (SR11) and 14 000 BP (Pta 2299) from Cooke's third trench, and it is worth recalling his (1963, p. 97) initial uncertainty with regard to the scraper-dominated MSA industry from comparable but less disturbed levels in his first trench. This industry is probably related to a similar scraper-dominated but undated MSA assemblage from Shashabugwa Shelter elsewhere in the Matopos (Walker in prep.). The deposit matrix at both sites is more leached than the overlying LSA units, suggesting that the older assemblages were both followed by an occupational hiatus. It is only possible to put a maximum age on the MSA at Pomongwe Cave as there are dates from the underlying layer. Of these one date of about 21 000 BP (SR 10) should be ignored as the laboratory was not satisfied with it (Robins & Swart 1964) and it is stratified below a date of c. 35 000 BP (SR 39; Cooke 1963). Thus the final MSA in the Matopos remains essentially undated but could pre-date the Last Glacial Maximum. It needs to be remembered, however, that the Maleme industry shows some MSA traits, and even if it did not evolve directly from the late MSA in the Matopos, it had to be derived from a relict MSA technology that survived the glacial somewhere nearby. Other published open 'Tshangula' sites, such as Sawmills (Jones 1924), Khami Waterworks (Cooke 1957) and Sitanda Dam (Cooke 1969a), are difficult to assess as they are incomplete and/or have problems of contamination, and are all undated by absolute methods.

Our knowledge of the terminal Pleistocene contrasts strongly with the past 13 000 years. Over 460 LSA sites are known in the Matopos, a significant increase from the 30 or so MSA (Bambata and Tshangula) sites recorded. Research has shown that only two of the ten excavated LSA sites were used between 13 000 and 10 000 BP, whereas seven have occupational debris dating between 10 000 and 8000 BP (Walker in prep.), which could imply a relatively rapid population increase after the Late Glacial. This is in sharp contrast to the lack of acceptable occurrences dated to the LGM.

The only other part of Zimbabwe where any picture is emerging for this period is Mashonaland. Here several sites were excavated in the 1930s and have been investigated more recently. Cooke (1978) has proposed a Mashonaland LSA sequence beginning in the Early Holocene, based largely on his work at Diana's Vow (1979) and Martin's (1938) excavation at Nyazonga, but it is unlikely that between them these two sites have a complete sequence. Certainly, the remarkable uniformity of his stages does not accommodate the considerable differences noted by Robinson (1952) and Voigt and Walker (unpubl.) and present in other Mashonaland LSA assemblages (e.g. Schofield 1932, Goodwin 1934). This is in stark contrast with the diverse Matopos LSA sequence (Walker in prep). There are few dates for the northeastern LSA, but on the basis of the dated Duncombe Farm evidence (Walker & Wadley 1983) and associated pottery at some sites, assemblages with high adze or concave (spokeshave) components are probably late Holocene. Several surface collections support the conclusion from the Diana's Vow study that the Pomongwe industry has no scraper-dominated Early Holocene counterpart in Mashonaland (Cooke 1978), and the LSA has closer affinities to traditions in Zambia than to the south.

At most sites where both the LSA and MSA are present, they are separated by a disconformity, and few sites have any indication of Terminal Pleistocene occupation. One possible exception is Zombepata Cave where Cooke (1971) recognized a Tshangula industry. Unfortunately, leaching has masked the events of the past 25 000 years. The inventories indicate a Terminal Pleistocene assemblage with both MSA and LSA components, but some of the dates are juxtaposed, and it is difficult to decide how serious the mixing has been. It is certainly not easy to correlate with a similar aged assemblage also originally described as Tshangula from Duncombe Farm, and dating to nearly 20 000 years ago (SR 243; Hitzeroth 1971). A recent re-analysis of this assemblage (Walker & Wadley 1983) has shown that it shares many features with the Terminal Pleistocene early Nachikufan industry of eastern Zambia (Miller 1969, Phillipson 1977) and Robberg industry of eastern South Africa (Deacon 1978). The key features of this assemblage are the microlithic nature of the tools and the high production of backed bladelets suitable as arrow inserts. This is the only reliably dated assemblage between 22 000 and 14 000 BP in Zimbabwe. There may have been another early Nachikufan-like component at Pfupi Shelter (Robinson pers. comm.), but here the entire LSA deposits were treated as a single assemblage (Robinson 1952). As elsewhere in the country, Holocene sites are much more numerous than Upper Pleistocene sites in Mashonaland, which possibly implies rapid population growth (Table 9.2).

Research in other parts of Zimbabwe has been more limited, with systematic investigations usually restricted to one or two excavations. Five excavations in the western lowveld (Robinson 1964, Cooke & Simons 1969, Walker in press a) and four in the eastern mountains (Martin 1938, Robinson 1958) have not yielded any evidence for human occupation during the Terminal Pleistocene. These excavations have only yielded Holocene and/or Upper Pleistocene assemblages.

Table 9.2   Periods definitely or apparently represented in 46 Stone-Age excavations covering Upper Pleistocene and Holocene in Zimbabwe

	Approximate Age			
Region	Holocene (Developing LSA)	LGM (Early LSA)	Late Upper Pleistocene (Late MSA)	Upper Pleistocene (Bambata)
Southwest	25	0	5	9
Northeast	12	2	2	5
Other	6	0	1	1
Number of sites	43	2	8	15

Discussion and conclusions

The present state of Stone-Age research in Zimbabwe indicates that the MSA is in need of urgent re-evaluation (Walker 1980a, Volman 1984, Cooke pers. comm.). Consequently it is difficult to decide which assemblages date either to the height of the Last Glacial or the immediately preceding millennia. Only a provisional assessment is possible at this stage (Tables 9.1, 9.2).

In Mashonaland only one excavated site has yielded clear evidence of Terminal Pleistocene occupation, but it is possible that a few others may have had short phases of habitation at this time.

Central Matabeleland has been better investigated, yet no sites can be confidently dated to the LGM. It seems likely, however, that a relict MSA technology survived in the northwestern interior of southern Africa, perhaps along the Zambesi or Okavango rivers, cut off from the mainstream of cultural innovation in the east (see also Phillipson 1977).

The first major conclusion, therefore, is that the numbers of humans were low in Zimbabwe at the height of the Last Glacial. This is based on the difficulty of finding sites of this age. It is, in fact, highly likely that human population was absent from southern and central Zimbabwe.

It can also be concluded that climatic factors greatly influenced prehistoric human settlement in Zimbabwe and population size grew relatively rapidly with the post-glacial amelioration (Walker in prep.). The lowveld is today a marginal area, and rivers draining the watershed have played an important role in supporting human life here (Walker in press a). If during glacial phases their catchments received appreciably less rain, people would have been unable to survive here without sophisticated technology. Moreover, the western and central watershed was apparently too cold and dry, and the eastern highlands too cold for human settlement.

The adoption of microlithic technology may have been the most significant response to the environmental deterioration, although it would be difficult to disprove coincidence. The small backed bladelets that appear at this time imply the introduction of the bow which would certainly have increased hunting success and offset some of the environmental limitations. The innovation of digging-stick weights at about this time (Cooke 1971, Walker 1980b) suggests that gathering technology may also have been improved in response to the greater importance of subterranean foods during climatic stress. Art may also have been developed at this stage to help cope with the worsening conditions by facilitating information flow (Walker in press b). However, there are as yet no good data on diet or social organization that would enable detailed comparison of this period with either the previous or succeeding ones. It would seem that the technology and strategies developed or adopted during the LGM were designed more for basic survival considering the low and discontinuous population, but they did enable the land to support higher populations when conditions improved (Table 9.2). Further work is clearly needed on this important period in Zimbabwe prehistory.

References

Armstrong, A. L. 1931. Rhodesian archaeological expedition (1929): excavations in Bambata Cave and researches on prehistoric sites in Southern Rhodesia. *Journal of the Royal Anthropological Institute* **61**, 239–76.

Cooke, C. K. 1957. The Waterworks site at Khami, Southern Rhodesia. *Occasional Papers of the National Museum, Southern Rhodesia* **3** (21a), 1–60.

Cooke, C. K. 1963. Report on excavations at Pomongwe and Tshangula Caves, Matopos Hills, Southern Rhodesia. *South African Archaeological Bulletin* **18** (71), 73–151

Cooke, C K. 1969a. A re-examination of the 'Middle Stone Age' industries of Rhodesia. *Arnoldia Rhodesia* **4** (7), 1–20.

Cooke, C. K. 1969b. Radiocarbon dates for the Rhodesian Stone Age. *Rhodesian Prehistory* **3**, 6–8.

Cooke, C. K. 1971. Excavations in Zombepata cave, Sipolilo district, Mashonaland, Rhodesia. *South African Archaeological Bulletin* **26**, 104–26.

Cooke, C. K. 1978. Myazongo rock shelter: a detailed reexamination of the cultural material. *Arnoldia Rhodesia* **20**, 1–8.

Cooke, C. K. 1979. Excavations at Diana's Vow rock shelter, Makori district, Zimbabwe Rhodesia. *Occasional Papers of the National Museum, Rhodesia* **A4** (4), 45–73.

Cooke, C. K. 1984. The industries of the upper Pleistocene in Zimbabwe. *Zimbabweia* **1**, 23–7.

Cooke, C. K. & P. S. Garlake 1968. The Tshangula (Magosian) site at Sitanda Dam, Tshipise Tribal Trust Lands, Beit Bridge, Rhodesia. 18th Expedition: Sijanje. *Rhodesia School's Exploration Society*, 22–34.

Cooke, C. K. & H. A. B. Simons 1969. Mpato Shelter, Sentinel Ranch, Limpopo River, Beit Bridge, Rhodesia; Excavation results. *Arnoldia Rhodesia* **4** (18), 1–9.

Cooke, C. K., R. Summers & K. R. Robinson 1966. Rhodesian prehistory reexamined. Part 1: The Stone Age. *Arnoldia Rhodesia* **2** (12), 1–7.

Cruz-Uribe, K. 1983. The mammalian fauna from Redcliff Cave, Zimbabwe. *South African Archaeological Bulletin* **38** (137), 7–16.

Deacon, J. 1978. Changing patterns in the late Pleistocene/early Holocene prehistory of southern Africa, as seen from the Nelson Bay Cave stone artefact sequence. *Quaternary Research* **10**, 84–111.

Deacon, J. 1982. The later Stone Age in the southern Cape, South Africa. Unpublished D. Phil. thesis, University of Cape Town.

Goodwin, A. J. H. 1934. The Rhodesian origin of certain Smithfield N elements. *Proceedings of the Rhodesian Science Association* **34** (1), 28–34.

Hattle, J. 1971. Rhodesian weather and climate. In *Bundu book of meteorology, rock climbing and wayfinding*, 7–31. Salisbury: Longmans.

Heine, K. 1978. Jüngquartär pluviale and interpluviale in der Kalahari (südliches Afrika). *Palaeoecology of Africa and the surrounding islands* **10**, 31–9.

Hitzeroth, L. 1971. Results of a Stone Age excavation from Duncombe Farm shelter, Concession, 1970. *Rhodesian Prehistory* **10**, 14–18.

Jones, N. 1924. On the palaeolithic deposits of Sawmills, Rhodesia. *Journal of the Royal Anthropological Institute* **54**, 276–86.

Jones, N. 1949. *The prehistory of Southern Rhodesia*. Cambridge: Cambridge University Press.

Klein, R. G. 1978. Preliminary analysis of the mammalian fauna from the Redcliff Stone Age cave site, Rhodesia. *Occasional Papers of the National Museum, Rhodesia* **A4** (2), 74–80.

Lancaster, N. 1981. Palaeoenvironmental implications of fixed dune systems in southern Africa. *Palaeogeography, Palaeoclimatology & Palaeoecology* **53**, 327–46.

Lineham, S. 1965. Rainfall in Rhodesia. In *Rhodesia: its natural resources and economic development*, M. C. Collins (ed.), 26–7. Salisbury: Collins.

Martin, C. 1938. A rock shelter on Nyazongo Mountain, Penhalonga district, Southern Rhodesia. *Occasional Papers of the Queen Victoria Memorial Library* **1**, 1–14.

Miller, S. F. 1969. The Nachikufan industries of the Later Stone Age in Zambia. Unpublished D. Phil. thesis, University of California.

Morley, J. J. & J. D. Hays 1979. Comparison of Glacial and Interglacial oceanic conditions in the south Atlantic from variations in calcium carbonate and radiocarbon distributions. *Quaternary Research* **12**, 396–408.

Nicholson, S. E. & H. Flohn 1980. African environmental and climatic changes and the general atmospheric circulation in late Pleistocene and Holocene. *Climatic Change*, **2** 313–48.

Phillipson, D. W. 1977. *The Later Prehistory of eastern and southern Africa*. London: Heineman.

Robins, P. A. & E. R. Swart 1964. Southern Rhodesian radiocarbon measurements. *Radiocarbon* **6**, 31–6.

Robinson, K. R. 1952. Excavations in two rock shelters near the Rusawi river, central Mashonaland. *South African Archaeological Bulletin* **7** (27), 108–29.

Robinson, K. R. 1958. Some Stone Age sites in Inyanga District. In *Inyanga: prehistoric settlements in Southern Rhodesia*, R. Summers (ed.), 270–309. Cambridge: Inyanga Research fund.

Robinson, K. R. 1964. Dombozanga rock shelter, Mtetengwe river, Beit Bridge, Southern Rhodesia: excavation results. *Arnoldia Rhodesia* **1** (7), 1–14.

Schofield, J. F. 1932. Salisbury Commonage sites. *South African Journal of Science* **29**, 772–7.

Street, F. A. & A. T. Grove 1979. Global maps of lake level fluctuations since 30 000 years BP. *Quaternary Research* **12**, 83–118.

Torrance, J. D. 1965. The temperature of Rhodesia. In *Rhodesia: its natural resources and economic development*, M. O. Collins (ed.), 28–9. Salisbury: Collins.

Voigt, E. & N. J. Walker Unpublished. The Later Stone Age of Rhodesia.

Volman, T. P. 1984. Early prehistory of southern Africa. In *Southern African prehistory and palaeoenvironments* R. G. Klein (ed.), 169–220 Rotterdam: A. A. Balkema

Walker, N. J. 1980a. Later Stone Age research in the Matopos. *South African Archaeological Bulletin* **35**, 19–24.

Walker, N. J. 1980b. The bored stones of Zimbabwe. *Rhodesian Prehistory* **19**.

Walker, N. J. in press a. The Later Stone Age of the western Lowveld, Zimbabwe. *Zimbabweia*.

Walker, N. J. in press b. The age of Stone Age art in Zimbabwe. *Australian Rock Art Research*.

Walker, N. J. in prep. The terminal and post Pleistocene hunter-gatherers of the Matopos.

Walker, N. J. & L. Wadley 1983. Evidence for an early microlithic industry at Duncombe Farm in Zimbabwe. *Cookeia* **1** (1), 4–13.

10 *A view from the south: southern Africa before, during, and after the Last Glacial Maximum*

JOHN PARKINGTON

Introduction

Holocene prehistory in southern Africa is reasonably well researched, in part because a substantial number of excavated rockshelter sequences preserve bone and plant materials in informative contexts. Regional research designs have helped us go beyond sequence construction and stone tool typologies. Within these regional frameworks a small series of sites preserve materials from earlier time-periods, notably the millennia since the Last Glacial Maximum (LGM). Thus it is now possible to try to interpret earlier very partial patterns against the more detailed and extensive information in Holocene contexts. We may be able to make only modest statements about the Terminal Pleistocene but we can see how different it was from later millennia and thus suggest alternative patterns of behaviour. In such interpretations, covering as they do the transformations of local climates from the extreme of about 20 000 years ago to the present, the role of environmental changes in stimulating behavioural changes is understandably highlighted by many researchers. Thus understanding the end of the Pleistocene necessarily involves both palaeoenvironmental and social reconstructions.

In this survey I adopt a three-part strategy. First, I present the patterns of site use from the Elands Bay Cave, which has an episodic history of occupation since the beginning of the Late Pleistocene (Parkington 1980, Volman 1984). After that I generalize to caves and rockshelters elsewhere in southern Africa by considering more briefly sites with similar depositional histories. And, thirdly, I move beyond the confines of caves and discuss patterns of settlement in the subcontinent against what is known of palaeoenvironments since about 20 000 years ago. I precede this with some general remarks on the kinds of data available and my attitude to them.

Settlement histories

A point of obvious significance is the extreme cave or rockshelter bias in the distribution of radiocarbon dates used here as elsewhere (H. Deacon & Thackeray 1984). It is hard to know whether this tells us more about recent archaeological strategies than it does about ancient settlement decisions. I take the view that the radiocarbon date set is primarily a document of changing patterns of cave use rather than of prehistoric settlement in general. But in the case of thorough regional surveys the date list can be turned into a document of more general relevance by considering the set of open-station assemblages reported, often well described, but perhaps only occasionally dated directly. The problem of moving from dated cave assemblages to undated open-site assemblages of similar typological character will be discussed later.

It may be asked what kind of reflection such a date list is of even the patterns of cave use. The Pleistocene–Holocene transition, of course, is a time-period of some interest to archaeologists and might thus be expected to be over-represented in date lists. Although it cannot be claimed that radiocarbon dates have randomly accumulated, and although we must admit that the distribution includes some noise (mixed samples, laboratory errors, pioneer dates), I take the view that the information content is high. The test of this assumption lies in the strength of patterning across a sample drawn from many sites and excavated by many different archaeologists. Some problems, such as the drowning of continental shelves and the very variable distribution of rockshelters, cannot be wished away but can be faced explicitly. In our interpretations of the date lists we must include consideration of the motives for cave use rather than open-air living and for relatively substantial relocation of population around the changing landscape.

Recently much effort has been expended on the attempt to understand past changes in ^{14}C production (Barbetti & Flude 1979, Barbetti 1980, Vogel 1980, 1983). Changes in the strength of the Earth's magnetic field, sunspot activity, and correlations with climatic change have been implicated. My point here is simply to raise the issue that some patterning in ^{14}C date lists could be an artefact of a changing set of carbon isotope ratios in the biosphere, a pulsing of the statistical likelihood of particular ^{14}C ages appearing in archaeological samples. Such effects need to be eliminated before we can speak of the dates as a reflection of human settlement decisions and densities.

A third issue, mentioned earlier, is the salient point that the small number of dated rockshelters is far surpassed by the set of possibly contemporary, surface sites where no organic materials are preserved. Can we indirectly age such assemblages by noting their typological relationships to others securely dated by ^{14}C? Although J. Deacon (1984) has had considerable success in arguing for time-related typological change in the Holocene it is nevertheless dangerous for us to assume that correspondence of assemblage character guarantees contemporaneity, and more so that the reverse applies. Such reasoning would be circular and will 'guarantee' only that the guiding principle will be fulfilled in the subsequent ordering of observations. We would never in this argument be capable of documenting contemporaneous variety in assemblage composition or geographic variability in technological or social behaviour.

In sum, I take the view that the use of caves was an episodic pattern of behaviour grounded in local regional settlement strategies. Some variability in contemporary toolmaking and economic behaviour may be anticipated, as between planned and expedient actions or between temporary and longer-term site use. I suggest that the distribution of dates can be understood in this way as a partial reflection of prehistoric land-use without reference to circular assumptions about tool manufacture and time. This in no way eliminates the possibility of discovering, rather than assuming, a time-related, formal trajectory when adequate blanket dating methods become available.

Elands Bay Cave

EBC (Fig. 10.1) is a substantial cave which houses a series of terminal Pleistocene loamy soils capped by Holocene shell-middens (Miller 1987). Underneath these, lying on the quartzite bedrock, is a stony lag deposit with superabundant stone tools of Middle Stone-Age character (Volman 1984). Stratigraphy is complex and locally variable but is summarized in Figure 10.2. It has become clear with an increasing number of radiocarbon dates that cave use came in a series of pulses, separated by time-periods of millennia when the cave was apparently rarely or never visited. I refer here, informally, to the five pulses as basal, lower, middle, upper, and uppermost.

The basal deposits have been highly compacted by the elutriation of fine material and the destruction of all organic components. The reduction in information content is enormous and, in any event, Volman's estimate of some 150 000–200 000 years for their age effectively removes them from the present discussion. The upper and uppermost deposits are shell middens with associated ash and grass bedding units of the second half of the Holocene. They, too, fall beyond the scope of the present discussion. The lower and middle units are, however, of direct relevance. The time-frame for the middle series is well established as between about 13 500 and 8000 years ago, while that of the lower series is less well established but includes dates of 20 180 years near the top and 45 000 years at the base. Pending further radiocarbon dates, I assume an intervening hiatus in occupation between 14 000 and 18 000 years.

The lower series, corresponding in time to the peak of the LGM in Europe, has not yet been extensively sampled. Faunal remains are fragmentary and comprise teeth and extremity parts of large bovids and equids, along with a wider range of body parts from small animals, such as tortoises, dune mole-rats, dassies, and the steenbok or grysbok (Klein & Cruz-Uribe 1987). Plant remains, apart from charcoal, are not preserved and a substantial component of large angular roof rock characterizes the lower sediments in these layers (Butzer 1979, Miller 1987). The stone tools are dominated by

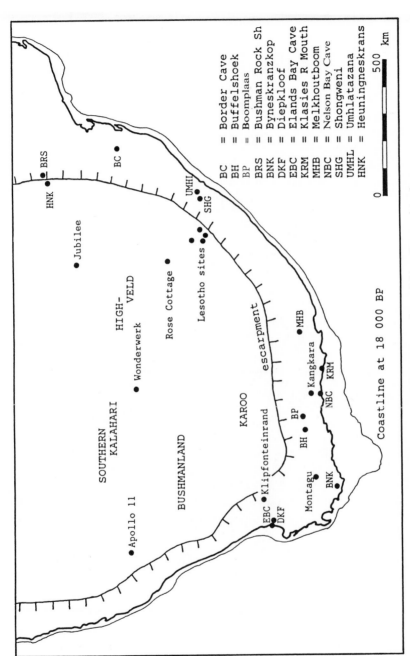

Figure 10.1 Principal sites in southern Africa discussed in the text.

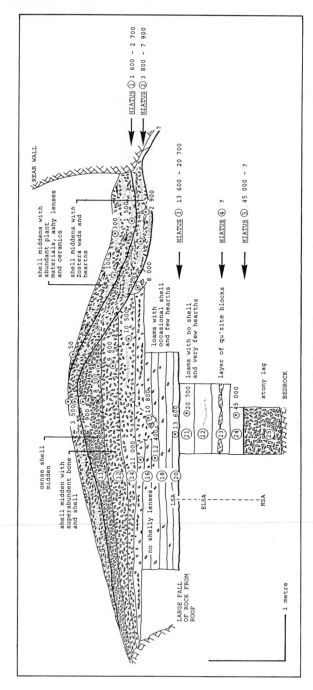

Figure 10.2 Elands Bay Cave stratigraphy.

irregular quartz chunks, some of which may have been cores but few of which correspond to any patterned type such as the bipolar pieces found higher up the sequence. It is possible, but not yet demonstrable, that this lower pulse actually includes the transition to the assemblages characteristic of the middle pulse.

The stone tools, bone and ostrich eggshell tools, and the faunal remains of the middle pulse show considerable, though gradual, change through time and clearly reflect the Terminal Pleistocene rise in sea-level that brought the coast to within a 100 m or so of the cave. Thus, although at 13 600 years ago there are fragments of shellfish and small numbers of bones of other marine animals in the deposits, these increase dramatically after 11 000 years ago and soon comprise the bulk of the excavated materials. Conversely, terrestrial animals decrease in relative proportions through time. The decline in the numbers of large grazing forms and increase in smaller browsing forms through this sequence has led Klein and Cruz-Uribe (1987) to postulate a decrease in grass cover contemporary with sea-level rise.

The stone-tool assemblage at 13 600 years ago is again heavily quartz-dominated, but the average size of pieces is considerably smaller than the 20 000-year-old assemblages and there are substantial numbers of tiny bipolar and single platform cores. The small bladelets removed from these cores are very infrequently retouched. Similar cores and bladelets are found in silcrete, but the other stone raw material of interest is fine-grained indurated shale. Although our shale class probably includes a range of rock types, there are significantly higher frequencies of these in this middle pulse than anywhere else in the site. These shales are regularly utilized, form larger size pieces than the quartz and include lots of informally flaked cobbles. We have singled out from these assemblages what we call naturally backed knives (NBK's) (Parkington 1988), artefacts made on wide, side-struck flakes removed from rectangularly bedded indurated shale. These tools were, without doubt, removed from the parent rock at the site of dykes that had metamorphosed the fine silt or mudstones in the central interior of southern Africa. They were subsequently brought or exchanged and lost or abandoned at EBC in small but consistent numbers between 13 600 and 8000 BP. Although these characteristics persist to 8000 years ago, it is significant that there is a drift after 11 000 years ago toward more grindstones, whetstones and palettes and fewer bladelets and bladelet cores. At 8000 there appear relatively large numbers of small- to medium-sized quartz scrapers (15–25 mm in maximum dimension).

Coincident with this drift in stone-tool assemblage character is a marked increase in ostrich eggshell, particularly in ostrich eggshell beads, both whole and broken during manufacture, and in bone tools and beads. Not unrelated, perhaps, is the shift mentioned earlier towards an increase in marine foods, which includes fish (Poggenpoel 1987), rock lobsters, marine birds (Avery 1987) and, of course, shellfish. The numbers of tortoise bones peak in these same levels.

A point of some significance here, dealt with in detail elsewhere (Parkington 1988), is the increased deposition rate in EBC once shells were being regularly returned to the site. This implies that the easily visible increase in faunal remains from that time is even more dramatic when converted to an estimate of bone per unit time, rather than bone per unit volume of deposit. I have estimated at least a one hundredfold increase in the amount of food debris in EBC per unit time after 11 000 years ago.

I have suggested (Parkington 1988) that a coherent interpretation of this package of changes would be that, as sea-level rose and the coastline shifted east toward EBC, people rescheduled their use of the cave. The increase in numbers of small, relatively easily gathered food parcels (tortoises, ostrich eggs, shellfish) and in the numbers of bone and stone artefacts used in tool shaping (whetstones, grindstones) and broken or unfinished decorative items is consistent with an interpretation of increasing female presence at the site as it was rescheduled from some kind of expedient short-term use to home-base status. Of course the alternative is to describe these assemblages as belonging to successive cultural episodes (J. Deacon 1978), in this case Robberg followed by Albany.

The middle pulse at EBC represents a substantial amount of occupation debris, perhaps half of that still retained in the cave. I find it hard to believe that the visits to EBC were not integrated into a pattern that included sites now submerged under the Atlantic as well as quarries of indurated shale far into the interior. This particular phase of cave use must, then, owe its existence to decisions made by people as sea-level rose and environmental change rendered the site particularly attractive. None of the 75 or so other sites around the lower part of the Verlorenvlei contain this pulse and there are no nearby open sites, east of the current coastline, with assemblages we would consider contemporary. EBC must have been part of a widely spaced apparently cave-oriented network of sites. The exact relationship with landscape change is difficult to estimate because we have little idea what the critical thresholds for people were or what kinds of lags in geological and biological cycles there were (Parkington 1987).

Caves elsewhere

In Table 10.1 I have plotted all of the published radiocarbon dates for archaeological assemblages in southern Africa between 23 000 and 8000 years old. The correspondence between EBC and a more general pattern visible in the table, is even clearer when we look at the nature of cave use site by site. Thus there is no doubt at all that major sites such as Apollo XI (Wendt 1976), Boomplaas (H. Deacon 1979), Sehonghong (Mitchell 1988), Nelson Bay Cave (NBC) (J. Deacon 1978), and others have been episodically and thus presumably opportunistically used. Not only that, but some of the pulses identified at EBC recur at a number of sites over a surprisingly wide geographic area. All four of the sites mentioned previously, for example, have dated occupations at or around the LGM followed by variable but largely coterminous periods of non-occupation. Scrutiny of the placing of ^{14}C dates in

Table 10.1 ^{14}C dates from southern Africa

Years BP	Southern Namibia	Western Cape	Southern Cape	Eastern Cape	Natal Swaziland E TVL	Lesotho OFS	Northern Cape	Transvaal
8 000		★★	★				★	
		★	★	★			★	
								★
		★	★		★	★		
			★★					
			★★		★★		★★	★
		★						
	★	★	★		★★			
		★	★★		★		★	
		★★		★★	★★★		★★	
10 000		★★	★★★	★				
			★				★★	
	★	★	★★★	★	★			
		★★	★					
		★	★					
			★		★			★
			★				★	
	★		★★					
12 000			★		★	★	★★	
			★		★★	★		
	★	★★	★★		★		★★★	
					★			
	★				★★	★★		
	★				★	★		
					★★		★	
	★					★		★
	★	★			★		★	
14 000			★					
	★							
				★				
					★			
16 000								
			★					
			★			★		
18 000			★					
	★							
	★		★					
	★							
						★★		
	★★				★	★		
20 000		★				★		
					★	★		
						★		
			★★		★			
			★					
	★							
22 000	★							
			★			★		
			★					
					★			

Each ★ = one ^{14}C date.   E TVL, Eastern Transvaal; OFS, Orange Free State.

these stratigraphies makes it very clear that to assume an even rate of deposition between dates, as we once did, is not justified. On the contrary, it would be more consistent to argue that there was a widespread, if insubstantial, pulse of cave or rockshelter use at the LGM, followed by another beginning about 14 000 years ago. Cave use between 17 500 and 13 500 is very hard to locate in southern Africa.

The pulsing of ^{14}C dates in caves could, as mentioned earlier, be due to changes in ^{14}C production rather than in prehistoric behaviour. To test this, I plotted all the geological and palaeontological ^{14}C dates I could find for southern Africa (Butzer et al. 1973, Vogel & Visser 1981, Rust et al. 1984) on the assumption that dates derived from submerged beaches, peat deposits, silt sequences, and calcified roots should be independent of human choices but related to any global phenomena. The pulsing of the artefact-associated charcoal dates is not repeated in the geological series, from which I assume that the former reflect real behavioural patterns.

The coincidence in the timing of cave occupations claimed here is accentuated by further similarities in the artefactual assemblages at these sites. Thus J. Deacon (1978) has illustrated clearly the dramatic increase in bone tools at NBC exactly contemporary with that at EBC and including some identical forms (most notably hundreds of tiny double-pointed 'fish gorges'). Bone beads, ostrich eggshell, and decorated ostrich eggshell water-flask fragments appear to increase in number at Boomplaas and NBC (J. Deacon 1984) at the same time as they do at EBC, and could thus be incorporated into the argument I used earlier for that site. To judge by the less well understood patterns at Apollo XI, Bushman Rock Shelter, and elsewhere, the same may be true at a subcontinental scale. Again, while we could interpret the changes in a culture-replacement model, we should not lose sight of the nature of the changes. These are, I submit, in effect evidence of increasingly varied and diverse activities scheduled to take place at the caves and rockshelters we examine.

In terms of the cultural terminology currently in use it is interesting to note that there is no correspondence between pulses and cultural grouping. Rather we see the 22 000–17 500 pulse including the 'Early Late Stone Age' to Robberg transition and the later pulse encompassing assemblages conventionally labelled both Robberg and Albany. I would argue that at both EBC and NBC there is little justification in splitting these assemblage series into separate entities. At both the change is toward greater numbers of bone tools, greater varieties of manufacturing waste, fewer expedient quartz tools, along with an increasingly marine-based economy. We may be looking at a phase of rescheduling that is reflected at a subcontinental scale, suggesting that the explanation must be of comparable scale.

The timing of these pulses is rather hard to understand. The period of most extreme climates, arguably 22 000–18 000, seems not, as some claim (H. Deacon & Thackeray 1984), a period of archaeological invisibility but is relatively widely represented in the date list by comparison with the following three or four millennia. It is hard to square this with a model of increasing population in the period of amelioration after the LGM, especially as many would see essentially modern conditions established by 13 000 years ago. One could argue for a substantial time-lag between climatic amelioration and the decision to reoccupy caves and shelters in the mountainous fringes of the subcontinent, but the undoubtedly widespread set of 22 000–18 000 BP occupations render this difficult.

The clear association of this particular pulse (say 22 000–17 500) with hilly or mountainous terrain, and especially that of the high Drakensberg, offers us an interesting insight. Such altitudes do not intuitively strike me as likely refuges at the maximum conditions of oxygen isotope stage 2, although some regions may well have been optimal in terms of freshwater availability. Rather, I suggest, we should view the surviving set of occupations at this time as the tip of the iceberg, so to speak. My argument would be that if there was persistent and visible occupation of the high Drakensberg, the Cape Fold Belt and other escarpment regions, there may well have been even more people in the presumably milder climates of the then extensive coastal plains and, more arguably, in the central interior plains. Some such sites may no longer be available for study but some may simply remain as yet undated.

The cave orientation in the Terminal Pleistocene, noted from our good regional knowledge in the Elands Bay area, is repeated in other regions from which the other cave sequences come. Thus Apollo XI, NBC, Boomplaas, and Sehonghong are certainly not located in or near a swarm of similar Terminal Pleistocene assemblages in less informative open contexts. We are left with the impression that residential patterns in these regions involved the selection of a few caves, usually fairly large ones, with large-scale movement between them. The shift from expedient, almost transient, cave use to one reflected in a wider range of economic and technological remains may imply that these regions had not previously been central to settlement systems. One possibility is that through much of the time-period covered by the two pulses, people were primarily based either along the increasingly inundated coastal plains or in the increasingly arid interior. Both of these processes may have brought about a shift in the distributional centre of gravity by 10 000 to 8000 years ago, into the varied topography of the escarpment areas which ring the interior basin from Namibia through the Cape to Lesotho and the eastern Transvaal.

A general perspective

A large part of southern Africa is, for very good reason, missing from this cave-orientated survey of settlement density. The interior basin, comprising the current Karoo and grassland regions of the Cape, Orange Free State and the Transvaal, and penetrating the savannahs of Botswana, has few long-sequence caves. But there are, as Sampson has shown (1985) tens or even hundreds of thousands of archaeological assemblages, many on the surface and as yet undated. Those which Goodwin & van Riet Lowe (1929) would have called 'Smithfield A' and which Sampson (1974, 1985) now calls Lockshoek seem likely to date from the Terminal Pleistocene and thus to be relevant to our discussion. If there are 1000 of these sites in half of the Seekoei Valley (Sampson 1985) there must be 15 000 or more in the interior as a whole, although the exact distribution remains to be established. It is a sobering thought that they outnumber dated cave assemblages by some 200 : 1 or more. We might have allowed the tail to wag the archaeological dog.

One of the original type-tools of the old Smithfield A was the concavo-convex scraper, a form that is undoubtedly morphologically and probably functionally the equivalent of our naturally backed knives. Of course, situated as they are in those parts of the interior where dyke swarms make sources of undurated shale or hornfels superabundant, these assemblages are mono-lithically made from such rock. There is in the general absence of quartz no opportunity for these assemblages to resemble in overall composition the quartz domination of EBC and NBC. The question is obviously how the Smithfield A or Lockshoek assemblages relate to the pulses of occupation documented from the caves and shelters in the peripheral regions of the subcontinent.

J. Deacon suggested some time ago (1974) that the Lockshoek assemblages would date prior to 9500 years ago, helping to form the dearth of radiocarbon dates she noted from the interior between 9500 and 4500 BP. It was her view, and still is (pers. comm.) that increasing terminal Pleistocene aridity in the interior, particularly that part which is marginal to both the summer- and winter-rainfall systems, helped persuade 'Lockshoek people' to locate else-where. An estimate of the earliest date for the Lockshoek is less easy to make. Both J. Deacon (1974) and Sampson (1985) noted the presence of large scrapers in the Albany of the periphery and the Lockshoek of the interior and thus suspected the existence of contemporary but geographically separate develop-ments. They would place an early boundary of about 12 000 years, the beginnings of the Albany, for the beginnings of the Lockshoek. I would not be surprised to see some Lockshoek assemblages as contemporary with so-called Robberg assemblages with dates going back eventually to at least 13 600 and perhaps 17 500 years ago.

There does seem to be evidence, albeit preliminary and scattered, to suggest wetter circumstances in the interior, where researchers have noted higher water tables at several times between 20 000 and 13 000 years ago. Although these observations have yet to be orchestrated into a coherent score (but see Butzer 1984, Deacon et al. 1984, Kent & Gribnitz 1985), there is considerable evidence of higher lake, spring or pan levels in southern Botswana (16 255–15 610 BP, Lancaster 1977, 1979), along the Ghaap escarpment of the northern Cape (16 000–14 000 BP, Butzer et al. 1978), in the southwestern Kalahari (17 000–15 000 BP, Heine 1982), and in now dry pans of the northwestern Cape (for some time prior to 13 670 BP, Kent & Gribnitz 1985). There is still considerable discussion as to whether these periods of more available water were due to increase in summer or winter rains, but substantial and apparently repeated wetter than present intervals seem to be widely supported. Whether these can be made to fit the pulse-like nature of occupation debris in surrounding highland areas is a matter for future research.

Regardless of the success of this kind of analysis, we may well ask whether it is necessary for rainfall to have been higher in the interior for us to postulate a formerly substantial human presence. Surely present ethnographies and many Eurasian palaeolithic case studies in these volumes demonstrate that hunter–gatherers can and do exist in seemingly quite arduous environmental contexts, which are often limited by rainfall. I take the view that decisions to occupy particular segments of the landscape are made in the light of environmental circumstances but are also influenced by technological capabilities, the prior trajectory of settlement decisions, and the range of alternatives perceived as open at the time.

The relative invisibility of sites in the interior after 9500 years ago, should it prove a durable pattern, would seem to be inversely related to the increase in both cave and open sites in the surrounding mountainous fringes. There, as mentioned earlier, few sites penetrate beyond the Early Holocene, but particularly in the southern and eastern Cape, in Natal, and in parts of the western parts of the Cape and Namibia, sequences pick up from about 9000 years ago. Indeed, the much described Wilton assemblages abound in the Cape Fold Belt, in other rugged terrain, and in the present coastal plains from that date, spreading only after 4500 or so 'back' into the interior (J. Deacon 1984), J. Deacon et al. 1984). Obviously, in the very varied terrain of southern Africa we cannot hope for neat patterns, but it seems here we have a moderately clear relationship between interior basin, surrounding uplands and escarpment, and now partly submerged continental margins, that remains coherent over a 20 000-year period.

Conclusion

As a set of working hypotheses I advance the following suggestions as to the history of human settlement in the southern part of southern Africa leading up to and out of the LGM.

1   During the period from about 22 000 BP to 17 500 BP settlement in the interior of southern Africa is as yet undocumented. In the highland fringes of the subcontinent, including the current coastal areas of the Cape Fold Belt, largely ephemeral but widespread occupations are known. These assemblages are characterized by very extensive fracturing of fine-grained rocks, often quartz, by bipolar techniques, particularly after about 20 000 BP, and would correspond to the 'Early LSA' and earliest 'Robberg' of other authors (Deacon 1978, 1984, Mitchell 1988). During this time a very extensive coastal foreland west and south of the present coast was exposed

but is no longer available for study. Assemblages are all in caves or rockshelters; none of those in the Cape show any evidence of karoo interior contents, and faunal assemblages are dominated by a heads and tails pattern of large animal body parts. Given that this is the maximum cold part of isotope stage 2, I argue that a highland/escarpment pattern of settlement is counter-intuitive and that complementary settlement in the coastal regions should be hypothesized. The expedient tool use in highland/escarpment shelters may imply that these are occupations by only a segment of social groups, arguably males on transient hunting excursions.

2   During the period from 17 500 to 14 500 BP the pattern is similar but with the difference that even in the highland/escarpment region occupations are very rare. The reasons for this are not clear.

3   During the period 14 500 to about 11 500 BP there is abundant evidence in the highland/escarpment region for the renewed occupation of caves and rockshelters. Again the visits may have been brief, the nature of the occupying groups incomplete and most tool assemblages making expedient use of locally available rocks. At least at Elands Bay Cave the assemblages of this period resemble those of the earlier pulse but with the difference that they now include NBKs undoubtedly made in the interior near the dyke sources of hornfels. The existence of NBKs in a large number of interior sites reinforces the suggestion that occupation of the previously unoccupied central interior region of southern Africa may have been possible by now. Radiocarbon dates from shelters that circumscribe the interior confirm this. Faunal assemblages are, as in the earlier pulse, somewhat modest and suggest small numbers of animals per millennium. No burials and few other stratigraphic features are known.

4   Between 11 500 and 8000 years ago many of these same caves and rockshelters, and arguably additional ones, in the highland/escarpment regions are more regularly reoccupied. Stone tool assemblages still contain naturally backed knives (NBK's), and many inland karoo sites ('Lockshoek') may belong in the earlier part of this time-range. From the perspective of Elands Bay Cave, several major changes since prior to 11 500 may have social and settlement significance. In this period we have located five burials, including one newborn individual, at least one large ash feature, a stone arrangement of unknown function, a significant increase in the quantity and range of all kinds of manufacturing debris, and an increase in faunal remains per millennia that is probably more than one hundredfold. I believe this is evidence for the broadening of site function as the site was rescheduled. In a sense, Terminal Pleistocene people have been 'herded' into the inner fringes of the continental shelf by the final rise in sea-level. The centre of population distribution may at this time, to judge from site numbers, have been firmly in the interior.

5   After about 9000 years BP an increasingly arid interior dissuades people from extensive settlement there and helps redistribute population back along the better-watered highland/escarpment region. Most archaeological

sequences are found here. Ironically, the Holocene may have been the only portion of the past 25 000 years when excavations have coincided with the centres of population distribution. Previously we may have been viewing a changing ecological and social landscape from the very marginal vantage points still accessible to field research. By implication the core area of LSA population distribution in the southern part of southern Africa may have lain at its southern, now submerged, extremity.

References

Avery, G. 1987. Avian faunas from Verlorenvlei sites. In *People and places: papers in the prehistory of the western Cape*, J. Parkington & M. Hall (eds), 164–91. Oxford: BAR International Series 332.

Barbetti, M. 1980. Geomagnetic strength over the last 50 000 years and changes in atmospheric 14–C concentration: emerging trends. *Radiocarbon* **22**, 192–9.
Barbetti, M. & K. Flude 1979. Geomagnetic variation during the Late Pleistocene period and changes in the radiocarbon time scale. *Nature* **279**, 202–5.
Butzer, K. W. 1979. Geomorphology and geo-archaeology at Elandsbaai, western Cape, South Africa. *Catena* **6**, 157–66.
Butzer, K. W. 1984. Late Quaternary environments in South Africa. In *Late Cainozoic palaeoclimates of the southern hemisphere*, J. C. Vogel (ed.), 235–65. Rotterdam: A. A. Balkema.
Butzer, K. W., G. J. Fock, R. Stuckenrath & A. Zilch 1973. Palaeohydrology of a late Pleistocene lake, Alexandersfontein, Kimberley, South Africa. *Nature* **243**, 328–30.
Butzer, K. W., R. Stuckenrath, A. J. Bruzewicz & D. M. Helgren 1978. Late Cenozoic palaeoclimates of the Gaap Escarpment, Kalahari margin, South Africa. *Quaternary Research* **10**, 310–39.

Deacon, H. J. 1979. Excavations at Boomplaas Cave – a sequence through the Upper Pleistocene and Holocene in South Africa. *World Archaeology* **10**, 241–57.
Deacon, H. J. & J. F. Thackeray 1984. Late Pleistocene environmental changes and implications for the archaeological record in southern Africa. In *Late Cainozoic palaeoclimates of the southern hemisphere*, J. C. Vogel (ed.), 375–90. Rotterdam: A. A. Balkema.
Deacon, J. 1974. Patterning in the radiocarbon dates for the Wilton/Smithfield complex in southern Africa. *South African Archaeological Bulletin* **29**, 3–18.
Deacon, J. 1978. Changing patterns in the late Pleistocene/early Holocene prehistory of southern Africa as seen from the Nelson Bay Cave stone artefact sequence. *Quaternary Research* **10**, 84–111.
Deacon, J. 1984. *The Later Stone Age of southernmost Africa*. Oxford: BAR International Series 213.
Deacon, J., N. Lancaster & L. Scott 1984. Evidence for Late Quaternary climatic change in southern Africa. In *Late Cainozoic palaeoclimates of the southern hemisphere*, J. C. Vogel (ed.), 391–404. Rotterdam: A. A. Balkema.

Goodwin, A. J. H. & C. Van Riet Lowe 1929. The Stone Age cultures of South Africa. *Annals of the South African Museum* **27**, 1–289.

Heine, K. 1982. The main stages of the Late Quaternary evolution of the Kalahari region, southern Africa. *Palaeoecology in Africa* **15**, 53–76.

Kent, L. E. & K. H. Gribnitz 1985. Fresh water shell deposits in the north western Cape Province: further evidence for a widespread wet phase during the late Pleistocene in Southern Africa. *South African Journal of Science* **81**, 361–70.

Klein, R. G. & K. Cruz-Uribe 1987. Large mammal and tortoise bones from Elands Bay Cave and nearby sites, Western Cape Province, South Africa. In *Papers in the prehistory of the western Cape, South Africa*, J. E. Parkington & M. Hall (eds), 132–63. Oxford: BAR International Series 332(i).

Lancaster, N. 1977. Pleistocene lacustrine stromatolites from Urwi Pan, Botswana. *Transactions of the Geological Society of South Africa* **80**, 283–5.

Lancaster, N. 1979. Evidence for a widespread late Pleistocene humid period in the Kalahari. *Nature* **279**, 145–6.

Miller, D. 1987. Geoarchaeology at Verlorenvlei. In *Papers in the prehistory of the western Cape, South Africa*, J. Parkington & M. Hall (eds), 46–77. Oxford: BAR International Series 332(i).

Mitchell, P. J. 1988. *The early microlithic assemblages of southern Africa.* Oxford: BAR International Series 388.

Parkington, J. E. 1980. The Eland's Bay sequence: cultural stratigraphy & subsistence strategies. In *Proceedings of the 8th Pan African Congress of Prehistory & Quaternary Studies, Nairobi, September 1977*. R. E. Leakey & B. A. Ogot (eds); 314–20. Nairobi: The International Louis Leakey Memorial Institute for African Prehistory.

Parkington, J. E. 1987. Prehistory and palaeoenvironments at the Pleistocene – Holocene boundary in the western Cape. In *The Pleistocene Old World – Regional perspectives*, O. Soffer (ed.), 349–63. New York: Plenum Press.

Parkington, J. E. 1988. The Pleistocene/Holocene transition in the western Cape, South Africa: Observations from Verlorenvlei. In *Prehistoric cultures and environments in the Late Quaternary of Africa*. J. Bower & D. Lubell (eds), 197–106. Oxford: British Archaeological Reports S405.

Poggenpoel, C. A. 1987. The implications of fish bone assemblages from Eland's Bay Cave, Tortoise Cave & Diepkloof for changes in the Holocene history of Verlorenvlei. In *Papers in prehistory of the western Cape, South Africa*, J. Parkington & M. Hall (eds), 212–36. Oxford: BAR International Series 332.

Rust, U., H. H. Schmidt & K. R. Diety 1984. Palaeoenvironments of the present day arid south western Africa 30 000–5000 BP: results and problems. *Palaeoecology in Africa* **16**, 109–48.

Sampson, C. G. 1974. *The Stone Age archaeology of southern Africa.* New York: Academic Press.

Sampson, C. G. 1985. Atlas of Stone Age settlement in the Seacow Valley. *Memoirs of the National Museum at Bloemfontein* **20**, 1–116.

Vogel, J. C. 1980. Accuracy in the radiocarbon time scale beyond 15 000 BP. In *Proceedings of the 10th Radiocarbon Conference* M. Stuiver & R. Kra (eds), 210–18. *Radiocarbon* **22**.

Vogel, J. C. 1983. [14]C variations during the upper Pleistocene. *Radiocarbon* **25**, 213–18.

Vogel, J. C. & E. Visser 1981. Pretoria Radiocarbon dates II. *Radiocarbon* **23**, 43–80.

Volman, T. P. 1984. Early prehistory of southern Africa. In *Southern Africa prehistory and palaeoenvironments*, R. G. Klein (ed.), 169–220. Rotterdam: A. A. Balkema.

Wendt, W. E. 1976. 'Art Mobilier' from the Apollo XI Cave, South West Africa: Africa's oldest dated works of art. *South African Archaeological Bulletin* **31**, 5–11.

SOUTHERN ASIA, SUNDA AND AUSTRALIA

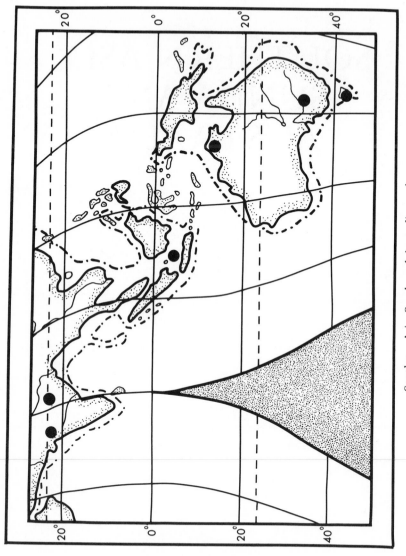

Southern Asia, Sunda and Australia: study areas

11 South Asian climate and environment at c. 18 000 BP

D. P. AGRAWAL, REKHA DODIA & MALA SETH

Introduction

In this chapter we present palaeoclimatic data for the period c. 18 000 ± 2000 BP, for South Asia. It is generally believed that c. 18 000 BP was the global peak after which the present type of interglacial conditions began to develop. In general terms this global climatic picture is correct, but in different latitudinal belts there were significant variations, as we will see below.

At the moment definitive evidence for South Asia is only available from northwest India – the Arabian Sea, Rajasthan, and Kashmir – which fall on a southwest to northeast transect. There are some scattered data from the rest of the subcontinent, but their poor resolution does not warrant inclusion here. We will also touch upon some relevant archaeological data for this period from Rajasthan and Kashmir.

The Arabian Sea

In recent years considerable data has come from the Arabian Sea cores and also from the coastal sites. Duplessy (1982) and Van Campo et al. (1982) have presented palynological, foraminiferal, and stable isotopic data from the Arabian Sea cores. Caratini et al. (1978) examined pollen from cores taken offshore from Muscat in Oman, in the Arabian peninsula. A vegetational sequence up to 35 000 BP was reconstructed, and at 18 000 BP a distinct arid type of vegetation was encountered. Van Campo et al. (1982) reported a correlation between oxygen isotopes and pollen records from the marine cores obtained from the northern Arabian Sea. The cores cover oxygen isotopic stages 1–6, thus spanning about 130 000 years. A correlation with the eustatic curve was also obtained, with interglacial intervals showing high sea-levels. The pollen spectra show relatively low frequencies of humid–tropical taxa, such as *Alchornea*, Apocynaceae, Meliaceae, etc., and high relative frequencies of the Mediterranean steppe taxa, such as *Artemisia*, *Colligonum*, Compositae, *Plantago*, *Erodium*, etc. at c. 18 000 BP, roughly coinciding with oxygen isotope stage 2. The benthic foraminifera show ^{18}O values up to +4‰ and up to

+3‰ for planktonic foraminifera. Thus there is a very good correlation between the glacial maxima and aridity shown by the pollen flora (Van Campo et al. 1982) and ^{18}O curves.

Sea-levels started rising only after 10 000 BP and reached +3 to +5 m above the present mean sea-level by the mid-Holocene. A sea-level curve was obtained from the west (Indian) coast by Agrawal & Guzdar (1972), Gupta (1972), and Gupta & Amin (1974), showing that marine transgressions were of the order of +5 m at c. 120 000 and 5000 BP. The marine pollen diagram from the arid tropical zone depicts fluctuations of the intensity of the seasonally reversed low-latitude wind systems and correlates littoral aridity with sea-level changes. The intensity of the monsoonal winds seems to be controlled by the Earth's orbital parameters, reaching maximum when insolation was strongest.

Rajasthan

The State of Rajasthan falls between 24°–30°N latitude and 70°–78°E longitude and contains the large Thar desert. On a west–east transect, precipitation increases from about 150 to 400 mm per year and is mainly the SW monsoon rain. It appears that 250–300 mm rainfall per year is the threshold beyond which sand dunes stabilize. Thus from west to east the dunes are stabilized with vegetation. We have sectioned some major dunes and studied the sequence of palaeosols they contain. For example, at Didwana (IR-6) dune there are five palaeosols marked by calcium carbonate nodules (Fig. 11.1). In between the palaeosols there is unweathered sand (Misra pers. comm.). It is obvious that whenever rainfall exceeded 250 mm per year, the dunes developed soils, and during periods of aridity sand dunes built up. It appears that the Thar desert is only 120 000 years old. It should be noted that at 20 000 and about 5000 BP palaeosols developed in the dunes. There are several ^{14}C dates on the pedogenic carbonates from Didwana dating to 20 000 ± 2000 BP (Agrawal et al. 1985). The mid-Holocene soil formation is confirmed by dates from the other sites.

It is interesting to note that the 20 000 BP palaeosol is associated with an ubiquitous Upper Palaeolithic industry, and the mid-Holocene occurrence with the Mesolithic settlements in western Rajasthan (Agrawal et al. 1980) and with the Indus civilization sites in the Ghaggar Valley (Agrawal & Sood 1982).

Singh et al. (1974) produced a pollen sequence from the salt lakes of Rajasthan and reported moister conditions in Phase IV (5000–3000 BP) than today. Their pollen diagram starts with the pre-10 000 BP period showing severely arid conditions. Agrawal et al. (1980) carried out palaeoclimatic and palaeosalinity studies of the Didwana salt lake up to a sediment depth of 6 m (Wasson et al. 1983). The pre-13 000 BP sediments show hypersaline conditions and a dune-building phase (Fig. 11.1). This obviously corresponds with the marine oxygen isotope stage 2 marked by glacial and arid conditions from the Arabian Sea, as explained above. This is also the period of the LGM at c.

18 000 BP. Between 13 000 and 6000 BP there were wide fluctuations in the salinity curves, but from 6000 to 4000 BP there is very low salinity, fresh water, indicating wetter conditions than today. This period is also marked by the rise of pre-Harappan and Harappan cultures in the area.

Kashmir

Kashmir falls between 32°–35°N latitude and 72°–80°E longitude and forms the northermost region of South Asia. Unlike the Arabian Sea and Rajasthan, where c. 18 000 BP is marked by a cold and arid climate, Kashmir shows climatic amelioration during this period. We will first discuss the data on which this inference is based and suggest explanations for this difference in the climatic pattern.

Pollen has been analysed by us from two bogs at Butapathri in Kashmir, and also from the Anchar and the Hokarsar lakes. Earlier Singh & Agrawal (1976) reported palynological changes after 15 000 BP from Toshmaidan which is at an altitude of +3000 m. The ^{14}C dates of 14 000–15 000 BP are from the contact between the organic and inorganic sediments at Toshmaidan and are in agreement with the dates generally associated with deglaciation following the last glacial period in several parts of the world. Thus Toshmaidan indicated a date of c. 15 000 BP for deglaciation in the Kashmir Valley. However, our work at the Butapathri bogs in Kashmir, at an altitude of +3000 m, showed a warm temperate and wet climatic condition around 17 000 BP, as indicated by the significant presence of thermophilous elements such as Carpinus, Corylus, Juglans, Ulmus, etc. After this warm temperate phase, the Butapathri pollen sequence shows a cool–warm–cool sequence. Elsewhere in the valley the mid-Holocene warm period is associated with dominance of Cerealia-type pollen, indicating agricultural activity (Dodia et al. 1985).

On the other hand there is a distinct palaeosol extending over the whole of the valley, dated to c. 18 000 BP (Kusumgar et al. 1980). It is therefore obvious that this soil, developed over loess, represents a climatic amelioration. Subsequently, Krishnamurthy et al. (1982) studied ^{13}C variations in the loess profile in the Burzahom in Kashmir. There are three palaeosols in the Burzahom sequence. The lower two show a range of −16 to −21‰ ^{13}C variation, thus indicating that probably the soils were a result of the decay of C4-type vegetation (Fig. 1 in Krishnamurthy et al. 1982). But for palaeosol-1, dated to c. 18 000 BP, the ^{13}C value is −25‰, indicating a dominance of the C3-type of vegetation, which grows under optimal climatic conditions.

There is circumstantial evidence that the Upper Palaeolithic culture in Kashmir is associated with the palaeosol dated to c. 18 000 BP. In Kashmir a small difference in temperature made it either habitable or inhospitable for early man. Recent work shows a good correlation between increase in the number of archaeological sites at c. 18 000, 5000, and 1800 BP. These coincide with the climatic optima in the valley (Agrawal 1985).

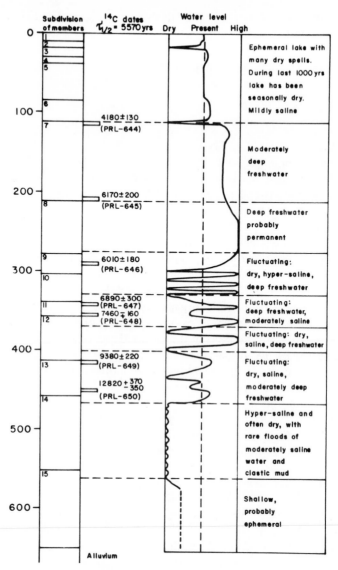

Figure 11.1 A diagrammatic summary of stratigraphy, salinity fluctuations, and lacustrine history of the Didwana lake. The scale on the left depicts depth in cm.

Thus there is strong evidence that *c.* 18 000 BP shows a definite climatic amelioration in the Kashmir Valley, as indicated by palynological, stable isotopic, pedologic, and archaeological evidence. The lack of similar correlation between Kashmir and Rajasthan could be explained by an early deglaciation in some parts of the world or, and perhaps more convincingly, by the explanation put forward by Duplessy (1982). He reports the strengthening of the northeastern monsoon and heavier winter precipitation during the period, as indicated by Arabian Sea core evidence of a weaker southwestern monsoon. An important factor here is that during the past 2.5 million years the rise (*c.* 5000 m) of the Pir Panjal range has effectively shielded off the Kashmir Valley from the southwestern monsoon. The present-day rainfall pattern in the valley is dominated by heavier winter rains, as opposed to the summer monsoon rains in the rest of peninsular India.

Conclusion

The South Asian subcontinent provides evidence of a cold and arid climate from the Arabian Sea cores and the lakes and sand dunes of Rajasthan for the period *c.* 18 000 ± 2000 BP. The evidence is based on pollen and oxygen isotope curves for the sea-cores and pollen, pedologic, and other data from Rajasthan. A cold and arid climate in this part of Asia is in concordance with the LGM at *c.* 18 000 BP. No significant human settlements are reported from Rajasthan immediately after the Upper Palaeolithic cultures (dated to *c.* 20 000 BP), that is during and after the *c.* 18 000 BP period, until the mid-Holocene.

In Kashmir, however, there is a distinct climatic amelioration, as indicated by palynologic, pedologic, and stable isotopic data, at *c.* 17 000–18 000 BP. The Upper Palaeolithic of Kashmir is probably associated with this period and a well-developed palaeosol on the loess. This divergence can be explained by the strengthening of the northeastern monsoon during the periods of weakening of the southeastern monsoon in South Asia.

Acknowledgements

We thank Drs S. Kusumgar and P. Sharma and Mr N. Juyal for help and discussions.

References

Agrawal, D. P. 1985. Cenozoic climatic changes in Kashmir: the multidisciplinary data. In *Climate and geology of Kashmir: the last 4 million years*, D. P. Agrawal, S. Kusumgar & R. V. Krishnamurthy (eds), 1–12. New Delhi: T. T. Printers & Publishers.

Agrawal, D. P. & S. Guzdar 1972. Quaternary studies on the western coast of India: preliminary observations. *Palaeobotanist* **21**(2), 216–22.

Agrawal, D. P. & R. K. Sood 1982. Ecological factors and the Harappan Civilisation. In *Harappan civilisation*, G. L. Possehl (ed.). New Delhi: Oxford and IBH.

Agrawal, D. P., R. V. Krishnamurthy & S. Kusumgar 1985. Physical Research Laboratory Radiocarbon date list V. *Radiocarbon* **27**(1), 95–110.

Agrawal, D. P., R. P. Dhir, R. V. Krishnamurthy, V. N. Misra, S. C. Nanda & S. N. Rajaguru (eds) 1980. *Arid zone research and development*. Jodhpur: H. S. Mann.

Agrawal, D. P., P. S. Datta, H. Zahid, R. V. Krishnamurthy, V. N. Misra, S. N. Rajaguru & K. Thomas 1980. Palaeoclimate, stratigraphy and prehistory in north and west Rajasthan. *Proceedings of Indian Academy of Sciences* **89**(1), 51–6.

Campo, E. van, J. C. Duplessy, M. Rossignal-Strick 1982. Climate conditions deduced from a 150 Kyr oxygen isotope–pollen record from the Arabian Sea. *Nature* **296**, 56–9.

Caratini, C., J. Bellet & C. Tissot 1978. Étude microscopique de la matière organique: palynologie et palynofacies. *Géochimie organique des sédiments marins profonds*, 265–307. Organ IV, Golfe D'Aden, Mer d'Oman: Centre National de la Recherche Scientifique.

Dodia, R., D. P. Agrawal & A. B. Vora 1985. New pollen data from the Kashmir bogs: a summary. In *Climate and geology of Kashmir: the last 4 million years*, D. P. Agrawal, S. Kusumgar & R. V. Krishnamurthy (eds). New Delhi: T. T. Printers and Publishers.

Duplessy, J. C. 1982. Glacial to interglacial contrasts in the northern Indian Ocean. *Nature* **295**, 494–8.

Gupta, S. K. 1972. Chronology of the raised beaches and inland coral reefs of the Saurashtra coast. *Journal of Geology* **80**, 357–61.

Gupta, S. K. & B. S. Amin 1974. Io/U ages of corals from Saurashtra coast. *Marine Geology* **16**, M79–M83.

Krishnamurthy, R. V., J. M. DeNiro & R. K. Pant 1982. Isotope evidence for Pleistocene climatic changes in Kashmir, India. *Nature* **298**, 640–1.

Kusumgar, S., D. P. Agrawal & R. V. Krishnamurthy 1980. Studies on the loess deposits of the Kashmir Valley and ^{14}C dating. *Radiocarbon* **22**(3), 757–62.

Singh, G. & D. P. Agrawal 1976. Radiocarbon evidence for deglaciation in north-western Himalaya, India. *Nature* **260**, 233.

Singh, G., R. D. Joshi, S. K. Chopra & A. B. Singh 1974. Late quaternary history of vegetation and climate of the Rajasthan desert, India. *Philosophical Transactions of the Royal Society of London* **269**(889), 467–501.

Wasson, R., J. Canberra, S. N. Rajaguru, V. N. Misra, D. P. Agrawal, R. P. Dhir, A. K. Singhvi & R. D. Kameswara 1983. Geomorphology, late Quaternary stratigraphy and palaeoclimatology of the Thar dune field. *Zeitschrift Geomorphologie* **45**, 117–51.

12 *Hunter–gatherers of the Terminal Pleistocene in Uttar Pradesh, India*

VIDULA JAYASWAL

Introduction

Stone-Age studies carried out in Uttar Pradesh in the past two decades have not only brought to light positive evidence for the existence of the Upper Palaeolithic stage in India, but have also provided a reliable geochronological base to the lithic cultural-sequence. The evidence for a complete and continuous history of the various Stone-Age cultures is remarkably well preserved in this area, a feature rarely found in other parts of the Indian subcontinent. Moreover, a good amount of data are also known with regard to the mode of Palaeolithic habitation and workshops. The region thus provides an excellent opportunity for the study of some basic issues relating to the settlement pattern and behaviour of early humans in general and those of the Terminal Pleistocene in particular. This chapter discusses the evidence for human cultures in the period between *c.* 22 000 and 14 000 BP, which coincides with the Upper Palaeolithic phase of our area.

Research history

The archaeological potential of the southern part of Uttar Pradesh has been brought to light by the investigations of two main research teams – those of the Allahabad University and the Banaras Hindu University. The former, under the leadership of G. R. Sharma, carried out exploration of the Banda, Mirzapur, and Allahabad districts and the excavation of a few sites in the 1960s and 1970s (Sharma 1973, 1975). P. C. Pant, from the Banaras Hindu University, also undertook fresh-field investigations in almost the same area, first in 1961–64 and later between 1968 and 1976. The present author participated in the latter field trip and also conducted excavations at two rockshelters in 1978 (Jayaswal 1983). The following discussions are based on the reports of Sharma (1975) and Pant (1982), and also my own field observations.

Pleistocene geology

The Quaternary stratigraphy of the region is best preserved along the banks of the rivers Belan and Seoti. These belong to the Ganga–Yamuna plains and the Vindhyan formations of the adjoining hills of Allahabad and Mirzapur districts (Fig. 12.1). Since none of these rivers joins the ocean directly, the changes in the sea-levels would have hardly influenced the nature of the river deposits in this area. Consequently, the river sediments, which are found in the form of alternating layers of gravels of different sizes, silts, and clays, are considered to represent regional climatic fluctuations. These deposits, divided into units, contain the lithic artefacts of various facies ranging from Acheulian to Mesolithic times (Fig. 12.2).

Upper Palaeolithic

The Upper Palaeolithic industries of the Belan–Seoti valley are clearly distinguished from the others in this impressive culture sequence. Unlike the earlier cultures, the industries of this phase can be dated with some amount of precision. There are two radiocarbon dates c. 25 790 BP (PRL 86) and 19 715 BP (TF 1245) for the Gravel III deposit (layer 4 of the schematic sequence, Fig. 12.2), that yielded the earliest Upper Palaeolithic industry. This is predominantly a blade industry of Upper Palaeolithic tradition. The dates indicate that the Gravel III was being formed between c. 25 000 and 19 000/ 18 000 BP. The succeeding period, which witnessed the formation of the 'blackish humus soil' (layer 3) lies directly above the Gravel III. Since it directly follows the earlier deposits with Upper Palaeolithic industry, it also falls within the scope of the present study. On these grounds it can reasonably be dated between 16 000 and 14 000 BP. It is pertinent to recall in this connection that the radiocarbon date available for Gravel IV, a 'pre-Neolithic' deposit coming much later in the sequence, is 10 030 ± 115 BP (SUA 1421) (Sharma et al. 1980, p. 27). The cultural remains obtained from the 'blackish humus soil' show continuity with an Upper Palaeolithic type blade industry associated with non-geometric microliths. This association suggests a transition from the Palaeolithic to the Mesolithic mode of life (Sharma 1975). Elsewhere we have argued that a small proportion of bladelets and microliths forms an integral part of even the earliest Upper Palaeolithic toolkit in this area (Jayaswal & Pant 1980). The basic difference between the two assemblages, from the Gravel III and the overlying soil, lies in the marked proportional increase of bladelets and microliths. The technotypological observations from these two layers provide a framework for the study of other comparable industries, usually very rich in lithic artefacts. These are found in the same region but in different geographical settings and are devoid of suitable material for absolute dating.

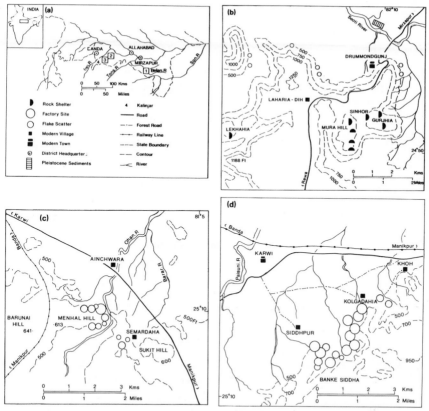

Figure 12.1 Stone-Age research in Uttar Pradesh showing the location of areas discussed in the text and the distribution of site categories. a, Upper Palaeolithic research areas in Uttar Pradesh; b, location of rock shelters and flake scatters near Laharia-Dih, area 1; c, location of factory sites and flake scatters near Ainchwara, area 2; d, location of factory sites and flake scatters near Kolgadahia, area 3.

Settlement evidence

The archaeological remains from the period 22 000–14 000 BP have been found in three different contexts. Each one of them has a particular geographical setting and throws light on the adaptive ecological behaviour of the contemporary population. These are:

(a) river valley sites;
(b) open-air factory sites on the hill slopes; and
(c) rockshelter habitations.

River valley sites

The main localities of this settlement category are found in Gravel III and the succeeding soil layer of the Belan and Seoti rivers. As has been discussed above,

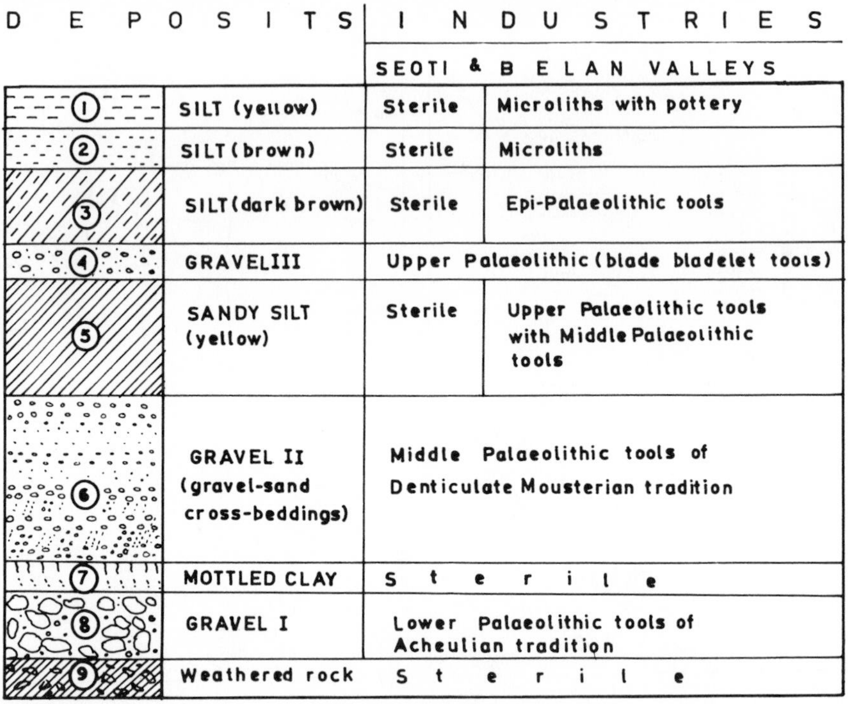

DEPOSITS		INDUSTRIES	
		SEOTI & BELAN VALLEYS	
------①------	SILT (yellow)	Sterile	Microliths with pottery
------②------	SILT (brown)	Sterile	Microliths
//////③//////	SILT (dark brown)	Sterile	Epi-Palaeolithic tools
∘∘∘④∘∘∘	GRAVEL III	Upper Palaeolithic (blade bladelet tools)	
//////⑤//////	SANDY SILT (yellow)	Sterile	Upper Palaeolithic tools with Middle Palaeolithic tools
∘∘∘⑥∘∘∘	GRAVEL II (gravel-sand cross-beddings)	Middle Palaeolithic tools of Denticulate Mousterian tradition	
\\\\⑦\\\\	MOTTLED CLAY	S t e r i l e	
∘∘⑧∘∘	GRAVEL I	Lower Palaeolithic tools of Acheulian tradition	
////⑨////	Weathered rock	S t e r i l e	

Figure 12.2 Schematic section of the Seoti and Belan geology and archaeology (after Pant 1982).

the Gravel III of the Belan–Seoti valley is reported to have yielded a blade industry of the Upper Palaeolithic tradition. This deposit is preserved only sporadically, and hence the implementiferous localities are also limited in number. A remarkably well-preserved Gravel III is exposed along the right bank of the Seoti near the village of Daiya in the Allahabad district. This was excavated at a number of places (Pant 1982, pp. 100–1) and it was possible to obtain a sizeable collection of artefacts from this horizon, which are considered to be representative of a wider group of localities. Furthermore, the techno-typological sequence and the geological composition of this horizon are similar to the Gravel III of the Belan Valley.

The technotypological details of the Daiya assemblage are presented in Table 12.1 (Pant 1982, p. 101). This shows an important feature of the Upper Palaeolithic toolkit, where, besides blade and flake elements, bladelets form an important component. Furthermore, microliths, though present only in small proportions, form another significant feature.

Comparable technotypological features are seen in the assemblages associated with the 'blackish humus soil'. However, the frequencies of bladelets and microliths increase in this phase and the microgravette point is the diagnostic tool type. The excavated assemblage from this horizon is numerically small

Table 12.1 Typological composition of the Daiya assemblage

Tool type	Numbers
triangle-atypical	1
backed bladelet	1
partially backed bladelet with marginal retouch	1
'federmesser'	1
endscraper	1
single-stroke axial burin	1
transverse burin	3
offset burin on proximal end	1
obliquely truncated bladelet with marginal retouch	1
truncated blade	1
notched blade	2
denticulated bladelet (side)	2
blade/bladelet with marginal retouch	2
convex side scraper	1
partially retouched blade	1
Total	20

and it is not possible to present a detailed technotypological analysis. The raw materials include various types of crypto-crystalline silica and fine-grained quartzite.

A small bone object claimed to represent a 'mother goddess' figurine was also discovered from the Gravel III (Misra 1977, Plate V). This specimen has also been identified as a harpoon fragment. It is the only positive evidence of boneworking/art from the Indian Upper Palaeolithic.

Open-air factory sites on hill slopes

The southern fringes of the Belan–Seoti valley are formed by the low hill ranges of the Kaimur (Fig. 12.1). Recent fieldwork in these hills in the Mirzapur and Banda districts has discovered numerous lithic workshops (Pant 1982). These workshops are located on the gentle hill slopes and the sides of small hillocks. Artefacts, in various stages of manufacture, are scattered in clusters in a number of localities. On the basis of the size and density of the clusters, as well as their technotypological features, these localities form two categories:

(a) knapping scatters of small dimensions; and
(b) large-sized workshops

SMALL KNAPPING SCATTERS

These occur mostly in the Allahabad and Mirzapur districts and are characteristic of the Belan–Seoti valley. Several scatters were discovered by Sharma and

Pant in this area, while on the southern slopes of the Kaimur range the main sites are Dayia, Itaha, Lakhanpur, Mahuackachcha, Orwa, Pahiha, and Mundva (Lal 1973, p. 36). Artefact clusters at these sites are not only small in dimension but are also located at wide intervals. The density and scale of these artefact-scatters are so small that they appear to be short-duration toolmaking locations, probably utilized by very small groups of people. For instance, the largest collections of artefacts, made by the Allahabad team from Mundva (Chandva), consisted of only 41 finished artefacts, 64 blanks, five cores, and 12 unidentifiable artefacts (Jayaswal 1978, pp. 186–7). Technotypological features of this assemblage correspond with the Daiya assemblage.

A further feature of the artefacts obtained from this group of sites is that more than one type of raw material was utilized for manufacturing implements. Besides chert, which dominates, chalcedony, agate, and quartzite are also used in varying proportions. In general there is a scarcity of all types of suitable raw material on the sites. This is shown by the very small amounts of unused raw material and debitage among these scatters. Crypto-crystalline silica is occasionally available in this area in the form of outcropping of veins in the hills. The nearest source for the small nodules and quartz pebbles appears to be the Son bed, which is 8–10 km away.

LARGE-SIZED UPPER PALAEOLITHIC WORKSHOPS

These were discovered near the villages of Siddhapur, Ainchwara, and Kalinjar in the Banda district (Fig. 12.1). Located on the slopes of low hills, each locality is drained by small seasonal rivers.

The Siddhapur valley, near the town of Karwi is littered with artefacts made of whitish and buff-coloured cherts. This valley was occupied during both the Middle and Upper Palaeolithic, as shown by the excavations in the middle of the valley in 1974 (Pant 1982, p. 109). The workshop sites are located on the slopes of the hills that surround the valley. The excavations recovered an assemblage from the lower part of the upper artefact horizon that appears to be later than the Daiya industry. The proportion of bladelets and non–geometric microliths is higher in the former than the latter. The artefacts from the upper part of this deposit, though made of similar raw material, belong technotypologically to a still later lithic tradition. The Middle Palaeolithic artefacts occur in a lower gravel, separated from the upper implementiferous deposit by a thick accumulation of sandy silt.

There is evidence, therefore, that two facies of artefact manufacture occurred in the Siddhapur Valley during the Palaeolithic and that there is no reliable way to separate one from the other from surface collections. Consequently, although extremely rich, this area cannot be fully utilized for the reconstruction of cultural sequences in the Upper Palaeolithic. In spite of this situation, two factors should be noted: first, the profusion in the area of suitable raw material in the form of small and medium-sized chunks; and, secondly, the large dimension and dense concentration of the artefacts. Closely spaced, they cover an area approximately 1.5 km in length along the slopes of several hills.

Table 12.2 Artefact classes in the Ainchwara assemblage

Artefacts	Numbers	Percentage
finished tools	534	20.35
partially retouched flake	183	6.97
partially retouched blade/bladelet	56	2.13
partially retouched nodule	20	0.76
retouched chip	72	2.74
unretouched flake	511	19.48
unretouched blade/bladelet	350	13.34
chip	228	8.69
core	591	22.53
unclassified	78	2.97
Total	2623	99.96

In the vicinity of Ainchwara village, situated about 11 km south east of Karwi (Fig. 12.1c) evidence has been found for rich Upper Palaeolithic tool-manufacturing localities. On the slopes of a hillock on the left bank of the small river Ohan, several thousand artefacts were found in a number of clusters. Each of these artefact concentrations contained finished tools, primary flakes, cores, lumps of raw materials, and debitage (Pant 1982, p. 114). The artefacts are made mostly on chert, but other rocks of fine-grained silica were also utilized. From one cluster of approximately 9 m^2 2623 artefacts were collected. The general composition is shown in Table 12.2, and the detailed typology in Table 12.3 (after Pant 1982, pp. 114, 115–16).

The industry has a high percentage of retouched artefacts, made in order of preference on flakes, blades, chips, bladelets, and nodules. Retouched chips, numbering 72, are a noteworthy feature of the Ainchwara industry. In addition, non-geometric microlithic forms, including lunates, backed and truncated bladelets, occur in small percentages, as well as denticulate and notched implements (Fig. 12.3). Most of the flakes in this collection are from core dressing, as shown by the presence of only two flake cores but 762 flakes. Among the flakes 249 were classified as primary core rejuvenation while 55 appeared to be accidental, produced during the removal of blades. Therefore, in spite of the large numbers of flakes, they do not form a significant artefact category in the Ainchwara industry. On the contrary, the blades and bladelets are the dominant technotypological elements. This feature is also corroborated by the classification of cores, of which 76% were used for obtaining blades and bladelets. Finally, there is a tendency to use the raw material exhaustively, both as cores and blanks. Even the chips have been retouched into implements.

Another important area for large workshops is found at Kalinjar, some 23 km south of Naraini in Banda district. The site is located on the right bank of the Baghain. Once again a series of Upper Palaeolithic factory sites were found on a small hillock where chert and other fine-grained silica were flaked

Table 12.3 Typological composition of the Ainchwara assemblage

Tool type	Numbers	Percentage
lunate	8	0.98
backed bladelet	17	2.08
truncated blade/bladelet	5	0.61
Blade/bladelet with one retouched side		
concave	13	1.59
straight	35	4.28
concavo–convex	10	1.22
convex	9	1.10
Total of blades/bladelets with one retouched side	67	8.20
Blade/bladelet with retouched sides		
both margins straight	7	0.86
one straight and other concave	6	0.73
one concave and other convex	4	0.49
both concave	5	0.61
Total of blades/bladelets with both retouched sides	22	2.69
Notched and denticulated tool		
notched blade	20	2.45
blade/bladelet with notch near base	6	0.73
blade/bladelet with notch near top	5	0.61
bladelet with abruptly retouched denticulated sides	4	0.49
denticulate on blade/bladelet	50	6.12
denticulate on flake	67	8.20
Total of notched & denticulated tools	152	18.60
Blade/bladelet with retouched top	10	1.22
backed blade	14	1.71
atypical borer	2	0.24
end-scraper	17	2.08
atypical endscraper	18	2.20
steep scraper on thick round flake/nodule	10	1.22
Burin		
offset burin	29	3.55
offset double burin	2	0.24
offset dihedral burin	6	0.73
transverse burin	8	0.98
single-stroke axial burin	1	0.12
axial burin on retouch	4	0.49
axial dihedral burin	6	0.73
axial burin	5	0.61
axial double burin	1	0.12
Total of burins	62	7.59
Side scraper on nodule	7	0.86
Transverse scraper	7	0.86
Double side scraper	5	0.61
Flake with more than two retouched sides	11	1.35
Wavy-edged side scraper	2	0.24

Table 12.3   cont.

Tool type	Numbers	Percentage
Convex–concave side scraper	4	0.49
Concave–straight side scraper	2	0.24
Concave side scraper	2	0.24
Straight side scraper	8	0.98
Convex side scraper	21	2.57
Flake with retouched top	11	1.35
Obliquely retouched flake	2	0.24
Retouched chips	72	8.81
Partially retouched flake	183	22.40
Partially retouched blade/bladelet	56	6.85
Partially retouched nodules	20	2.45
Grand total	817	100

into artefacts. Closely spaced artefact clusters were again noted and 1233 artefacts were collected from one location. The typological details of the retouched tool category are given in Table 12.4

The technotypological features of the Kalinjar industry conform to the Upper Palaeolithic phase of Uttar Pradesh in general and the Ainchwara industry in particular (Fig. 12.3). Microliths and bladelets form an integral part of the industry, though flake and blade elements are dominant. As in the Ainchwara industry, the proportion of flake cores (39.6% of the flakes) differ widely, suggesting that the flakes do not form a predominant feature of the industry. However, in contrast, the tendency to exhaustively utilize debitage and raw material is not marked in the material, and neither chips nor many preparation flakes have been retouched. Blades and bladelets together compromise 145 of the blanks, and the number of cores for these types is very high, 138 from a total of 171 cores (Pant 1982, pp. 125–6). It may be significant to note that suitable raw material, in the form of small and medium-sized pebbles, is abundant in the bed of the River Baghain so that the pressure of raw material scarcity never influenced lithic reduction strategies.

Rockshelter sites

The hill ranges in the vicinity of the Belan–Seoti valley are full of numerous rockshelters of varying dimensions. These lie south of Drummondganj in the Mirzapur district (Fig. 12.1b) and many contain Stone-Age materials. Excavations at Lekhahia (Sharma 1965, pp. 76–9), Baghaikhor (Verma 1965, pp. 73–5), Morhana Pahar (Verma 1965, pp. 73–5), Laharia-dih (Pant 1982, pp. 103–9, Jayaswal 1983, pp. 126–33), and Sinhor (Jayaswal 1983, pp. 126–33) suggest that these shelters were first occupied in the Upper Palaeolithic period.

The Mura-Gurjhia hills were extensively explored and two rockshelters

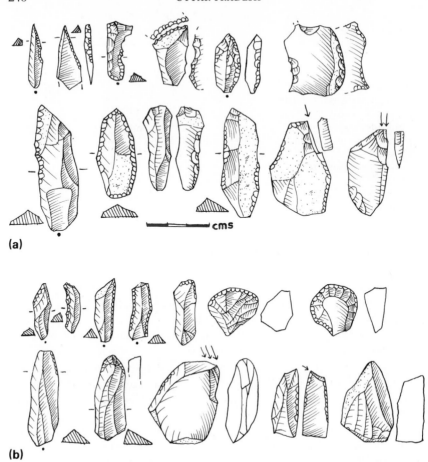

Figure 12.3   (a) Representative tool types from Kalinjar; (b) representative tool types
from Ainchwara.

excavated. Our findings suggest that only the larger shelters, more than
50 m² floor area, were inhabited. Those with smaller floor areas were found
to be devoid of paintings as well as other culture-remains (Jayaswal 1983,
p. 126).

Laharia-dih is the biggest rockshelter at Mura–Gurjhia. Half of the shelter
floor is covered by the partly collapsed overhanging rock and the remaining
floor area now measures only 10 × 7.5 m. When occupied by prehistoric
people, the shelter must have been almost double its present size. The cultural
deposits were very shallow. However, a large concentration of cultural-debris
was found lying just outside the mouth of the shelter where its accumulation
forms a small semicircular mound resting against the shelter floor (Fig. 12.4).
The two excavations carried out in 1977 (Pant 1982) and 1980 (Jayaswal 1983)
point to the existence of three artefact horizons which, from top to bottom, are
as follows (Fig. 12.5):

Table 12.4 Typological composition of the Kalinjar assemblage

Tool type	Numbers	Percentage
Triangle	1	0.23
Lunate	1	0.23
Backed bladelet	6	1.41
Backed blade	8	1.87
Backed blade with concave side	5	1.17
Backed flake	3	0.70
Backed flake with retouched side	2	0.47
'Federmesser'	1	0.23
Atypical 'Federmesser'	2	0.47
Burin		
axial burin on a notch	2	0.47
single stroke axial burin	3	0.70
axial burin on proximal end	2	0.47
axial dihedral burin with round end	2	0.47
axial burin	1	0.23
offset burin	2	0.47
transverse burin	1	0.23
flat-faced carinated burin	1	0.23
Total of burins	14	3.28
Endscraper		
nosed endscraper	1	0.23
typical endscraper	11	2.58
atypical endscraper	5	1.17
Total of endscrapers	17	3.98
Blade with one retouched side	10	2.34
Blade with both retouched sides	13	3.04
Blade with retouched margin and base	2	0.47
Blade with retouched top	4	0.94
Bladelet with retouched margin	4	0.94
Borer		
double borer	2	0.47
middle borer	9	2.11
side borer	14	3.28
atypical borer	5	1.17
Total of borers	30	7.03
Point		
narrow backed point	2	0.47
typical point on flake	3	0.70
atypical point	5	1.17
Total of points	10	2.34
Denticulate		
side-denticulate on blade	9	2.1
double side-denticulate on blade	2	0.47
side-denticulate on core	1	0.23
double-sided and top-denticulate on core	1	0.23
peripheral-denticulate on core	1	0.23

Table 12.4 cont.

Tool type	Numbers	Percentage
peripheral-denticulate on flake	1	0.23
side-denticulate on flake	25	5.85
double side-denticulate on flake	25	5.85
double side- and base-denticulate on flake	1	0.23
double side- and top-denticulate on flake	2	0.47
side- and top-denticulate on flake	3	0.70
Total of denticulates	71	16.63
Notched tool		
bladelet with notch close to base	2	0.47
bladelet with notch on top	1	0.23
bladelet with notch on side	8	1.87
blade with notch on top	2	0.47
blade with notch on side	7	1.64
flake with notch on top	1	0.23
flake with notch on base	1	0.23
flake with notch on side/sides	5	1.17
Total of notched tools	27	6.32
Side scraper and others		
angle scraper	2	0.47
transverse scraper	2	0.47
straight side scraper	4	0.94
convex side scraper	6	1.41
concave side scraper	7	1.64
zig-zag side scraper	2	0.47
concave–convex side scraper	2	0.47
double convex side scraper	2	0.47
double straight and convex side scraper	2	0.47
double straight side scraper	1	0.23
flake with retouched side base	3	0.70
flake with retouched top	90	21.08
flake with retouched top and base	1	0.23
Total of side scrapers and others	124	29.04
Partly retouched blanks		
partly retouched bladelet	4	0.94
partly retouched blade	6	1.41
partly retouched flake	62	14.52
Total of partly retouched blanks	72	16.86
Grand total	427	100

(1) The uppermost 10–20 cm deposit yielded a microlith and bladelet industry associated with pottery but no metal.

(2) The middle layer of 40–60 cm thickness also contained microliths and bladelets along with handmade pottery.

(3) The lower artefact deposit, *c.* 60 cm in thickness, produced an aceramic industry devoid of geometric microliths. The toolkit from this deposit

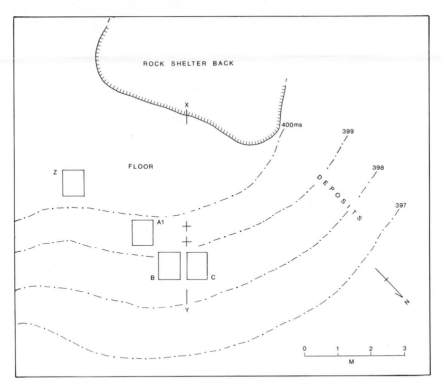

Figure 12.4 Location of trenches in the Laharia-Dih rockshelter.

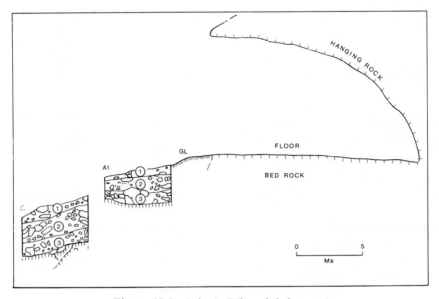

Figure 12.5 Laharia-Dih rockshelter sections.

has close technotypological parallels with the later Upper Palaeolithic assemblage of the Belan–Seoti valley, and hence deserves a detailed treatment.

The artefacts are made of crypto-crystalline silica as well as fine-grained quartzite and sandstone. The technotypological analysis clearly demonstrates (Table 12.5) that microliths and bladelets form a considerable proportion of

Table 12.5   Typological composition of the Laharian-dih assemblage

Tool type	Numbers	Percentage
Obliquely truncated backed bladelet	2	2.22
Obliquely truncated bladelet	5	5.56
Backed bladelet	13	14.44
Lunate	9	10.00
Microgravette point (two atypical)	7	7.78
Point on bladelet (obliquely worked edge)	4	4.44
Borer on flake	1	1.11
Endscraper bladelet	2	2.22
Round scraper on core rejuvenating flake	1	1.11
Burin		
offset burin (flake)	1	1.11
axial burin (flake)	2	2.22
single stroke axial burin with truncated base	1	1.11
axial burin on retouch	1	1.11
offset burin on proximal end	2	2.22
Total of burins	7	7.78
Backed blade	1	1.11
Blade/bladelet with one retouched side	6	6.67
Bladelet with both retouched sides	1	1.11
Flake with retouched top	1	1.11
Angle scraper	1	1.11
Simple concave side scraper	1	1.11
Transverse scraper	1	1.11
Notched and denticulated tools		
notched flake	2	2.22
notched blade	1	1.11
notched bladelet	1	1.11
bladelet with denticulated back	1	1.11
denticulated bladelet	2	2.22
blade with micro-denticulation	3	3.33
denticulated backed blade/bladelet with retouched margin (ventral)	2	2.22
denticulated flake	2	2.22
Total of denticulated and notched tools	14	15.56
Partially retouched flake	10	11.11
Partially retouched bladelet	3	3.33
Grand Total	90	100

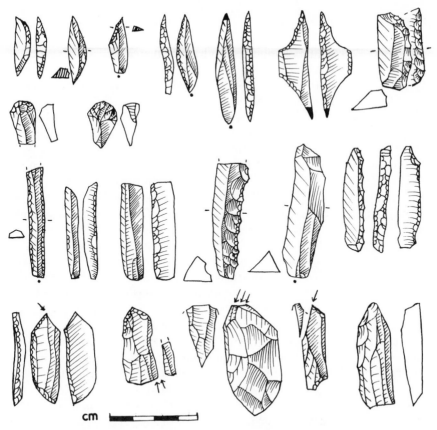

Figure 12.6 Representative tool types from Laharia-Dih.

microgravette point on backed blade/bladelet, lunate, borer, burin, and notched and denticulated tools. Backing of blades and bladelets is very common but there are also specimens with low-angle retouch (Fig. 12.6) mostly confined to the ventral face of the artefacts.

The proportion of intentionally detached flakes and corresponding core-types is small (Pant 1982; p. 106). Blades and bladelets are dominant in the unretouched group. However, initial microscopic scrutiny of the artefacts indicates that a number of the unretouched blades and bladelets were utilized, since they retain microchipping and striations along their sharp edges.

The earliest artefact level at Chopani-Mando, an open-air habitation site on the left bank of the Belan (Sharma *et al.* 1980, p. 36), closely parallels the technotypological trend of the Laharia-dih-iii industry (Pant 1982, p. 105). Thus it appears that the population of the late Upper Palaeolithic phase inhabited large-scale rockshelters as well as some open-air camp sites in the Belan–Seoti valley.

Discussion

The Upper Palaeolithic assemblages that have been preserved in the districts of Banda, Allahabad, and Mirzapur have been found in three different geographical settings. Stratigraphically, as well as on technotypological grounds, they fall into two chronological facies.

The industries of the earlier facies are concentrated in the Belan–Seoti valley, as represented by the Daiya assemblage. The limited number of knapping floors, invariably small in dimension, are located at the foot of the Kaimur ranges near Drummondganj. When combined with other evidence from the region it suggests that the valley was inhabited by small groups of people between *c.* 25 000 and 19 000 BP. It is surprising that they did not occupy the numerous rockshelters, some of which are located on the crest of the same hills where they regularly manufactured their implements.

The industries of the later facies appear to have a much wider area of distribution. Not only were the hill-top rockshelters in the Mirzapur district occupied, but in the Banda district there were also numerous factory sites. The large-scale flaking activities at these workshop and rockshelter sites, combined with the open-air locations, could be interpreted as an increase in population during the later Upper Palaeolithic phase, post-18 950 BP. However, there are reasons to believe that the basic technotypological traits of the earlier facies continued in this later phase, since the fundamental nature of the toolkits remained more or less the same, apart from the marked increase in microlithic and bladelet elements. I would further like to suggest that variations in the technotypological features of the Banda and Mirzapur sites appear as regional differences rather than as evidence for culture change. The concentration of large numbers of factory sites in Banda district is perhaps due to the availability of surplus raw material, since the river beds of Banda are rich in various types of crypto-crystalline silica pebbles, whereas the rivers of the Mirzapur area appear to be deficient in this respect.

Outside Uttar Pradesh, remains of the Upper Palaeolithic period are scanty. This reflects the limited nature of fieldwork and the very recent recognition of lithics from this period in the Indian subcontinent (Jayaswal 1978, pp. 174–93). On present evidence, sites of this period are distributed either in small, widely separated regional clusters or as isolated, sporadic scatters. Noteworthy areas are Renigunta (Murty 1968, pp. 83–101), Cuddapah (Raju 1985, pp. 147–56), and Kurnool districts (Murty & Reddy 1976, pp. 214–26) in Andhra Pradesh; Jalgaon district in Maharashtra (Sali 1985, pp. 137–56); and Pushkar region in Rajasthan (Allchin *et al.* 1978). These recent discoveries take the form of small concentrations of sites. The limited distribution and localized concentrations of sites in the Terminal Pleistocene contrasts strongly with the widespread and more or less uniform distribution of both the preceeding and succeeding humid phases, i.e. the Middle Palaeolithic and the Mesolithic periods, respectively.

It should also be pointed out that Uttar Pradesh is the only region where the geochronological and archaeological evidence has been studied in detail. In the other regions the investigations are selective, covering one aspect or the other. For instance, important evidence regarding the origin and development of the Upper Palaeolithic in five recognizable stages was obtained from Patne in Jalgaon district (Sali 1985, pp. 137–45). A ^{14}C date for the fourth stage gives an age of 25 000 ± 200 BP. The Palaeolithic climate at this time is described as 'semi-arid, more or less similar to the present day' (Sali 1985, p. 144). However, in spite of all these details the data relating to settlement size and pattern in each of the five stages in the region are lacking. In another example, three Upper Palaeolithic sites are reported from Cuddapah by Raju (1985, pp. 147–56). The surface scatter of artefacts at these sites appears to belong to knapping debris. However, in this case the chronological and climatic details are missing.

The arid zone of northwestern India, the Thar desert and surrounding areas, experienced short climatic cycles of dry and humid conditions during the Terminal Pleistocene and Early Holocene (Allchin et al. 1978, pp. 320–6). There is evidence for the persistence of a humid phase from the Middle Palaeolithic to the early Upper Palaeolithic. At 18 000 BP conditions were marked by lower precipitation, and arid conditions prevailed. It was noted that Middle Palaeolithic sites were very common but that Upper Palaeolithic sites were rare. The latter generally occur near water sources. In the succeeding Early Holocene at c. 10 000 BP, humid conditions prevailed once again and numerous Mesolithic sites can be found in both the desert and surrounding areas. The Rajasthan evidence points to some correlation between long-term climatic conditions and the density of regional occupation. However, the detailed settlement pattern of the two Upper Palaeolithic phases still has to be worked out.

The preceding discussion suggests that the relationship between regional settlement histories and climatic change in the Terminal Pleistocene in India can only be viewed in very general terms. Upper Palaeolithic industries are currently few in number and are confined to the edge of the hills that border the alluvial plains. These areas lie some distance from the major rivers but are traversed by several small, perennial streams. Later in the Mesolithic the sites are both more numerous and occur in different ecological contexts. The preferred habitats became river banks, horse-shoe lake margins, sand dunes, hill slopes, plateaus, rockshelters, as well as coasts. Further work is needed to clarify the nature of this transition.

References

Allchin, B., A. Goudie & K. Hegde 1978. *The prehistory and palaeogeography of the great Indian desert*. London: Academic Press.

Jayaswal, V. 1978. *Palaeohistory of India (a study of the prepared core technique)* Delhi: Agam Kala Prakashan.

Jayaswal, V. 1983. Excavation of a painted rock-shelter at Laharia-Dih, Mirzapur district. Bulletin of the Department of Ancient Indian History, Culture & Archaeology, Banaras Hindu University, No. 1, 126–33.

Jayaswal, V. & P. C. Pant 1980. Microlithic succession in India: a case study of Uttar Pradesh. *Indian pre-and protohistory 1980*. Allahabad: Allahabad University.

Lal, B. B. 1973. *Indian Archaeology 1969–70 – a review*. Delhi: Archaeological Survey of India, 36.

Misra, V. D. 1977. *Some aspects of Indian archaeology*. Allahabad: Prabhat Prakashan.

Murty, M. L. K. 1968. Blade and burin industries near Renigunta on the southeastern coast of India. *Proceedings of the Prehistoric Society* **34**, 83–101.

Murty, M. L. K. & K. T. Reddy (1976). Significance of lithic finds in the Cave area of Kurnool. *Asian Perspectives, Journal of Archaeology and Prehistory of Asia and the Pacific* **18** (2), 214–26

Pant, P. C. 1982. *Prehistoric Uttar Pradesh (a study of Old Stone Age)*. Delhi: Agam Kala Prakashan.

Raju, D. R. 1985. The Upper Palaeolithic industries of Cuddapah District, Andhra Pradesh. In *Recent advances in Indo-Pacific Prehistory*, V. N. Misra & P. Bellwood, (eds), 147–156. New Delhi: Oxford & IBH.

Sali, S. A. 1985. The Upper Palaeolithic culture at Patne district Jalagaon, Maharashtra. In *Recent advances in Indo-Pacific prehistory*, V. N. Misra & P. Bellwood, (eds), 137–45. New Delhi: Oxford & IBH.

Sharma, G. R. 1965. Comments on 'Mesolithic phase in the Prehistory of India'. In *Indian prehistory – 1964*, V. N. Misra & M. S. Mate (eds), 76–9. Poona: Deccan College Post Graduate and Research Institute.

Sharma, G. R. 1973. Stone Age in the Vindhyas and the Ganga Valley. In *Radiocarbon and Indian archaeology*, D. P. Agrawal & A. Ghosh (eds), 106–10. Bombay: Tata Institute of Fundamental Research.

Sharma, G. R. 1975. Seasonal migrations and Mesolithic lake cultures of the Ganga Valley. Presidential address, Indian Prehistoric Society, Delhi.

Sharma, G. R., V. D. Misra, D. Mandal, B. B. Misra & J. N. Pal 1980. *Beginnings of agriculture (Epi-Palaeolithic to Neolithic: excavation at Chopani-Mando, Mahadaha and Mahagarha)*, Studies in History, Culture and Archaeology, Vol. IV. Allahabad: Allahabad University.

Verma, R. K. 1965. Comments on 'Mesolithic Phase in the Prehistory of India'. In *Indian prehistory – 1964*, V. N. Misra & M. S. Mate (eds), 73–6. Poona: Deccan College Post Graduate and Research Institute.

13 *From Late Pleistocene to Early Holocene in Sundaland*

PETER BELLWOOD

Introduction

The geographical focus of this chapter is the region known generally as 'Sundaland', that is the Malay Peninsula and the islands of Sumatra, Java, Borneo, and adjacent small island groups. These locations lie on the extensive and now mainly submerged Sunda continental shelf, which during the Last Glacial Maximum (*c.* 18 000 BP) would have been fully exposed as a subcontinent with an area of more than two million square kilometres (Fig. 13.1). The Quaternary literature published over the past two decades indicates that the environmental changes that swept this region between 18 000 and 6000 years ago would have had the potential to be very dramatic indeed, particularly those correlated with the rise in sea-level of over 100 m.

The purpose of this chapter is to examine existing evidence that pertains to the question of human cultural adaptation in Sundaland during this period. Before doing so, however, it is necessary to present some background information. In terms of Sundaland climate and environment one may distinguish between an equatorial rainforest zone with a relatively non-seasonal (ever-wet) climate, represented by the greater portions of Sumatra, Malaya, and Borneo, and a flanking monsoonal forest zone which is characterized by a winter dry season of varying length (Fig. 13.1). This latter zone includes most of Java, and the greater portion of the islands of Wallacea, (Philippines, Sulawesi, Moluccas, and Lesser Sundas). The vast majority of the present population of the region inhabits this seasonal monsoonal zone, which offers the soil, sunlight, and vegetation conditions most conducive to agriculture.

At the LGM the general environment of Sundaland would have differed from that of today in several major respects. Highland temperatures would certainly have been cooler than now (Maloney 1983, Flenley 1985), and the same may have been true, although with more scope for debate, of temperatures in the tropical lowlands (Rind & Peteet 1985). There is also a quantity of geomorphic and botanical evidence which suggests that annual rainfall would have decreased, and that the zone of seasonal climate with a dependable dry season would have increased in area at the expense of the equatorial ever-wet zone (Verstappen 1975, van Steenis 1979). The equatorial rainforest, however, would probably not have been broken up to the same extent as that suggested in the recent literature for equatorial Africa and Amazonia.

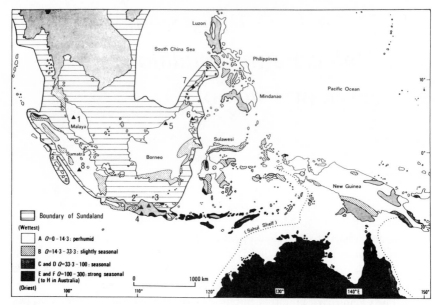

Figure 13.1   Map of rainfall types in Island Southeast Asia, modified from Whitmore 1984a, Fig. 4.1, with Sundaland and selected archaeological sites superimposed. Q is defined as (dry months/wet months) × 100, and this index reflects present-day vegetation closely. For a detailed vegetation map of the region see Whitmore 1984b. Archaeological sites are as follows; 1, Kota Tampan; 2, Ngandong; 3, Sangiran; 4, Pacitan; 5, Niah; 6, Tingkayu; 7, Tabon; 8, Tianko Panjang.

The exposed surface of the now-drowned lowland portions of Sundaland at 18 000 BP would perhaps have supported an inland mosaic of both ever-wet and monsoonal rainforest (Whitmore 1981, Walker 1982), with swamp and peat forest behind a very extensive mangrove fringe in the coastal regions. According to Biswas (1973, p. 245), describing the results of core analyses from the bed of the South China Sea off eastern Malaya, 'Brackish lagoons and bays existed at the centre of the basin bordered by widespread mangrove swamps and forests, obviously one of the largest mangrove colonies ever known in the history of the world.' Whether such a watery yet food-rich environment (mangrove swamps are generally well endowed with shellfish and crustacean resources) supported large Pleistocene populations we may never know, since the relevant archaeology will by now have been submerged or washed away. Nevertheless, it may be worth noting that such environments today, which exist in large areas of eastern coastal Sumatra and western Borneo, tend to support low densities of traditional or tribal population, whether of food-gatherers or cultivators, and there is no a priori reason to assume that they would have supported unusually high densities during the Pleistocene. Many of the Sundaland coastal soils may also have been hypersaline, especially in times of sea-level retreat (Chappell & Thom 1977), and these would probably have been unexploitable by human populations.

During the period of overall sea-level rise between 18 000 and 6000 BP (still-stands and minor regressions during this period are here ignored as being too fine grained for archaeological application) the great Sundaland sub-continent was drowned to produce its present land and sea configuration. The area of dry land was eventually reduced to less than half of its former extent, and the river systems of the regions now occupied by the South China and Java Seas were truncated rather dramatically. It is quite possible that a number of large mammal species became locally extinct during this period; examples include the Malayan tapir, *Cuon* sp. (a wild dog), and the Javan rhinoceros on Borneo (Cranbrook 1987), and the elephant and clouded leopard on Java (Bellwood 1985a, Table 1.1). Superficially, one might suggest that human hunting caused these extinctions, but acceptable evidence on this matter is really non-existent. Indeed, it is important to note that several zoologists who have commented on these extinctions have not found it necessary to invoke causation. Medway (1977), for instance, suggests increasing forest density as a major factor, while Heaney (1984) favours the processes of island formation and geographical niche fragmentation. Large mammals, including carnivores, and also small mammals with circumscribed environmental preferences, appear to have been the most drastically affected.

The environmental changes that may be presumed to have occurred across Sundaland between 18 000 and 6000 BP were, therefore, substantial. Increasing rainfall and expansion of rainforest, enormous changes in the geographical distributions of land and sea, and complex patterns of biological extinction and speciation may all have combined to offer one of the greatest adaptational challenges ever to the human populations of the region.

My purpose in this chapter is to examine whether the cultural results of such challenges can be identified in the archaeological record. Many results can be expected to be archaeologically invisible, especially in a tropical landscape characterized by rapid geomorphic change, but there are still three questions for which available data make the asking worthwhile:

(a) Was there any change in the pattern of equatorial rainforest habitation and exploitation during the period under consideration?
(b) Did the sea-level rise have any major impact on human population movements and economic development?
(c) Is any technological change recognizable in the stone tool record across the Pleistocene–Holocene boundary?

Equatorial rainforest exploitation

A substantial number of archaeological assemblages in Sundaland are known to belong to the time-period under consideration. I will not consider here the so-called 'chopper-chopping tool' or Pacitanian-type assemblages, which have often been suggested to have Middle or Late Pleistocene dates (a topic discussed

critically by Bartstra 1983, and Hutterer 1985). One point, however, concerning these 'early' industries is worthy of note, and this is that all have been
recovered from the monsoonal regions of Island Southeast Asia; Java,
southwestern Sulawesi, the Lesser Sundas, and possibly northern Luzon. No
convincing examples come from the equatorial zone at all, although I think we
have to be aware that equatorial rainforests can present difficult conditions for
the recognition of ephemeral stone tool scatters. Nevertheless, there is no
evidence, as yet, for hominid occupation of the ever-wet equatorial rainforest
zone until about 40 000 years ago, a circumstance that I believe parallels that for
the equatorial West African rainforest.

When we turn to the more securely radiocarbon-dated industries of the
period between 40 000 and 10 000 years ago we find basically the same
situation. Prior to the Holocene the only substantial traces of human occupation in the present equatorial rainforest belt come from the West Mouth of
the Niah Caves in Sarawak (Majid 1982), from the Tingkayu Valley and
Madai–Baturong sites in eastern Sabah (Bellwood 1988), and from Tabon
Cave on Palawan (Fox 1970). The industry from Kota Tampan in northwestern Malaya is sealed by Toba ash which has been dated to *c*. 30 000 BP (Stauffer
et al. 1980), and is thus most probably also of Upper Pleistocene date.
However, although this site is almost within the equatorial rainforest belt now
it may not have been so at the time of occupation; Verstappen (1975, pp. 26–7)
has suggested that this area of the Malay Peninsula may have experienced a
drier climate and tree-savanna vegetation during Pleistocene glacials.

The equatorial sites just listed, with the possible exception of Kota Tampan,
are all within the equatorial rainforest zone now, and most probably were
during the LGM, even if climatic conditions then were a little drier and more
seasonal than today. However, the real 'core' regions of lowland equatorial
rainforest in southern Malaya, eastern Sumatra, and much of inland Borneo
show no signs of Pleistocene human occupation at all. Again, this may simply
reflect invisibility of the prehistoric record, although it should be noted that
within this core region cave complexes that have been examined by fieldwor-
kers do not reveal traces of any ancient human occupation; these include the
Payakumbuh Caves in central Sumatra (my own observations), and several
complexes in inland Sarawak (Harrisson 1970, Hanbury-Tenison 1980). The
impression of Late Pleistocene site distribution that is available at present thus
suggests that equatorial rainforest core regions were not inhabited by human
groups, despite the occurrence of some fringe penetration as represented at
Niah and in Sabah.

During the Holocene there is quite a dramatic change in the northwestern
part of the equatorial rainforest belt in this rather negative picture of human
equatorial adaptation. In northern and central Malaya and northeastern
Sumatra a prolific record of Hoabinhian cave and shell-midden occupation
commenced, and in all cases where radiocarbon dates are reported, or coastline
correlations are possible, the occupations fall within the past 10 000 years
(Bellwood 1985a, pp. 159–75). Occupation also started at this time in the

Tianko Panjang Cave near Lake Kerinci in the central Sumatran highlands (Bronson & Asmar 1975), but there is no evidence as yet for a similar adaptation in the southern lowlands of Sumatra or in inland Borneo.

The absence of signs of human habitation in these latter core regions of the equatorial rainforest belt, prior to the agricultural period (post-5000 BP), is an observation of some ethnographic significance. The rainforests of lowland southern Sumatra and central Borneo do support small populations of food-gatherers today, of whom the Kubu of Sumatra and the Punan (or Penan) of Borneo are the best known. However, it would probably be a mistake to assume that this lifestyle has a pre-agricultural antiquity in these particular regions. Basically, the Kubu and Punan share a Southern Mongoloid phenotype with surrounding cultivators, and they also speak Austronesian languages related to those of their near neighbours. Hoffman (1983) has recently presented a convincing case for a derivation of the Punan from agricultural communities in relatively recent times, partly as a result of specialization in the collection of forest products for trade. If a similar argument with less emphasis on trade can be applied to the Kubu, then we are left with the observation that the equatorial rainforest zone of Island Southeast Asia has no really ancient food-gathering tradition at all.

It is worthy of note here that the Negrito populations, who have probably had a much longer prehistory of hunting and gathering than the groups just mentioned, are today found well to the north of the core equatorial zone in central and northern Malaya and the central and northern Philippines. There is no evidence to support the prior existence of a major Negrito population in Sumatra or Borneo; had they once existed throughout these equatorial islands then one would still expect to find populations of them in remote forested regions, as one still can in Malaya and in the Philippines. In the case of Borneo, vast areas of the interior are uninhabited by aboriginal populations (Wurm & Hattori 1983, maps 41–2), and until recently supported unbroken primary rainforest. It is therefore unlikely that the agriculturalists, who occupy many river valleys in Borneo today, could have assimilated previous interior food-collecting populations completely, had they once existed. The Negritos, as far as can be ascertained, evolved in the seasonal monsoonal regions outside the equatorial belt proper.

The observations which I would present, therefore, concerning the antiquity of equatorial rainforest occupation in Sundaland, as based on the evidence at present available, are four in number: no verified occupation at all by *Homo erectus*, fringe northeastern occupation after 40 000 years ago, Hoabinhian expansion into Malaya and Sumatra after 10 000 years ago, and virtually no occupation at all in the core regions along the Equator until some time after 5000 years ago.

The impact of the post-18 000 BP sea-level rise

As noted above, I am unable to see any compelling environmental evidence that would suggest that the low-lying portions of Sundaland, exposed above sea-level at 18 000 BP, would have been very attractive for human settlement. There would doubtless have been a small and scattered population, perhaps focused in coastal regions where mangroves abutted against lowland monsoonal forest (if such environments existed), and there might also have been some degree of seasonal movement through regions under periodically flooded swamp forest. While some episodes of coastal drowning might have been very rapid during the overall period of post-glacial sea-level rise, the ultimate result of the marine transgression would have been a doubling of coastal length on Sundaland (Dunn & Dunn 1977), and presumably an improvement of environment for coastally oriented populations, such as those responsible for the Hoabinhian shell-middens in northern Sumatra.

From this perspective, the Hoabinhian occupation of inland Malaya, evident after about 10 000 years ago, cannot be seen as a result of population retraction from an encroaching coastline, and may instead reflect innovations in hunting or trapping technology; perhaps the bow and arrow, or, with less likelihood, the blowpipe. This occupation, however, seems to have restricted itself to the northwestern fringes of the equatorial rainforest zone, and never appears to have led to a spilling over of an inland rainforest-dwelling population into southern Sumatra or Borneo. Why this did not occur is naturally something of a mystery, unless one simply accepts the hypothesis, which I am obviously supporting to some degree in this chapter, that the core regions of equatorial rainforest in Sundaland were relatively impervious to human settlement before the widespread availability of agriculture.

On the present evidence, therefore, the post-glacial sea-level rise cannot be seen to have had any major impact on human settlement or economy in Sundaland. This conclusion is at variance with my earlier opinion (Bellwood 1976, p. 164) that the transgression caused resource stress, and ultimately, a local transition to an agricultural economy. For reasons that lie outside the scope of this chapter, I no longer regard this as a viable hypothesis. Neither can I accept the hypothesis that the sea-level rise caused population crowding and consequent migration out of Sundaland, a viewpoint favoured independently by Gibbons & Clunie (1986; see Bellwood 1987b for comment) and Thiel (1987).

Post-18 000 BP lithic technology

The stone-tool industries found throughout Southeast Asia in the period between 18 000 and 6000 BP are based on a pebble/core tool and utilized flake technology; a very basic method of stone reduction exemplified by the mainland Hoabinhian, and by island sequences in sites such as the Niah and

Tabon Caves, and the Madai–Baturong sites in Sabah (for a review of these industries see Bellwood 1985a, Ch. 6, Bellwood, 1987a). There are, at present, three unusual variations which differ from the norm, and all seem to belong to time-spans outside the main focus of this chapter:

(a) the Tingkayu biface industry of Sabah which on present evidence appears to be older than 18 000 BP (Bellwood 1984);
(b) an occurrence of a prepared core technology in the Leang Burung 2 shelter in southwestern Sulawesi, which again seems to be older than 18 000 BP (Glover 1981);
(c) a widespread occurrence of microlithic technology (small blades, backed flakes, small points) in parts of the Philippines, Sulawesi, and Java, in all dated situations occurring after 7000 BP (Bellwood 1985b, Glover & Presland 1985).

These variant technologies cannot, at present, be related in any decisive way to local environmental adaptations following the LGM in either Sundaland or Sulawesi, and cases can be made for all three, which would involve some degree of introduction from outside sources. The post-7000 BP small-blade and microlithic industries, nevertheless, do belong to a period when sea-level would have been becoming relatively stable following its post-glacial rise, and many aspects of their distribution might reflect greater familiarity and skill with watercraft. Sites of this type have not, however, been found within the Sundaland or central Sulawesi equatorial zone, and they seem to reflect a hunting technology in seasonally dry environments with relatively open vegetation, and correspondingly high mammal biomasses. Wild banteng cattle in Java, for instance, can occur at densities of up to 15 animals per 100 hectares in savanna grasslands, but only 1–2 animals per 100 hectares in rainforests (Pfeffer 1974).

The basic stance that I have taken in the chapter, therefore, is that cultural changes in Sundaland during the period between approximately 20 000 and 5000 years ago might have taken place without a great deal of direct, local, environmental causation. It may be better, indeed, to look at them within the perspective of the East and Southeast Asian region as a whole. On this scale, it may be that the environmental changes at the end of the last glaciation did have some very profound ultimate effects on the human cultures of the region, the most important being the development and expansion of agriculture in regions to the north of Sundaland, and the consequent beginning in Sundaland itself of an episode of post-5000 BP population growth and equatorial rainforest exploitation, which still continues today.

References

Bartstra, G.-J. 1983. Some remarks upon fossil man from Java, his age, and his tools. *Bijdragen tot de Taal-, Land- en Volkenkunde* **139**, 421–34.

Bellwood, P. S. 1976. Prehistoric plant and animal domestication in Austronesia. In *Problems in economic and social archaeology*, G. de G. Sieveking, I. H. Longworth & K. E. Wilson (eds), 153–67. London: Duckworth.

Bellwood, P. S. 1984. Archaeological research in the Madai Baturong region, Sabah. *Bulletin of the Indo-Pacific Prehistory Association*. **5**, 38–54.

Bellwood, P. S. 1985a. *Prehistory of the Indo-Malaysian Archipelago*. Sydney: Academic Press.

Bellwood, P. S. 1985b. Holocene flake and blade industries of Wallacea and their predecessors. In *Recent advances in Indo-Pacific prehistory*, V. N. Misra & P. Bellwood (eds), 197–206. New Delhi: Oxford & IBH.

Bellwood, P. S. 1987a. The prehistory of Island Southeast Asia. *Journal of World prehistory* **1**, 171–223.

Bellwood, P. S. 1987b. The impact of sea-level changes on Pacific prehistory. *Journal of Pacific History* **22**, 106–8.

Bellwood, P. S. 1988. *Archaeology in South-eastern Sabah*. Sabah Museum Monograph 2, Kota Kinabulu.

Biswas, B. 1973. Quaternary changes in sea-level in the South China Sea. *Bulletin of the Geological Society of Malaysia* **6**, 229–56.

Bronson, B. & T. Asmar 1975. Prehistoric investigations at Tianko Panjang Cave, Sumatra. *Asian Perspectives* **18**, 128–34.

Chappell, J. & B. Thom 1977. Sea levels and coasts. In *Sunda and Sahul*, J. Allen, J. Golson & R. Jones (eds), 275–92. London: Academic Press.

Cranbrook, Earl of 1987. A review of fossil and prehistoric remains of rhinoceroses in Borneo. *Sabah Museum and Archives Journal* **1**, 50–110.

Dunn, F. L. & D. F. Dunn 1977. Maritime adaptations and the exploitation of marine resources in Sundaic Southeast Asian prehistory. *Modern Quaternary Research in Southeast Asia* **3**, 1–28.

Flenley, J. R. 1985. Man's impact on the vegetation of Southeast Asia: the pollen evidence. In *Recent advances in Indo-Pacific prehistory*, V. N. Misra & P. Bellwood (eds), 297–306. New Delhi: Oxford & IBH.

Fox, R. B. 1970. *The Tabon Caves*. Manila: National Museum of the Philippines.

Gibbons, J. R. H. & F. G. A. U. Clunie 1986. Sea level changes and Pacific prehistory. *Journal of Pacific History* **21**, 58–82.

Glover, I. C. 1981. Leang Burung 2: an Upper Palaeolithic rock shelter in South Sulawesi, Indonesia. *Modern Quaternary Research in Southeast Asia* **6**, 1–38.

Glover, I. C. & G. A. Presland 1985. Microliths in Indonesian flaked stone industries. In *Recent advances in Indo-Pacific prehistory*, V. N. Misra & P. Bellwood (eds), 185–95. New Delhi: Oxford & IBH.

Hanbury-Tenison, R. 1980. *Mulu: the rainforest*. London: Weidenfeld & Nicolson.

Harrison, T. 1970. The prehistory of Borneo. *Asian Perspectives* **13**, 17–46.

Heaney, L. R. 1984. Mammalian species richness on the Sunda Shelf. *Oecologia* **61**, 11–17.

Hoffman, C. L. 1983. *Punan*. University Microfilms International.

Hutterer, K. L. 1985. The Pleistocene archaeology of Southeast Asia in regional context. *Modern Quaternary Research in Southeast Asia* **9**, 1–24.

Majid, Z. 1982. The West Mouth, Niah, in the prehistory of Southeast Asia. *Sarawak Museum Journal* **31**.

Maloney, B. 1983. The terminal Pleistocene in Sumatra, Indonesia. *Quaternary Newsletter* **39**, 1–9.

Medway, Lord 1977. The Niah excavations, and an assessment of the impact of early man on mammals in Borneo. *Asian Perspectives* **20**, 51–69.

Pfeffer, P. 1974. Fauna of humid tropical Asia. In *Natural resources of humid tropical Asia*, 295–306. Paris: Unesco.

Rind, D. & D. Peteet, 1985. Terrestrial conditions at the last glacial maximum. *Quaternary Research* **24**, 1–22.

Stauffer, P. H., S. Nishimura & B. C. Batchelor 1980. Volcanic ash in Malaya from a catastrophic eruption of Toba, Sumatra, 30,000 years ago. In *Physical geology of Indonesian island arcs*, 156–64. Kyoto University, Japan.

Steenis, C. G. G. J. van. 1979. Plant geography of East Malesia. *Botanical Journal of the Linnaean Society* **79**, 97–178.

Thiel, B. 1987. Early settlement of the Philippines, Eastern Indonesia and Australia-New Guinea: a new hypothesis. *Current Anthropology* **28**, 236–41.

Verstappen, H. T. 1975. On palaeo climates and landform development in Malesia. *Modern Quaternary Research in Southeast Asia* **1**, 3–36.

Walker, D. 1982. Speculations on the origin and evolution of Sunda-Sahul rainforests. In *Biological diversification in the tropics*, G. Prance (ed.), 554–75. New York: Columbia UP.

Whitmore, T. C. 1981. Palaeoclimate and vegetation history. In *Wallace's Line and plate tectonics*, T. C. Whitmore (ed.), 36–42. Oxford: Clarendon Press.

Whitmore, T. C. 1984a. *Tropical rainforests of the Far East*, 2nd edn. Oxford: Clarendon Press.

Whitmore, T. C. 1984b. A vegetation map of Malesia at a scale 1 : 5 million. *Journal of Biogeography* **11**, 461–71.

Wurm, S. A. & S. Hattori (eds) 1983. *Language atlas of the Pacific area, Part II*. Canberra: Australian Academy of the Humanities.

14 From Kakadu to Kutikina: the southern continent at 18 000 years ago

RHYS JONES

People had managed to colonize the Australian continent perhaps 20 000 years before the peak of the Last Glacial Maximum (LGM), conventionally targeted at 18 000 years ago. To do this they had to cross at least 80–100 km of open ocean, even during climatic phases when the sea-level was lower than at present. These deep straits, together with areas of fully oceanic islands constitute the region of 'Wallacea' situated in the eastern part of the Indo-Malay archipelago, and separating the continental shelf of Sunda on the Asian side, and of Sahul on the Australian. The latter consists of Australia proper, together with the subcontinental sized island of New Guinea and to the south, Tasmania and Kangaroo Island.

The oldest dates for human occupation of Australia come from a variety of site types, and are widely distributed across the continental land mass (Jones 1988). Dates of about 38 000 were obtained for stone tools and hearths in sites within clay river terraces near Perth in the extreme southwest (Pearce & Barbetti 1981). In this region is also located Devil's Lair, a cave in soft limestone, where superimposed levels containing stone tools, burnt animal bones, and hearths were excavated dating back to some 32 000 BP, with a possibility of some small flakes in levels dated at 35 000–37 000 BP (Dortch 1984). In the southeast of the continent, a series of aeolian deposits, bordering now fossil river and lake systems on the Willandra and lower Darling Rivers, have revealed freshwater shell-middens dated back to about 37 000 BP (Bowler 1976a). In one of these lunette-shaped sand dunes at Lake Mungo numerous archaeological remains, including freshwater mussel-midden scatters, fish and other animal bones, stone tools and ochre, were common in units dated to between 26 000 and 32 000 BP. At the Mungo site, human remains were found as cremated and smashed bones heavily cemented with calcium carbonate and dated to 26 000 BP (Bowler *et al.* 1970). A deep excavation in the lunette showed some stone flakes *in situ* 1.5 m below the remains just described, and for the record a ^{14}C result was obtained on a small sample of charcoal, which gave a value indistinguishable from background (Shawcross & Kaye 1980).

The northeastern coast of New Guinea, near the Huon Peninsula, is one of the most rapidly uplifting coastlines in the world, where the Australian continental plate is overriding the Pacific one. A series of uplifting coral terraces can be seen up to an elevation of 60 m above present sea-level, and these have been dated by uranium series radiometric methods to give one of the key sequences of variation in sea-level over the Upper and Middle Pleistocene period. Behind each of the fossil coral reefs are deposits associated with the back lagoon and contemporary shoreline of that reef. Gullies in some of these deposits associated with reef terrace IIIa revealed stone tools eroding from them, the stratigraphic integrity of the site being confirmed by excavations. Dates on the reef itself and on a sealing volcanic ash, showed the tools to be at least 40 000 years old and perhaps somewhat older (Groube *et al.* 1986). The tools included large, unifacially flaked axe-like objects, some up to 2.5 kg in weight and with pronounced grooves on their sides. These 'waisted blades' are presumed to have been hafted in some way and, despite their antiquity, their most likely use might have been ring-barking trees or otherwise modifying the vegetation, perhaps to enhance the growth of plants suitable for food, such as yams, sugar cane, bananas, and tree fruits.

These field data, all obtained during the past 10–15 years' research, already indicate that a wide range of ecological zones had been occupied by more than 30 000 BP. Presumably this also implies different subsistence strategies for which we have some direct evidence in the archaeological record, and some which must be inferred. Laying aside these oldest sites and coming forward to a period say 25 000 BP, I have long held the view that most of the major ecological zones of the Greater Australian continent had been colonized by this time and successful subsistence strategies had been developed to deal with them (Jones 1973). This terrain extended latitudinally from the Equator to 43° S, and altitudinally from the tropical seashore to the high intermountain valleys at 2000 m. It included tropical savanna, the desert scrublands, and the temperate forested zones of the south (Jones 1987a, 1989, Smith 1987). Recently, evidence has been obtained that people also crossed several oceanic water barriers to the large islands of the western Pacific rim, such as New Ireland in the Bismarck group, where basal dates of 33 000 BP have been obtained from a shell-midden at the cave of Matenkupkum (Allen *et al.* 1988). In this midden were remains of marine reef gastropods, marine fish, and stone tools made from worked cobbles. More spectacular evidence for a competent sea-going capacity at this time, comes from the date of 28 000 years from basal occupation levels at Kilu Cave on Buka Island in the North Solomons group (Wickler & Spriggs 1988). This would have required a straight journey of 180 km over open sea from the nearest large island, New Ireland, and with a land target giving an angular projection of only 30°. There are two small inland groups in between, but even so, minimum open-sea distances would have involved crossing 70 km. The Kilu layers also contained reef shellfish, marine fish, and stone tools, some of the latter with residue evidence for cutting tubers of some sort.

Ice-Age climatic regime in the south

The last 25 years have also seen a fundamental increase in our knowledge of late Pleistocene climatic changes and their environmental consequences in Australia. A summary of this data base was presented in the *First CLIMANZ Conference* in 1981 (Chappell & Grindrod 1983) where a series of key time-slots were considered separately; these included the period at *c.* 32 ky, 18 ky and 15 ky BP, the latter indicating ameliorations from the glacial conditions. A series of influential syntheses by Bowler and various co-workers has placed these events into their continental geographical contexts and offered some explanation in terms of climatic modelling (Bowler 1976a, 1976b; Bowler *et al.* 1976; Jones & Bowler 1980). The present brief summary draws heavily on these syntheses. During the period 30 000 back to perhaps 50 000 years ago, the conditions in Australia were effectively wetter than they are at present (Fig. 14.1). Using Prescott's climatic index[1] of precipitation over evaporation, effective moisture conditions of at least index value number 2, now found only along the eastern seaboard and the coastal fringe of the tropical north, then extended between 500 and 1000 km inland, with only the northwest coast and the Great Australian Bight having relatively dry conditions close to the then coastline. This regime meant that extensive river and lake systems in western New South Wales, and in the drainage leading from southwestern Queensland into the Lake Eyre basin, contained permanent water. Even the desert core had a moisture regime similar to that of the Adelaide district or Tennant Creek today, perhaps equivalent to dry Mediterranean or semidesert scrub conditions.

As the global climate moved towards the LGM, the average temperature dropped by 5–8° C. Over most parts of the continent it was not this temperature change as such which was most decisive, but rather the associated reduction in the atmospheric water cycle, and changes in the location of the major wind systems. In northern Australia, and possibly southern New Guinea, these changes were magnified by the exposure of most of the continental shelf in what is now the Arafura Sea, the Gulf of Carpentaria, and the Great Barrier Reef areas. These present-day, warm, shallow seas are the sources of most of the contemporary tropical cyclones, which make a major contribution to the tropical rainfall budget. The dominant influence on the climate of southern Australia is the circulation of air masses derived within the southern ocean and the circum-Antarctic region. These result in westerly winds driving rain-bearing cold fronts that provide present-day winter rain. During the LGM, it has been estimated that the edge of the winter pack ice around the Antarctic continent may have extended approximately 1000 km north of its present position, and that the Antarctic polar front may have been situated at 45°, i.e. only a few hundred kilometres to the south of Tasmania (Hays *et al.* 1976). This would have pushed the westerly wind stream northwards and, because of the constriction of the temperature gradient, would have resulted in intensified pressure systems with increased average wind speeds (Bolwer 1978, p. 150).

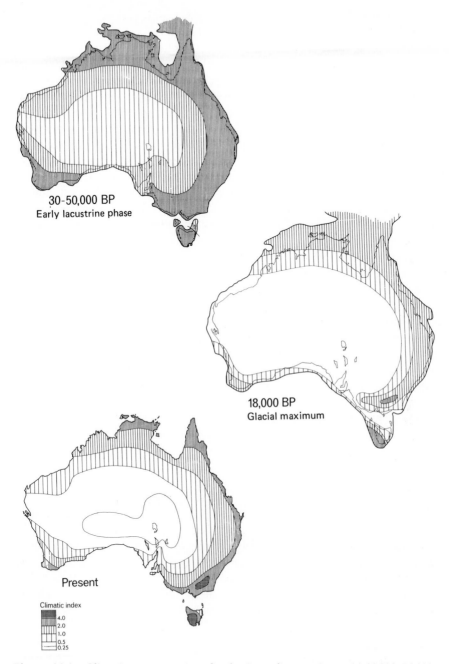

Figure 14.1 Climatic reconstructions for the Australian continent: (a) 30 000–50 000 years ago; (b) 18 000 years ago; (c) present conditions, using Prescott's effective moisture climatic index.

Geomorphological work on the Australian continental land-dune systems shows this to have been active, following the lines of a gigantic anticlockwise swirl, covering most of central and southern Australia. The lake systems such as at Mungo began to dry into ephemeral lakes at about 23 000–26 000 years ago, with the formation of bordering gypsum clay dunes, and by 18 000 BP were mostly dry. Mobile sand was driven from the Lake Eyre area southeast-wards into the tablelands of New South Wales, and even spilling over the Great Dividing Range into the upper river basins of the Pacific drainage rivers. The floor of Bass Strait was exposed, with a partly brackish enclosed lake in the middle (Blom 1988) and continental linear dunes were blown southeastwards along this floor and across the northeastern tip of Tasmania. The picture over much of the continent at the LGM is therefore one of generally arid, windy, dusty conditions (Fig. 14.1). Bowler (1978, p. 158) has compared these conditions to the situation in an equivalent latitudinal continental zone north of the Equator, namely northern China and Mongolia, when extensive loess units were deposited.

Glacial conditions existed in two areas. In the mountain zones of Tasmania and the highlands of southeastern Australia, valley glaciers were formed with small ice sheets on suitable elevated plateaus. The tree line was perhaps 1000 m below its present level, leaving extensive periglacial zones vegetated by alpine communities (Bowler *et al.* 1976). The mountain spine in New Guinea rises to peaks of 5000 m above sea-level and, although situated close to the Equator, these supported extensive mountain glaciers during the Last Ice Age (Loeffler 1972). The tree line was depressed to about 2500 m, with extensive 'islands' of mountain alpine grasslands which may have supported a high density population of marsupial herbivores.

Kakadu: the tropical savanna

A key location for understanding the prehistory of the Australian tropics is the Kakadu region of the Northern Territory. This corresponds to the drainage systems of the South and East Alligator Rivers, and the western edge of the Arnhem Land escarpment. This latter forms a sinuous wall of quartzite and sandstone cliffs more than 100 km long, and up to 200 m high in places. There are numerous gorges, which give access to the rugged plateau to the east. The escarpment overlooks the floodplains of the Alligator Rivers, which are seasonally flooded in the wet season to form extensive freshwater and brackish water wetlands.

On this plain are also numerous outliers ranging in size from a few hectares to the Djawumba massif and the Mt Brockman-Nourlangie Rock massifs, which are 16 km and 6 km long, respectively (Fig 14.2). These outliers, in geologically distant time, once formed part of the escarpment, and from an ecological point of view are very important since they afford refuges from the wet-season inundation, and give fire protection to sensitive plant communities

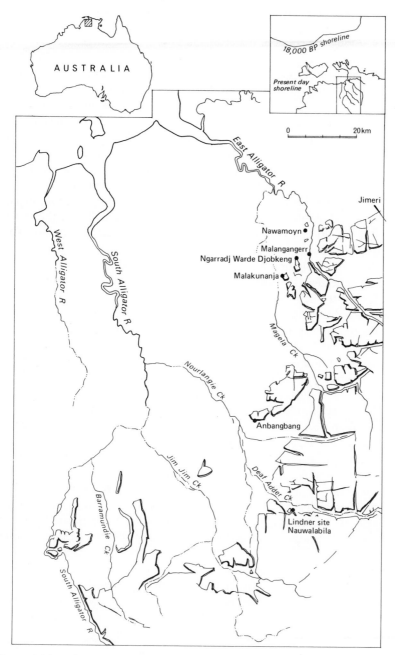

Figure 14.2 Pleistocene archaeological rockshelters in the Kakadu region of western Arnhem Land.

in the dry season. Because of the close geographic proximity of these major land-form types, the region displays a high degree of plant community diversity. Along the edges of the cliffs and in protected gorges are numerous disjunct populations of monsoonal rainforest communities and associated vine thickets. These are, in general, fire sensitive and are probably relicts from a once continent-wide distribution in the tropics of Australia. In contrast, the sand plains at the foot of the cliffs and on the plateaus behind are clothed in open savanna woodland with eucalypts (e.g. *E. tetradonta* and *E. mimiata*) and seasonal grasses. This zone is readily fired at the end of the dry season. The streams draining the escarpment and the main outliers contain a diverse fish fauna with more species represented than in the entire Murray–Darling Rivers drainage system in south eastern Australia. The wetlands nowadays contribute one of the major habitats in Australia for birds (especially geese, ibis, brolga, ducks, etc.), and reptiles, including the saltwater crocodile. It is partly because of this rich biological diversity that the area has been declared a National Park and is a World Heritage property.

The first archaeological excavations in the region were carried out by McCarthy & Setzler (1960) in 1948 at rock shelters on two small outliers near Oenpelli close to the mouth of the East Alligator River. These were shallow deposits probably only dating back 1000 years. The discovery of Pleistocene sites in the region was made by Schrire (formerly White), during her doctoral research between 1964 and 1966 (White 1967a, 1967b, 1967c, Schrire 1982). Since then separate field surveys and excavations have been made by Kamminga & Allen (1973) in the early 1970s; by Allen (1977, Barton 1979, Allen & Barton 1989) in the late 70s, and by a team led by myself in the early 1980s (Jones 1985a, 1988). During the course of this work, seven rockshelter sites have been found with either direct ^{14}C dates or reliable age-depth extrapolations, indicating basal occupation levels extending more than 10 000 years into the late pleistocene (Fig. 14.2, Table 14.1). These are located on a north-south axis of 80 km, either associated with outliers or within the floors of plateau valleys (Jones & Johnson 1985a, pp. 53–8, 66–8, 1985b, pp. 178–83, Jones & Negerevich 1985, pp. 2–7). Of these, four sites, namely Nawamoyn, Malangangerr, Malakunanja II, and the Lindner site, Nauwalabila I, all have artefact-bearing deposits dated directly to cover the 18 000-year period under review.

At this time, as has been outlined in the previous section, the global sea-level being 150 m below its present level, the coastline was situated some 300 km to the north, and the Alligator Rivers were cut into trenches below their present floodplains (Hope *et al.* 1985, p. 238, Woodroffe *et al.* 1986). Obviously, the river plain and swamp deposits did not then exist, since they were formed during the first phase of flooding between 7000 and 6000 years ago. Probes through these deposits have shown them to be lying on coarse red sands and gravels of Pleistocene age, derived from slope wash from the laterite-capped plains immediately adjacent (Hope *et al.* 1985, p. 234). These plains are essentially erosional surfaces, and thus are not a suitable location for the

Table 14.1 Stratigraphy and chronology of Pleistocene sites in the Alligator Rivers region (after Kamminga & Allen 1973, Gillespie & Temple 1976, 1977, Schrire 1982, Jones 1985a)

Sites	Years BP	Dates	Stratigraphy	Depth	Level
Nawamoyn	21 450 ± 380	ANU-51	yellowish-brown to brown coarse loamy sand	80 cm	IIIB
Malangangerr	22 900 ± 1000	ANU-77b	basal mottling in yellowish-brown sand	134–144 cm	IIIb
Ngarradj Warde Jobkeng	8 690 ± 125	SUA-165	brown sandy deposit	175 cm	
Malakununja II	18 040 ± 300	SUA-265	yellowish sand	190–215 cm	
Jimeri I	10 790 ± 200	GAK-632	brown sand	55– 60 cm	III
Anbangbang I	> 6 000		pink rubble	85–120 cm	III
Nauwalabila I	> 30 000		decayed sandstone rubble	277–286 cm	L29/80–81

preservation of stratigraphic deposits. However, at the foot of the escarpment and many of the outliers are extensive aprons of sand with a flat slope. Some of these sandsheets have been redeposited to form a complex series of fills within the edges of the valleys. These sandsheets have been dated as part of our 1981 archaeological investigations (Hope *et al.* 1985, pp. 229–31, 236, Jones & Johnson 1985b, pp. 173–83), and more recently in major independent geo-morphic studies (East *et al.* 1987, p. 15). Some of these sandsheets were accumulating during the 18 000-year period, and the oldest phases of sandsheet formation in the Magela Creek, a major tributary of the East Alligator River, have been dated by TL methods to extend back to 35 000 BP at least (East *et al.* 1987). The ultimate source of these sandsheets was material derived from the stripping of upland soils, and they probably had complex causes due to natural processes, and also due to the impact of man through burning practices. In all four shelters with stratifed Pleistocene deposits mentioned above, the strati-graphic columns themselves consist of sandsheet material that had accumulated around the rock outcrops forming the shelters. The outcrops stand out from the sandsheet plain, and the processes of formation of the deposits within the shelters were integrally related to the broader processes of sandsheet formation on a valley-wide scale.

At the shelters of Malangangerr and Nawamoyn, the basal sands were dated between about 24 000 and 18 000 BP (Schrire 1982, pp. 89, 118), They both contained stone tool assemblages that were typologically similar. The flaked tools consisted of horse-hoof core tools and thick flakes of quartzite, often with steep lateral retouch, forming steep-edged scrapers. Sometimes these edges showed working into small concave notches and may have been used as spokesheaves for the manufacture of spear or digging sticks shafts. Such tools are typical of Pleistocene assemblages elsewhere in Australia, such as the Mungo site, (New South Wales) dated to about 26 000 BP (Bowler *et al.* 1970) or in the lower levels of Kenniff Cave (Queensland), dated back to 19 000 BP (Mulvaney & Joyce 1965). The great surprise concerning the Kakadu sites, however, was that with the flaked scrapers were also found carefully made, small edge-ground hatchet heads with well-worked grooves or waists around their middle portions. These axes were made from igneous rocks of various types and their shape strongly suggested that they had been hafted. At the time of their discovery, they were the oldest edge-ground axes in the world; some three times as old as the oldest 'Neolithic' axes of western Asia and Europe. Since then, similar-aged axes have been found in Japan (Oda & Keally 1973, Ikawa-Smith 1979), and of course they are analogous to the 'waisted blades' of New Guinea, dated in the highlands at Kosipe to 26 000 BP (White *et al.* 1970), and at several other sites (Bulmer & Bulmer 1964, Bulmer 1966, 1975, Mountain 1979, 1981), back in time to the Huon finds of 40 000 BP (Groube *et al.* 1986). In the Kakadu sites the acid sandy soils did not allow any conservation of bone material in these Pleistocene levels.

A major problem with the stratigraphy of these Kakadu sites was that the top of the sands seemed to date to 18 000 or 20 000 BP and were directly overlain by estuarine shell-midden deposits with basal dates of 7000 and 6500 BP. Was there a genuine hiatus in occupation, which may have corresponded in time to the LGM, as Schrire herself suggested (White 1967a, Schrire 1982); or was this break due to some post-depositional erosion of the sandsheet in these particular sites, so that the shell-midden was laid down on a stratigraphic unconformity? To resolve this question was one of the major research aims of our field campaign (Jones 1985b, p. 19). To do this we choose the Lindner site Nauwalabila I within the enclosed Deaf Adder Gorge, some 75 km south of Malangangerr and Nawamoyn (Fig 14.2). I had visited this site in June 1972, and had been struck by the fact that its floor was contiguous with the level of the almost flat sandsheet which extended from the foot of the escarpment across almost the entire valley. Thus if one were to excavate, say a metre, into this floor, then the people who had occupied it would have been living on a valley surface that was also a similar depth below its present position. A pilot excavation in 1973 (Kamminga & Allen 1973) showed a depth of over 2 m of sand, containing artefacts, with a ^{14}C date of 20 000 BP at a depth of between 1.7 and 1.9 m.

Our own excavations were carefully conducted, with excavation units measuring 0.5 m^2 and about 3 cm in depth. Our stratigraphic column measured 2.85 m in depth, within which were 80 superimposed excavation units. Although our control pit only measured 1 m^2 in area it was placed immediately adjacent to Kamminga's pit. From the control pit were recovered 30 000 pieces of flaked stone, and in every one of 240 excavation units artefacts were present. The excavation revealed about 2.5 m of sand, resting on a further 0.4 m of heavily weathered rubble. The ^{14}C dates that we obtained fitted well with those from Kamminga's work, allowing a consistent depth–age correlation curve to be posited. The basal 0.5–0.7 m of the sand is undated but its base is believed to be of the order of 30 000 years old, with the rubble considerably older. There was no apparent hiatus in the column throughout the LGM.

What was interesting about this column was that the new fine-grained data seemed to have a different 'shape' to more broadly grouped information from older excavation methods. Here, there seemed to be 'pulses' of occupation densities separated by a background density of site use. I have speculated elsewhere as to the 'ethnographic reality' behind such phenomena (Jones 1987b, pp. 23–6). In the lowermost levels, from probably 30 000 to about 7000 BP the background density of artefacts was at a rate of about 0.4–1.5 pieces per kilogram of deposit.[2] There were peak pulses which extended in depth over several excavation units, and consisted of 6–8 pieces per kg. These values became higher in mid-Holocene times, with the background rising to about 5–8 artefacts per kg of deposit, with peaks of 16 per kg. Finally during the past 3000 years, values increased to a consistent density of about 35 pieces per kg, before falling back during the past 1500 years to about ten per kg. It must be remembered that after 6000–7000 years ago, the primary productivity of the region increased markedly, due to the arrival of the sea at its present level and the formation of dense mangrove swamps (Hope *et al.* 1985, Woodroffe *et al.* 1986). It can also be noted that although on average the density of artefacts increased significantly through the sequence, there were still some pulses within the 18 000–30 000-year period greater than much of the 'background' in Holocene levels.

The arid zone

The Nauwalabila I site showed that, at least within the relatively rich Kakadu region, there had been continuous occupation of the inland northern savanna, right through the 18 000 BP glacial arid 'spike'. One of the major problems of Australian field prehistory over the past decade has been to establish whether or not there had been occupation of the arid heart of the continent prior to Terminal Pleistocene times (Bowdler 1977, Jones 1987b). About nine sites have now been discovered from within the true arid zone and away from large river systems that document occupation by at least 24 000 years ago (Brown 1987, Smith 1987, Veth 1987). The first problem has thus been solved. There remains, however, a secondary question of whether or not, once having gained occupation, this was maintained throughout the stress of the LGM. Opinions seem divided, but this is shaping up as one of the key problems in Australian prehistory over the next decade. At Colless Creek, a narow gorge in dolomite, leading off the Barkly Tableland into the southern Gulf of Carpentaria (Magee & Hughes 1982), Hiscock (1985, p. 87) excavated rockshelters with artefact-bearing deposits to beyond 17 000 BP to an estimated basal date of about 20 000 BP. He argued that this and other sequences in the area implied a decisive and long-term retreat of the pre-18 000 inhabitants from the broader landscape, into isolated refugia such as the better watered gorges during the LGM (Hiscock n.d., quoted in Veth 1987, p. 107); a constriction of range which persisted for many millennia until reoccupation in mid-Holocene times.

A contrasting view comes from Smith's (1987) work in the very heart of the desert. His excavation at Puritjarra, a huge sandstone rockshelter situated within a dunefield in the MacDonnell ranges northwest of Lake Eyre not only demonstrated human presence back to beyond 22 000 BP, but also continuous occupation throughout the Last Glacial arid phase. However, the density of occupation during this period was low. Veth (1988) has sharpened the discourse by reference to biogeographic studies which have divided the arid zone into key subregions. Most important, from the point of view of distribution of many animal species, have been the relatively better-watered refugia, such as around the central mountain ranges near Alice Springs. Linking these are several strategic corridor zones, open during wet phases and closed during arid ones. It is clear that an understanding of the dynamics of human occupation of the two-thirds of the Australian continent, which even under present-day climatic conditions is classified as arid or semiarid, will depend on detailed regional studies and finely calibrated stratigraphic sequences. Smith (1988) has argued that the use of grass seeds, such as those of *Panicum* as evidenced by the archaeologically visible large sandstone grinding-slabs, was restricted to mid-Holocene times. The first pioneers into the desert may have had to use tubers, such as those of *Ipomoea*, as a staple vegetable food (D. Yen, pers. comm.).

There has been considerable argument within the literature, that in order to be able to survive the erratic seasonal and longer-term environmental stresses associated with occupation of the arid regions, the prehistoric Aboriginal people had also to develop broad-ranging social networks capable of responding to 'feasts and famines'. During modern ethnographic times, the key manifestation of such social links has been the great religious ceremonies. A potential archaeological record of such social activity is art, which within central Australia seems to have involved a similar set of motifs, depicted on a wide range of media, including being painted on rock walls and pecked into the faces of rocks. The motifs of modern times seem to meld with those of the past. Modern painters depict their totemic ancestors and the travelling tales of the Dreamtime in terms of patterns of circles, geometric designs of rows of dots and the tracks of animals, mostly birds such as emus, macropods, and sometimes people. Depictions of what are called 'ancestral heroes' are also part of the symbolic set. It has long been thought that some art comprising this complex of motifs has been ancient. Panels of such art pecked into the back wall of a cave in Cape York Peninsula was covered with deposit, carbon-dated to 13 000 BP (Rosenfeld *et al.* 1981). Recently a new method of dating the silicate mineralogical skin that often covers many such pecked designs within desert regions of Australia has been developed. Using the cation ratios dating method, Dorn and associates (1988) have suggested that some silicates covering large panels of decorated dolomite rocks near Manahill in the full arid region of northeastern South Australia, are dated consistently to between 16 200 ± 2450 BP, through three samples dated to *c.* 19 000 BP, one at 21 000 BP, back to the oldest at 31 000 BP. In the depths of Koonalda Cave on the desolate, dry limestone Nullarbor Plain near the Great Australian Bight, there are panels of art scraped by hands in the soft calc surface of the cave walls; up to 280 m in from the entrance and almost 80 m down from the surface of the ground. Fragments of a burnt torch-stick and charcoal at the foot of a tight squeeze, decorated with deeply incised lines, gave a value of 19 900 ± 200 (V92) (Wright 1971, p. 28).

Tasmania

The island of Tasmania measures 64 000 km^2 in area; it is mountainous, with the highest peaks rising to just over 1500 m; and being located between 40° and 44° S, its western half is exposed to the strong, rain-bearing winds of the Roaring Forties. There is a marked rain shadow effect, with rainfall over some of the western mountain ranges reaching values of 4300 mm, being amongst the wettest in Australia and having the least number of sunshine hours (Christian & Sharp-Paul 1979, p. 19). In contrast, some parts of the Midland Valley in the lee of the mountains receive as little as 400 mm, with formation of salt lakes in some restricted localities. This climatic gradient has strongly influenced the vegetation, with rainforest and wet sclerophyll associations in the west, and dry sclerophyll *Eucalyptus* woodland, or open grassy plains in the east. At present, Tasmania is separated from the Australian mainland by 150 km of the often rough seas of Bass Strait.

The key to Tasmania's prehistory lies in the submarine ridge between the northern part of the Furneaux Group of islands in the eastern Strait and Wilson's Promontary on the mainland (Jennings 1971). The critical sill between the 55 m and 65 m isobaths, means that a sea-level drop to those levels would have resulted in the difference between a plain 100 km wide and a strait 100 km wide. In my previous accounts of Tasmanian prehistory, I have followed the data base then available that initial human colonization occurred as the sea-level was dropping to its Last Glacial minimum (Jones 1984, p. 54). Correlation with Chappell's (1983, Fig. 105) sea-level curve, showed that the landbridge opened at about 23 000 BP and remained dry until 12 000 BP. However, recent basal dates of 30 000 BP from two rockshelters in south central Tasmania now suggests that the first people had used an earlier low-sea episode, which may also have exposed the bridge between *c.* 37 000 and 29 000 BP (Cosgrove 1989). The first discovery of stratified Pleistocene occupation deposits south of the Bassian Sill occurred in 1974, at Cave Bay Cave, a large raised sea cave on Hunter Island, off northwest Tasmania (Bowdler 1974) (Fig. 14.3). Major excavations at this site revealed a series of hearths and other occupation debris within clays dated to between about 22 000 and 18 000 BP (Bowdler 1984). In Tasmania itself, a chance find in 1976 of stone flakes within a cemented breccia in the limestone Beginner's Luck Cave, Florentine Valley (Goede & Murray 1977), dated initially to 12 000 BP, and later to 20 000 BP, signalled the possibility of finding occupation sites within densely forested country that was not occupied by Aborigines during the time of 'ethnographic contact' in the early 19th century. Fundamental palaeoenvironmental research has shown that glacial conditions in south central Tasmania, where the Florentine Valley is situated, might well have supported some open tundra-like or alpine herb-field vegetation, in a region where nowadays some of the tallest trees in the world grow.

A major conservation political struggle concerning a proposed series of hydroelectric dams on the lower Gordon River system of south west Tasmania, led to archaeological investigations of belts of Ordovician-aged limestone running along the floors of some of the threatened valleys, in particular that of the Franklin River. In 1981, extremely rich occupation deposits between 14 000 and 20 000 BP were found in Fraser (now Kutikina) Cave (Kiernan *et al.* 1983). Between 1982 and 1986, a series of expeditions led to the discovery, within various valleys of the westward flowing Gordon–Franklin drainage system, of about a further 20 limestone or dolomite cave

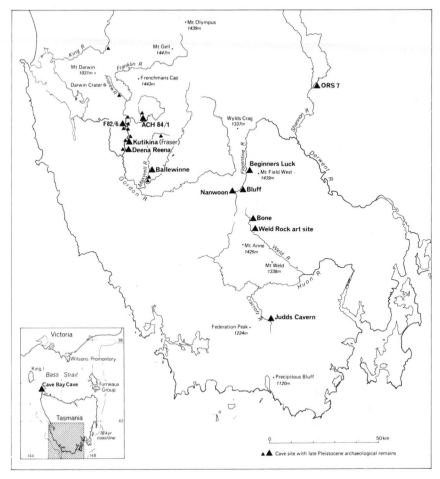

Figure 14.3 Limestone and dolomite cave sites with late Pleistocene archaeological occupation evidence.

sites containing archaeological remains either directly dated or, on geomorphological grounds, inferred to date from the same Last Glacial timeperiod (Blain *et al.* 1983, Jones & Allen 1984, Harris *et al.* 1988). Some of these sites formed part of the cultural data base which successfully gained for the Franklin Valley its status as a World Heritage property. More recent field research, some of it again stimulated by a political struggle to extend the World Heritage area to the east, to include what are known as the Southern Forests, led during 1987 and 1988 to the discovery and exploratory excavation of several more occupied carbonaceous rockshelters and caves in the valleys of the Florentine, Weld, and Cracroft rivers (Jones *et al.* 1988, Allen *et al.* 1988, Cosgrove 1989). These all flow to the southeast of Tasmania.

The Kutikina sequence

In March 1981, a small pilot excavation was made into the side of a partially eroded bank within the floor of Kutikina Cave (formerly Fraser Cave), where surface artefacts indicated the existence of occupation deposits (Kiernan *et al.* 1983). The stratigraphic sequence was only 1.3 m deep resting on bedrock, but consisted of a complex of superimposed layers, many with hearths and burnt earth features, and with high densities of stone artefacts and fragments of animal bones. The top of the deposit was sealed by a soft layer of stalagmite, under which was a thin sterile slick of clay. This rested directly on top of a complex of limestone rubble, blackened with charcoal, and containing numerous hearths. A charcoal sample from the top of this complex gave a value of 14 840 ± 930 BP (ANU 2781) (Kiernan *et al.* 1983, p 28). The lower half of this rubble complex was markedly browner in colour, with fewer charcoal lenses, and with the limestone fragments larger and more angular. Geomorphologically, this seemed somewhat similar to the '*éboulis*' rubble of French cave glacial deposits, and had been derived by frost shattering the limestone bedrock. Dates of 17 020 ± 310 and 15 670 ± 530 BP (ANU 2782 and 2783) in reverse stratigraphic order were obtained from within this rubble (Kiernan *et al.* 1983). The basal part of this rubble was intercalated with lenses of water-laid sandy silts, which were sterile of occupation debris. The date of this phase is unknown since the small charcoal sample obtained from the lowermost artefact–bearing rubble lenses was too mineralized to be dated. Under the rubble unit was a set of alluvial units, consisting of gravels with heavy concentrations of manganese salts precipitated within them. The uppermost gravels contained a few rolled stone tools and some charcoal dated to 19 770 ± 850 BP (ANU 2785) (Kiernan *et al.* 1983). These rested on sterile, manganese-rich gravels, which, in turn, lay on some heavily weathered sandstone cobbles, which elsewhere in the cave probably resulted from an earlier glacial episode.

The sequence, in summary, documents a change within the time-frame of the Last Glacial cycle, from a humid phase shortly prior to 20 000 BP, when there was enough surface vegetation to mobilize manganese, to the succeeding one, when the stratigraphic column became overwhelmed by an angular limestone rubble in a loamy matrix, believed to be the produce of mechanical weathering in cold, drier conditions. The role of human intervention can not be underestimated, since the earliest deposits to contain stone artefacts also have charcoal, perhaps the result of burning the hill slopes outside, with consequent ground slope instability. With the apparent human abandonment of the cave in Terminal Pleistocene times, there was also a virtual cessation of accumulation of deposit.

The onset of extremely cold conditions in western Tasmania probably started some 24 000 years ago, as documented by slope instability on the coast-facing margin of the West Coast Range some 50 km north of the cave. Conditions of maximum cold occurred at *c.* 18 000–19 000 BP as shown by driftwood fragments dated to $18\,800 \pm 500$ BP (ANU 2533), within proglacial silts immediately underlying glacial outwash gravels at an altitude of only 230 m, at the foot of this range (Kiernan *et al.* 1983, p. 29). These silts had flowed over and smothered flowering specimens of alpine cushion-plants *Donatia novae-zelandiae*, now only found in relict locations above the tree-line on the Central Plateau of Tasmania. Reconstruction of glacial snow-line altitudes show it to have been depressed to 1000 m at the headwaters of the Franklin River, corresponding to an average temperature depression of about 6.5°C. Within the upper Franklin Valley was a glacier, 12 km long, probably contiguous with ice on the upper Derwent, which had overriden the low divide between the two valleys. These ice bodies were adjacent to the ice sheet which formed on the Central Plateau itself. Further downstream along the Franklin catchment were further smaller cirque and valley glaciers, notably around the Frenchman's Cap mountain group (1443 m), only 25 km north of Kutikina Cave. Pollen analysis from sites in central Tasmania have shown the area to have been largely treeless and vegetated with alpine herb-fields during this glacial maximum period. By extrapolation to the southwestern valleys, it is probable that their lower slopes were equally open at this time. The distinctive *Nothofagus*-dominated rainforest species must have had refuges in the region, most likely along the river bottoms.

The edge of the continental shelf is located close to the present western Tasmanian shoreline, so the 18 000 BP coast was not appreciably further west than the present one. The floor of Bass Strait was, however, almost totally exposed, not only on the eastern Bassian Ridge but also on the western margin from northwestern Tasmania, through King Island to the Mornington Peninsula (67 m isobath). In the centre of the plain lay a depression with a maximum depth of about 80 m below present sea-level. During the LGM a large lake, measuring perhaps of the order of 100 by 250 km in area and 16 m deep was formed, with no outlet to the sea (Blom 1988). Piston-core samples from the bed of this lake have revealed it to have been brackish, with some brief saline episodes. It is likely to have acted as a large evaporimeter, with reduced runoff into it compared with present-day river flows, due to the glacial drier conditions. The microfossils within the lake-bed deposits show this lake to have been relatively unproductive with a paucity of bottom fauna (Blom 1988, p. 96).

Kutikina: stone tool assemblage

All the deposits were wet-sieved with a minimum 3 mm mesh. Altogether from the small excavation, some 37 000 pieces of flaked stone were recovered at an average density of 70 000 artefacts per cubic meter. Since several of the basal silt lenses were sterile, some occupation units had higher densities. Analysis of the sequence has not yet been completed (Jones *et al.* in prep), but it is apparent that it can be divided into two techologically distinct halves. In the lower part, from excavation unit 13 down to the basal unit 20, some 60% to

70% of all artefacts were made from quartzite and most of the rest from quartz. At unit 12, a sharp change occurred, when from there up to the top unit, the industry was dominated by quartz, which accounted for over 90% with most of the rest being made from quartzite. The change was archaeologically 'instantaneous' from one excavation unit to the next, and was stratigraphically associated with only the thinnest silt lens within the lower limestone rubble unit. It has not yet been precisely dated, but judging from the geomorphological evidence, it occurred within the coldest period between 16 000 and 18 000 BP, perhaps closer to the older value.

The artefacts within the lower assemblages had been made mostly from quartzite cobbles, which would have been readily available from the river banks nearby. The cobbles were smashed directly onto the middle of their flattest faces, causing them to split into halves or quarters. These latter chunks were then used as cores for further flake production, all stages of the reduction sequence being present in the occupation layers. Many flakes showed secondary retouch on their edges to form notches and rough denticulates, and the thicker flakes and some core fragments had steep, step-flaked edges. These tools seemed typical of later Tasmanian assemblages, especially the Holocene sequence from the Rocky Caves on the coast of northwest Tasmania (Jones 1971).

In complete contrast were the tools from the upper assemblage at Kutikina, which consisted almost entirely of tiny round-edged 'thumbnail' scrapers. Most of these were made from quartz. The process of manufacture for many consisted of hitting small elongated quartz pebbles in a bipolar manner. This resulted in thin lamellar flakes with a slightly twisted axis being detached from cores that ended up as *pièces écaillées* or scalar cores. The lamellar flakes were then snapped off to form quadrangular or square segments, whose edges were finally rounded by fine marginal retouch. In an excavated volume of only 0.22 m^3, there were 160 examples of these 'thumbnail' scrapers. Typically they measured some 20 mm by 15 mm in area and about 8 mm thick, but some were as small as 11 mm by 7 mm in area and 5 mm thick.

When we first studied these tiny thumbnail tools, we assumed that they had been hafted and that they represented some specialized function. To test these ideas, a specific research project was set up with Tom Loy who has pioneered the analysis of plant and animal material residues on stone tools. First, it was shown that residues did not occur on the curved retouched edges of these tools, but rather on their unretouched sharp flake component. Secondly, there were no indications either from gums or use wear of any hafting of these tools (Loy & Jones in prep.). It seems clear that they had been hand held, the retouched curved edges having been made to facilitate being held, and that the sharp unretouched edges were the 'business ends' as far as functions went. Thirdly, a study was carried out comparing the residues on statistically controlled samples of 'thumbnails' from the upper assemblage as opposed to the large flake-scrapers of the lower (Loy & Jones in prep.). Surprisingly, in both samples evidence for somewhat similar broad-range functions were found. Some 30–40% of tools from both samples had probably been used for cutting meat and other butchery functions; boneworking accounted for 20% of functions, whereas evidence for plant working of various kinds was found in about 15%. Evidence for woodworking was found on about 10% of tools in both assemblages (Loy & Jones in prep.).

If these results can be confirmed by further studies at Kutikina, and more generally in other contemporary late Pleistocene sites in southwest Tasmania, what is fascinating about them is that they show that the apparently specialized shaped 'thumb nail' scrapers, had exactly the same generalized set of functions as the typologically generalized flake-scrapers. Why, then, the typological differences between the assemblages below and above the unit 12/13 divide? Are we dealing here with styles of artefact manufacture independent of function, or with 'cultures' in Childe's (1956) sense? Did the difference between the assemblages in units 13 and 12 signify an incursion into the region of a different style of manufacture of stone technology or, even more radically, of a different group of people? Some of these speculations bear directly onto explanations for similar kinds of stone tool changes within the Upper Palaeolithic of western Europe at almost exactly the same time-period, such as the change from the 'Solutrean' to the 'Gravettian'.

Darwin Glass and Darwin Crater

In small numbers, but consistently within the upper excavation units, there were pieces, mostly tiny flakes, of Darwin Glass. This is a true natural glass, almost black in colour, formed as an impactite during the collision of a large meteorite with the Earth's surface. The energy of impact formed a crater a kilometre wide and several hundred metres deep, situated in the southern part of the Andrew Valley, a tributary of the Franklin, and which was only discovered by science in the mid-1970s (Fudali & Ford 1979). Glass fragments had been found on eastward-facing slopes of Mt Darwin in the West Coast Range during alluvial mining operations early this century, when the geological oddity of the material was noted, there being no evidence for vulcanism in the geology of the region. The impact melted some of the terrestrial bed-rock and threw tiny globules of it out to the west in a shock wave of some sort, since Stoke's Law of friction would have precluded the present distribution of glass fragments, if the normal air column had been in place. Fission-track and K–Ar dates on the glass show this event to have occurred some 0.7 million years ago. Fudali & Ford (1979, p. 292), while stating that this event 'ejected more impact-generated melt by a large factor, than any other known terrestrial meteorite crater of comparable size', also found that the size of individual glass pieces and their density on the ground fell off exponentially as one moved west from the crater's rim.

We visited this remote site in February 1984 in order to see under what circumstances Darwin Glass suitable for tool manufacture might have been obtained by the prehistoric people (Jones & Allen 1984, p. 94). The crater itself has been filled by clays and peats and is under extremely heavy *Leptospermum* ti–tree vegetation. The western rim of the impact crater coincides with the steep slope of a natural hill, and inspection of the beds of streams cut into the superficial deposits showed small pieces of glass eroding out of them. Another and perhaps more easily accessible source of the material might have been afforded by great trees falling over in storms, and their tangle of roots being ripped off the thin soil mantle. We inspected several such root-masses and were able to collect perhaps a dozen small pieces of Darwin Glass from each. Under the likely open glacial conditions, access to the surface slope deposits might have been easier than today.

The biggest pieces of glass that we collected measured 40 mm long, but they were typically about 10 mm long and 5 mm broad. Inspection of the glass flakes at Kutikina led us to the belief that they had been produced through bipolar flaking of the natural globules. To do this, a piece about 10 mm long would have been the smallest practical size for a core, and to hold even these in an upright position on an anvil would probably have required the use of strips of grass or bark, lest smashing the glass-core cut the fingers. From the rim of the crater, our transect surveys supported Fudali & Ford's (1979) previous finding that the size of the primary pieces of glass decreased markedly as one moved more than about 0.5 km to the west of the crater rim. Therefore we are confident that the source of the Darwin Glass in Kutikina and other Pleistocene occupation caves of southwestern Tasmania can be pinned down to this restricted location. The Frenchman's Cap massif with its numerous peaks, showing evidence of the geomorphic action of mountain glaciers of the Last Ice Age, are clearly visible from the rim of the Darwin Crater, only 15 km away to the west, the other side of the deep gorge of the Franklin.

The glass was obviously highly prized. Kutikina is situated some 26 km to the south–southeast of Darwin Crater, but given the broken nature of the terrain, it would have required several days' walk to get there, even under open conditions. A few glass flakes were found in most of the upper levels of the site down to unit 14. It seems tempting to associate these with the typological change to the thumbnail scrapers which occurred at about the same time. Clearly, a larger sample needs to be excavated at Kutikina, and with probably finer stratigraphic control, to elucidate these points. At least one well-formed thumbnail scraper had been made from Darwin Glass (unit 5). In the upper levels there were also a few flakes and thumbnails made from other high-quality cherts, which had been obtained from rocks (probably Cambrian) up to 50 km to the north of the cave. The original sources of all these exotic materials support an impression gained from other evidence that there was considerable movement along a north–south axis, which accords well with the 'grain' of the country.

Kutikina: animal bone

The site was extremely rich in animal bones, which have been analysed by Geering (1983). Altogether some 250 000 bone fragments were recovered from the small excavation, at an average density of 68 kg m^3. Some of the limestone rubble units had densities ranging between 100 and 200 kg of bone per m^3. Within some occupation units up to 70% of the bones showed signs of charring or even heavier calcination; and few units had less than 20% of burnt bones. This evidence of burning, the pattern of bone fragmentation, and the species composition were all in accordance with criteria, developed by Balme (1980) for Western Australian limestone caves and by Bowdler (1984) from Cave Bay Cave, that these bones were overwhelmingly the result of human deposition. Their association with hearths and stone tools strengthened this conclusion.

Of the species represented, as measured in terms of minimum numbers based on the frequency of the most numerous bone element, no less than 75% were of one species, viz. the red-necked wallaby, *Macropus rufogriseus*. A further 12% were wombat, *Vombatus ursinus*. The remaining 13% consisted of 15 species, of which the small macropod, *Thylogale billardierii*, made up 2.5% and the marsupial carnivores, including the Tasmanian Devil (*Sarcophilus harrissii*), 3%. The red-necked wallaby weighs about 15 kg and nowadays tends to live in open wooded or scrub country. The wombat is a heavier and less mobile animal with an underground sett, and today is found in the wetter, colder part of Tasmania. The Kutikina bone assemblage is highly unusual for Tasmanian archaeological sites, in the dominance of the two large animals (87%), with the virtual absence of murids, small marsupial bandicoots, and birds. In previous papers, I have speculated as to whether or not this reflected a highly targeted hunting strategy on the part of the palaeohunters (e.g. in Kiernan *et al.* 1983, Jones 1987b,c). Part of the problem in resolving this question is that the Last Glacial ecosystem of colder, drier conditions under extensive alpine herb-fields does not exist at the present day, and so modelling of past ecological relationships and marsupial population densities does not have the benefit of field studies under analogous conditions. Red-neck wallabies can exist in high densities, and support considerable hunting pressure. During 1976, some 300 000 ± 80 000 red-necked wallabies were believed shot for fur production in Tasmania by licensed non-commercial hunters, without any effect on their population numbers (Johnson 1977, p. 58). Ride (1970, p. 46) has described how two does and a buck of this species were introduced to the Canterbury province in the eastern half of the South Island of New Zealand in 1870. The climate there is dry and cold in winter. The population thrived and expanded to pest proportions; government records show that 70 000 animals were killed in control programmes between 1948 and 1965, not counting the tallies of private shooters.

Within the deposits there were also a few bone points. These were stout sharp-tipped awls or jabbing points made from the fibulae of wallaby. Similar points were found in the 18 000 BP levels at Cave Bay Cave, and also in Early Holocene levels at Rocky Cape. Based on the use, polish, and shape of the Rocky Cape points, I (1971) have previously speculated that they may have been used as awls and reamers to punch eyelets in skins for the manufacture of cloaks or rugs, as was recorded ethnographically in the cool wooded areas of southeastern Australia. Preliminary analysis of the Rocky Cape points by Tom Loy shows some with mammal blood congealed in cracks on their surfaces; and similar investigations are planned for the Kutikina ones. General consider-ations of the likely heat losses to be suffered by people without clothing in these glacial-edge conditions forces the conclusion that fur capes or other substantial clothing would have been necessary to prevent hypothermia. The ethnographically recorded Tasmanian Aborigines of the late 18th century were naked, with only some people wrapping a wallaby-fur over one of their shoulders; often women in order to carry their babies. The Rocky Cape sequence documented the gradual decline in manufacture of bone tools in Early and mid-Holocene times (Jones 1971).

Other sites in the Franklin catchment

Several other cave sites, although not yet investigated in such detail as Kutikina, give general support to its sequence and extend the range of information. The largest occupied cave is Deena-Reena, discovered in March 1982 (Blain et al. 1983, Jones et al. 1983). This cave is situated 4 km south of Kutikina, on the same eastern bank of the Franklin River, but about 150 m away from it, high up in a bluff of limestone. Our explorations revealed at least 350 m of passage. The main chamber is 4 m wide, up to 6.5 m high, and extends horizontally for about 40 m where it bifurcates. The floor has two large natural erosion gullies up to 4 m deep, which reveal the stratigraphy. Stone artefacts were found in the walls of both these gullies, the majority in the one closest to the entrance and about 10–16 m away from it.

The deposit was capped by a thin carbonate flowstone, as at Kutikina. This lay on a complex of rubble layers 0.5 m thick, themselves overlying about a metre of clayey sands on a basal deposit consisting of coarse gravels of cobbles of quartzite and sandstones. Thin layers of charcoal, with stone tools and animal bones, all of which seemed to be wallaby, were seen within the rubble and the uppermost part of the clayey sands. A charcoal layer just at the top of the rubble and immediately underlying the carbonate flowstone gave a date of 13 400 ± 770 BP (ANU 3558). Three small samples from within the same thin charcoal lens in the uppermost part of the clayey sands gave medial values of 17 800, 19 100 and 20 500 BP respectively (ANU 3139, 3331, 3332), their standard errors showing them to be not significantly different from each other, the pooled value being 19 150 ± 1370 BP (J. Head pers. comm.). This sample immediately predates the rubble, which as at Kutikina, seems clearly related to the LGM. Stone tools from within the rubble and associated with the 19 000 BP date have not yet been fully analysed, but they seem consistent with the lower part of the Kutikina sequence. The clay deposit beneath the date was closely inspected. A few charcoal specks from its upper part were collected and await accelerator mass spectrometer (AMS) analysis. However, there were no artefacts nor any other sign of human activity within the lower part of the clay. It is likely that the basal gravels may belong to a previous glacial episode.

The upper part of the Kutikina sequence also gets support from two further rockshelter sites. One, as yet unnamed, F/82/6 (Jones *et al.* 1983, p. 66) 7 km north of Kutikina, is a small limestone shelter with a surface area of about 2.5 m by 1.5 m, with stone artefacts on the surface, cemented by carbonate flowstone. A ^{14}C sample collected from immediately beneath this flowstone, gave a value of 13 850 ± 1470 BP (ANU 3562). On the confluence of the Acheron River with the Jane, which in turn flows into the Franklin, is a dolomite outcrop with two rockshelters containing stone artefacts. The unnamed ACH/84/1 (Jones *et al.* 1983, pp. 93–4) was a shelter about 20 m long, with a stream running through part of it today. An uneroded fragment of a bank was inspected and found to contain stone tools. Three radiocarbon samples were obtained from this, which gave a stratigraphically consistent sequence from between 12 500 and 16 000 BP (Jones *et al.* 1983). The stone tool assemblage had a similar concentration to that at Kutikina and, again, most of the tools consisted of small thumbnail scrapers made from quartz and using the same bipolar reduction technique. The fauna seemed to be dominated by red-necked wallaby. There was also *in situ*, two flakes of Darwin Glass. The Darwin Crater is situated 24 km to the northwest of the site, but with deeply dissected country in between. Finally, one can mention one open site, exposed in the upper banks of the Franklin River near F/82/6. Stone tools were seen eroding out of the section and a small excavation yielded charcoal, which gave a date of 17 100 ± 1350 BP (ANU 3562). This shows that there is a possibility of finding open sites dated to the LGM as well as cave sites.

The Weld and the Florentine: new investigations

The Weld flows south eastwards to the Huon River and thus to the D'Entrecasteaux Channel. The Florentine rises within a kilometre of the headwaters of the Weld, but flows northeastwards to join the Derwent and then southeast to Storm Bay. Some tributaries of the westward-flowing Gordon River headwaters also flow to within a kilometre or two from tributaries of the Florentine. The actual watersheds between these drainage systems consist of open plateau valleys and the relief is so subdued that one is barely conscious of moving from one to the other. This contrasts with the surrounding mountain ranges, which, in the case of Mt Anne, Mt Field West, Mt Weld, and Wyld's Crag, rise to between 1330 and 1430 m, amongst the highest mountains in Tasmania and all supporting small glaciers during the Last Ice Age. The rivers also, as they flow away from the watershed, often cut deep and rugged gorge systems in their middle reaches. Thus even though the country in general is hard, the actual passage from one river system to another would have been relatively easy.

Bone Cave is a small vertical cave in a dolomite bluff overlooking the Weld.

Its archaeological potential was recognized in the early 1980s and a radiocarbon sample taken from the side of a small erosion pit gave a date of 16 000 BP (Goede & Bada 1985, p. 159). A small, carefully controlled excavation in 1988 showed dense occupation units down to a depth of 0.7 m, when work was temporarily terminated (Allen *et al.* 1988). As in the Franklin sites, there was again a thin carbonate capping to the deposit. A series of four carbon dates are in stratigraphic order, ranging from 13 700 ± 860 BP (Beta 26509) towards the top of the sequence down to 16 820 ± 110 BP (Beta 26512) at the base of the excavation (Allen *et al.* 1988). A metal probe into the floor revealed the presence of at least another 0.3 m of deposit, which may span the LGM. Stone artefacts were estimated to be at a density of at least 20 000 flakes per m^3, and thus of the same order as at Kutikina. There were cores and large flakes, suggesting that some tool manufacture took place at the site. Some of the cores were steep-sided and some had further fine retouch, suggesting indications of use. There were also biopolar cores and the flakes derived from them. Many of the flakes had lateral retouch and could be classified generally as flat scrapers. There were also numerous tiny thumbnail scrapers in both the middle and lower part of the excavated deposit. This would correspond in time to the occurrence of these tools in the Franklin catchment sites.

Raw materials were mostly fine-grained quartzites available from cobbles in the river. Many cobbles had been used as cores. However, in contrast to Kutikina, there was also a wide range of other raw material exotic to the immediate locality. These included crypto-crystalline cherts and hornfels (indurated mudstone), which may have been derived from the Florentine to the east; chalcedony and jasper; and, finally, large numbers of crystal quartz possibly from Mt Weld to the southeast. In contrast to the Franklin sites, milky quartz was rare. Fascinatingly, a single flake of Darwin Glass was obtained from the middle unit. Bone Cave is 100 km in a direct line from Darwin Crater.

Animal bone, at about 55 000 fragments per m^3, was again present at densities reminiscent of Kutikina. The faunal assemblage from the topmost unit (above the 13 000 BP date) had features suggesting that most of the bone had been accumulated as a result of natural causes, probably by large marsupial carnivores such as the Tasmanian Devil, with infrequent human use. However, within the middle and lower units (between 13 000 and 17 000 BP), it is believed that most of the bone present was due to human actions. Macropods were most common, wombat was frequent, and dasyurids were present. Amongst the macropods, it is believed that the large eastern grey kangaroo *M. giganteus* was commonly represented. This is in contrast with the Kutikina assemblage. The Weld valley is nowadays drier than the Franklin and is wooded with wet sclerophyll, with huge *Eucalyptus obliqua* trees rising above wet scrub and rainforest patches. It is likely that this environment may have been more conducive to the kangaroo, which nowadays is restricted in Tasmania to the dry open eucalypt forests of the eastern ranges. Several bone tools were also obtained, mostly solid awls and a spatula made from wallaby fibulae. There was also a stout blunt point made by grinding the end of a fracture of a macropod tibia.

Bluff Cave, Florentine Valley

This is a small limestone shelter situated at an altitude of 400 m asl in the upper Florentine Valley. It was discovered and excavated by R. Cosgrove in early 1988. A stratigraphic sequence contained archaeological material down to a depth of 0.6 m, below which was a unit of a yellow silty clay resting on manganese-encrusted cobbles (Cosgrove 1989), as at the base of both Kutikina and Deena-Reena. The lowest unit containing archaeological material was a brown clay (Unit 3), which Cosgrove (1989) believes might have originally been derived from the yellow deposit below. He obtained two carbon samples from the very base of this unit at a depth of 0.6 m, which both gave values of 30 000 BP (Cosgrove 1989). If confirmed by further work, the significance of these dates for our understanding of how the first human colonization of Tasmania occurred has been discussed above. Higher up within the same unit 3, were three further dates; one of 24 000 BP at a depth of 0.35 m, one of 27 800 BP at a depth of 0.42 m, and one of 23 600 BP at a depth of 0.53 m. The reasons for the reversals need further investigation, but it seems that this part of the deposit dates from just prior to the LGM. In contrast to the Franklin sites of Kutikina and Deena-Reena, there was no limestone rubble layer, which might reflect milder climatic conditions during the 18 000 peak in this more easterly valley. From a strictly geomorphic point of view, the rubble unit in the western sites gives an independent indication of the coldest temperature regime; and stratigraphically it provides a good buffer against any hypothetical movement of material within the more plastic clay units. The sequence at Bluff Cave was again capped by carbonate flowstone. A carbon sample from within it gave a value of 11 600 BP and one from 10 cm below the surface, within layer 2 (a cemented brown deposit) gave one of 13 100 ± 110 BP (Beta 25381) (Cosgrove 1989). The very top of layer 3, at a depth of 15 cm, had a date of 13 830 ± 220 BP (Beta 25878) (Cosgrove 1989).

The density of stone artefacts at 30 000 flakes per m³, was similar to the Franklin sites. In terms of typological types, the Bluff Cave assemblages are described as being similar to the southwestern sites. There were thumbnail scrapers in Bluff, which made their appearance there soon after the level dated to 24 000 BP. Cosgrove (1989) believes that this means that the technological changes occurred in the Florentine Valley area some 6000–7000 years before they occurred in the Franklin. My instincts are that such a profound technological change as was demonstrated in the Kutikina sequence would have to be bounded fairly tightly in time and space. My prediction is that, eventually, the event will be fairly precisely dated. At present either the Bluff Cave date is wrong, or the Kutikina one is, or both are. Clearly this is an issue for further field research. In Bluff Cave five pieces of Darwin Glass were also found, showing that the occupants of this site were also in some way linked to the broader stone-material trading system and/or seasonal movements of the western groups. Other raw materials at this site were, however, different from those of the southwest, and included cherts, chalcedony, crystal quartz, agate, and the classical material of later eastern assemblages, namely indurated mudstone or hornfels.

The fauna at this site was also rich, and like Bone Cave, included kangaroo and bird, as well as red-necked wallaby and wombat. At Bluff, there were also some remains of platypus (*Ornithorhynchus*) and consistently in most layers, some shell of emu eggs. These are an important seasonal indicator, suggesting late-winter or early-spring visitation at this site.

At Nanwoon Cave, also on the Florentine, a piece of human occipital bone was found as a surface find at the base of an exposed section in a chute behind the talus. Everything in the stratigraphy at this site was consistent with the other caves, and we are of the opinion that there is a high probability that this human bone dates from the late Pleistocene. If this is so, then it is the oldest piece of human bone so far found in Tasmania. Anatomically, it is extremely gracile, delicately formed, with thin walls; a full anatomical description of it has been made by S. Webb (in Jones *et al.* 1988, pp. 10–13). The specimen is consistent in gracility with the Mungo 1 hominid, dated to *c.* 26 000 BP, and is in strong contrast to the extremely robust, with large cranial morphology, displayed by Terminal Pleistocene and Early Holocene hominid series from Kow Swamp and other areas in northern Victoria. The full significance of the Nanwoon fragment cannot be ascertained at present, given the paucity of comparative prehistoric material from Tasmania.[3]

Rock art

In the Kutikina excavation many pieces of ochre were found, including lumps of high-quality iron ore, within the rubble (*c.* 18 000 BP) levels. This haematite must have been brought into the site from a considerable distance away. In all of our work in the Franklin–Gordon caves, many of which were discovered and explored for the first time in our expeditions, no trace of any rock art was found. This prompted the comment, in the conclusion to the first phase of our field research, that no matter how many other apparent similarities there seemed to be between the archaeological record of these palaeo-Tasmanians and that of their contemporaries in southwestern Europe, this absence of rock art was a major difference (Blain *et al.* 1983 pp. 80–1). Three new discoveries have transformed the Tasmanian data base.

The first occurred in 1986 in the remote valley of the Maxwell River, a tributary of the Gordon and only some 12 km due east from the lower Franklin. Here, during a primary exploratory survey, five dolomite caves or rockshelters were found to contain stone tools; including one cave, M86/2, with a deposit more than 0.7 m deep, containing a rich assemblage of stone tools, with thumbnail scrapers and also bone tools (Harris *et al.* 1988). Another cave, Ballawinne[4], had over 100 m of passage. Situated some 20 m from the entrance and in total darkness, were 16 hand-stencils of at least five different individuals. One hand showed either amputation of the middle finger at the first joint, or the fact that the finger had been bent over prior to being stencilled. Also on the walls were small patches of ochre paint. In addition, on five rock-wall protuberances near the entrance to the passage that led down to the stencil gallery, there were large patches of what were described in the field report as 'blood red ochre colouring . . . [which] . . . may have acted as some kind of warning marker to a special area of ritual significance' (Harris et al. 1988). The second find occurred in September 1987 at Judd's Cavern on the lower Cracroft Valley, a southern tributary of the Huon, and thus within the same catchment as the Weld (Jones et al. 1988, pp. 13–20). The third was made in May 1988 during the Weld excavation, when an as yet unnamed cave (TASI, no. 3614) was found near the occupied Bone Cave. The decorated cave was surveyed to have over 100 m of passage, and in one section, 40–50 m in from the entrance in total darkness, there were three red hand-stencils placed on the low ceiling of the cave. None of the stencils was complete and the surfaces of two were covered with a calcium carbonate deposit.

Judd's Cavern in Ordovician limestone was first discovered by a pioneering explorer in 1896 and then lost for more than half a century. It is one of the largest river caves in Australia, with over 1.7 km of explored passage. The valley into which the cave river flows is surrounded by mountains and from its mouth, one can see Federation Peak (1224 m), probably the toughest mountain in the whole of Tasmania and first climbed in the mid-1950s. Lobes of last glacial moraines stem from this massif and also down the valley, close to the cave itself. The art was found mostly in a large, high alcove, 30–35 m in from the entrance, at the very limit of light penetration. It consisted of several panels of hand-stencils and also individual stencils. In one case, the stencils seemed to have been placed as a composition in a narrow sloping track between two shallow ridges of wall-rock. In other areas, there were extensive panels of paint, some on flat wall surfaces and others on rocky columns on the side of the main passage tunnel above the river course. There was something about the purple-brown, shining colour of this paint that reminded me of a series of rock-art sites that I had visited recently (with P. Gorecki) in the Sepik River district of New Guinea, where human blood had been used as a constituent. Accordingly, four tiny samples of pigment were collected from different panels and tested for blood residue by T. Loy (Jones et al. 1988, pp. 17–20). Tests, including anti-mammal Immunoglobin G test, involving colloidal gold Stapylococcal Protein A (gold + Sp A), showed the presence of mammalian blood in two of the panel samples. We are proceeding with further tests to try to ascertain whether or not the blood is human. The alcove area, where most of the art is located, is heavily encrusted with large stalagmites, which cover most of the walls and extend from ceiling to floor in thick columns. The art is found on the few patches of limestone rock not covered by the carbonate. In several instances stalagmites have grown down in front of the stencils, showing that they had definitely formed after the stencil had been blown onto the wall. The main phase of stalagmite formation in this region occurred in Late Glacial and perhaps Holocene times. Every single occupied cave site in southwestern Tasmania has a top date of about 13 000 BP, where the occupation deposits have been sealed by carbonate. We are confident that the art at Judd's Cavern and the other two cave sites belong to the same Late Glacial phase as the occupation deposits, i.e. that they are earlier than 13 000 BP. The technical possibilities of directly dating the blood residue, using AMS techniques have not escaped us.

Furthest south

The southern part of Tasmania was the most southerly place that humans out of Asia were to reach during the great geographical expansion of mankind in Upper Pleistocene times. During a recent voyage from Antarctica and on returning to the southern, storm-swept coast of Tasmania, I was forcibly reminded that in this sector of the globe, from longitude 166°E of New Zealand to longitude 60°W of the coast of Patagonia, Tasmania was the southernmost landmass on which trees grew. I admit that I still express some reservation about the claimed 30 000 BP antiquity for human colonization of South America. In any case, there is no evidence for any occupation of the southern tip of the American continent or of the Magellanic region prior to final Pleistocene times. It is likely that during the height of the Last Ice Age, the hunters of the western Tasmanian valleys were then the southernmost humans on Earth. They alone may have experienced the high latitude, glacier-edge conditions of a southern Ice Age. Even on the preliminary data that we have gathered so far, what strikes me is how similar were many of the climatic and topographic conditions of southwestern Tasmania to some mountain regions of western Europe, such as the Pyrenees, the south German Albs (Weniger, Vol.1, Ch. 9) and the northwestern Greek mountains (Bailey and Gamble, Vol 1, Ch. 8). If we are interested in investigating human responses to parallel climatic and environmental changes, then a comparison of the palaeo-Tasmanians with their Upper Palaeolithic contemporaries of western Europe may have considerable theoretical interest.

Within the Tasmanian situation, one is of course acutely aware of the tentative nature of the data base and of the huge lacunae within it. Where, for example, are the Last Glacial sites of the drier eastern Tasmania? No evidence has been found yet of any inland occupation in the east older than 4000–6000 BP.[5] Is this due to a lack of accurate searching, or were the eastern Tasmanian plains and hill ridges too cold and dry, with dusty storms blowing in from the west? The pattern of occupation within the southwestern caves all seems to finish within a remarkably well-defined time-period at about 13 000–13 400 BP. Was this due to the rapid and catastrophic flooding of the western Bass Strait, which occurred at precisely this time-period, and which may have led to the collapse of a well-integrated seasonal pattern of movement, north–south along the valley corridors of western Tasmania? The end of the Ice Age led to a spread of the rainforest and what had once been the domain of people became an abandoned rainforested wilderness. In many case, our own exploration during the past eight years, took the first human beings into caves abandoned 13 000 years ago. I have, on several occasions, referred to the region as containing quite literally the 'lost valleys of the Ice Age'. On Heard Island in the Southern Ocean, and not far from the sub-Antarctic Convergence, I saw valley glaciers tipping down to the sea; and on the shore only grass tussocks and herb-fields across which cold katabatic winds blew. In my mind's eye, I thought of southern Tasmania during the Last Ice Age through a set of three 10s: Heard Island is 10° of latitude to the south of Tasmania; the average temperature was then close to 10°C colder; and the time was slightly more than 10 000 years ago.

Notes

1 $I = \dfrac{(P)^{0.7}}{E}$

2 To convert to cubic measurements, it is worth noting that one cubic metre of deposit weighs approximately 1000 kg.
3 The specimen is under the custodianship of the Tasmanian Aboriginal Centre at their Keeping Place in Oyster Cove.
4 After the general term in most Tasmanian Aboriginal languages for red ochre.
5 I exclude the ORS 7 sandstone shelter on the Shannon, an upper tributary of the Derwent, 30 km east of the Florentine confluence, discovered by Cosgrove in early 1988 and dated by him as 17 000 BP at least, and possibly extending back to 30 000 BP (Cosgrove in press).

References

Allen, H. 1977. Archaeology of the East Alligator Rivers region, western Arnhem Lane. Unpublished seminar paper. Department of Anthropology, University of Auckland.
Allen, H. & G. Barton 1989. Ngarradj Warde Djobkeng and the prehistory of Arnhem Land. *Oceania Monographs*. Sydney: University of Sydney.
Allen, J., R. Cosgrove & S. Brown 1988. New archaeological data from the Southern Forests region, Tasmania: A preliminary statement. *Australian Archaeology* **27**, 75–88.
Allen, J., C. Gosden, R. Jones & J. P. White 1988. Pleistocene dates for the human colonisation of New Ireland, northern Melanesia. *Nature* **331**, 707–9.

Balme, J. 1980. An analysis of charred bone from Devil's lair, Western Australia. *Archaeology and Physical Anthropology in Oceania* **15**, 81–5.
Barton, G. 1979. Ngarrdj Warde Jobkeng (sic) rock-shelter, western Arnhem Land: An analysis and assessment of the flaked stone assemblage. Unpublished MA thesis, University of Auckland.
Blain, B., R. Fullager, D. Ranson, J. Allen, S. Harris, R. Jones, E. Stadler,

R. Cosgrove & G. Middleton 1983. The Australian National University – Tasmanian National Parks and Wildlife Service archaeological expedition to the Franklin and Gordon Rivers, 1983: A summary of results. *Australian Archaeology* **16**, 71–83.

Blom, W. M. 1988. Late Quaternary sediments and sea-levels in Bass Basin, south eastern Australia. A preliminary report. *Search* **19** (2): 94–6.

Bowdler, S. 1974. Pleistocene date for man in Tasmania. *Nature* **252**, 697.

Bowdler, S. 1977. The coastal colonization of Australia. In *Sunda and Sahul: Prehistoric studies in southeast Asia, Melanesia and Australia*, J. Allen, J. Golson & R. Jones (eds), 205–46. New York: Academic Press.

Bowdler, S. 1984. Hunter Hill, Hunter Island. *Terra Australis 8*. Canberra: Department of Prehistory, Research School of Pacific Studies, Australian National University.

Bowler, J. M. 1976a. Recent developments in reconstructing late Quaternary environments in Australia. In *The origins of the Australians*, R. L. Kirk & A. G. Thorne (eds), 55–77. Canberra: Australian Institute of Aboriginal Studies.

Bowler, J. M. 1976b. Aridity in Australia: Age, origins and expression in aeolian landforms and sediments. *Earth-Science Reviews* **12**, 279–310.

Bowler, J. M. 1978. Glacial age aeolian events at high and low latitudes: A southern hemisphere perspective. In *Antarctic glacial history and world palaeoenvironments*, E. M. van Zinderen Bakker (ed.), 149–72. Rotterdam: A. A. Balkema.

Bowler, J. M., R. Jones, H. Allen & A. G. Thorne 1970. Pleistocene human remains from Australia: A living site and human cremation from Lake Mungo. *World Archaeology* **12**, 39–60.

Bowler, J. M., G. S. Hope, J. N. Jennings, G. Singh & D. Walker 1976. Late Quaternary climates of Australia and New Guinea. *Quaternary Research* **6**, 359–94.

Bulmer, S. 1966. The prehistory of the Australian New Guinea Highlands. Unpublished MA Thesis, University of Auckland.

Bulmer, S. 1975. Settlement and economy in prehistoric Papua New Guinea: A review of the archaeological evidence. *Journal de la Société des Océanistes* **31**(46), 7–75.

Bulmer, S. & R. Bulmer 1964. The prehistory of the Australian New Guinea Highlands. *American Anthropologist* **66**(4), 39–76.

Brown, P. 1987. Pleistocene homogeneity and Holocene size reduction: The Australian human skeletal evidence. *Archaeology in Oceania* **22**, 41–67.

Chappell, J. M. A. 1983. Sea-level changes 0 to 40 ka. In *Proceedings of the 1st CLIMANZ Conference, Howman's Gap, Victoria, 8–13 February 1981: A symposium of results and discussions concerned with late Quaternary climatic history of Australia, New Zealand and surrounding seas*, J. M. A. Chappell & J. Grindrod (eds), 121–2. Canberra: Department of Biogeography and Geomorphology, Australian National University.

Chappell, J. M. & J. Grindrod (eds), 1983. *Proceedings of the 1st CLIMANZ Conference, Harman's Gap, Victoria, 8–13 February 1981: A symposium of results and discussions concerned with late Quaternary climatic history of Australia, New Zealand and surrounding seas*. Canberra: Department of Biogeography and Geomorphology, Australian National University.

Childe, V. G. 1956. *Piecing together the past: The interpretation of archaeological data*. London: Routledge & Kegan Paul.

Christian, G. S. & A. Sharp-Paul 1979. *Lower Gordon River scientific survey: Description of the biophysical environment*. Hobart: Hydro-Electric Commission, Tasmania.

Cosgrove, R. 1989. Thirty thousand years of human colonization in Tasmania – new Pleistocene dates. *Science* **243**, 1706–8.

Dorn, R. I., M. Nobbs & T. A. Cahill 1988. Cation-ratio dating of rock-engravings from the Olary Province of arid South Australia. *Antiquity* **62**, 681–9.

Dortch, C. 1984. *Devil's Lair, a study in prehistory*. Perth: Western Australian Museum.

East, T. J., A. S. Murray, G. C. Nanson & R. L. Clark 1987. Late Quaternary evolution of Magela Creek sand-beds channels. In *Alligators Rivers Research Institute Annual Research Summary 1985–86*, 14–17. Canberra: Australian Government Publishing Service.

Fudali, R. F. & R. J. Ford 1979. Darwin Glass and Darwin Crater: A progress report. *Meteorites* **14**, 283.

Geering, K. 1983. Preliminary analysis of the faunal remains from Kutikina Cave, Franklin River, 1981 excavation. Unpublished manuscript. Canberra: Australian Heritage Commission.

Gillespie, R. W. & R. B. Temple 1976. Sydney University natural radiocarbon measurements III. *Radiocarbon* **18**, 96–109.

Gillespie, R. W. & R. B. Temple 1977. Radiocarbon dating of shell midden. *Archaeology and Physical Anthropology in Oceania* **12**, 26–37.

Goede, A. & P. Murray 1977. Pleistocene man in south central Tasmania: Evidence from a cave site in the Florentine Valley. *Mankind* **11**, 2–10.

Goede, A. & J. L. Bada 1985. Electron spin resonance dating of Quaternary bone material from Tasmanian caves – a comparison with ages determined by aspartic acid racemization and C^{14}. *Australian Journal of Earth Sciences* **32**, 155–62.

Groube, L., J. Chappell, J. Muke & D. Price 1986. A 40 000 year old occupation site at Huon Peninsula, Papua New Guinea. *Nature* **324**, 453–5.

Harris, S., D. Ranson & S. Brown 1988. Maxwell River archaeological survey 1986. *Australian Archaeology* **27**, 89–97.

Hays, J. D., J. Lozano, N. Shackleton & G. Irving 1976. Reconstruction of the Atlantic Ocean and western Indian Ocean sectors of the 18 000 BP Antarctic Ocean. In Investigations of Late Quaternary paleoceonography and paleclimatology, R. M. Clive & J. D. Hayes (eds). *Geological Society Memoir* **145**, 337–72.

Hiscock, P. 1985. The need for a taphonomic perspective in stone artefact analysis. *Queensland Archaeological Research* **2**, 82–97.

Hiscock, P. n.d. Pleistocene abandonment of arid central Australia.

Hope, G., P. J. Hughes & J. Russell-Smith 1985. Geomorphological fieldwork and the evolution of the landscape of Kakadu National Park, In *Archaeological research in Kakadu National Park*, R. Jones (ed.), Canberra: Special Publication No. 13. 229–40.

Ikawa-Smith, F. 1979. Technological traditions in late Pleistocene and early Holocene Japan. Paper presented to 14th Pacific Science Congress, Khabarovsk, 21–24 August.

Jennings, J. N. 1971. Sea level changes and land links. In *Aboriginal man and environment in Australia*, D. J. Mulvaney & J. Golson (eds), 1–13. Canberra: Australian National University Press.

Johnson, K. A. 1977. Methods for the census of wallaby and possum in Tasmania. *Wildlife Division Technical Report 7712*. Hobart: National Parks and Wildlife Service, Tasmania.

Jones, R. 1971. Rocky cape and the problem of the Tasmanians. Unpublished PhD thesis, University of Sydney, Sydney.

Jones, R. 1973. Emerging picture of Pleistocene Australians. *Nature* **246**, 275–81.

Jones, R. 1984. Hunters and history: A case study from western Tasmania. In *Past and present in hunter gatherer studies*, C. Schrire (ed.), 27–65. New York: Academic Press.

Jones, R. (ed.) 1985a. *Archaeological research in Kakadu National Park*. Canberra: Australian National parks and Wildlife Service, Special Publication No. 13.

Jones, R. 1985b. New research aims, Aboriginal liaison and field strategy. In *Archaeological research in Kakadu National Park*, R. Jones (ed.), 17–29. Canberra:

Australian National Parks and Wildlife Service, Special Publication No. 13.

Jones, R. 1987a. Pleistocene life in the dead heart of Australia. *Nature* **328**, 666.

Jones, R. 1987b. Hunting forbears. In *The flow of culture: Tasmanian studies*, M. Roe (ed.), 14–49. Canberra: Australian Academy of the Humanities.

Jones, R. 1987c. Tasmania's ice-age hunters. *Australian Geographic* **8**(4), 26–45.

Jones, R. 1988. The southern continent: an episode in human colonization. In *Perspectives in human biology: The University of Western Australia 1987 Octagon Lecture Series*, N.W. Bruce, L. Freedman & W. F. C. Blumer (eds), 75–98. Perth: Centre for Human Biology, the University of Western Australia.

Jones, R. 1989. East of Wallace's Line: issues and problems in the colonisation of the Australian continent. In *The human revolution*, P. Mellars & C. Stringer (eds). Edinburgh and Princeton: Edinburgh University Press and Princeton University Press, in press.

Jones, R. & J. Allen 1984. Archaeological investigations in the Andrew River Valley, Acheron River Valley and at Precipitous Bluff, southwest Tasmania, February 1984. *Australian Archaeology* **19**, 86–101.

Jones, R. & J. M. Bowler 1980. Struggle for the savanna: Northern Australia in ecological and prehistoric perspective. In *Northern Australia: Options and implications*, R. Jones (ed.) 3–31. Canberra: Research School of Pacific Studies, Australian National University.

Jones, R. & I. Johnson 1985a. Rockshelter excavations: Nourlangie and Mt Brockman massifs. In *Archaeological research in Kakadu National Park*, R. Jones (ed.), 39–76. Canberra: Australian National Parks and Wildlife Service, Special Publications No. 13.

Jones, R. & I. Johnson 1985b. Deaf Adder Gorge: Lindner site, Nauwalabila I. In *Archaeological research in Kakadu National Park*, R. Jones (ed.), 165–228. Canberra: Australian National Parks and Wildlife Service, Special Publications No. 13.

Jones, R. & T. Negerevich 1985. A review of previous archaeological work. In *Archaeological research in Kakadu National Park*, R. Jones (ed.), 1–16. Canberra: Australian National Parks and Wildlife Service, Special Publications No. 13.

Jones, R., R. Fullagar & D. Ranson. in prep. Analysis of stone tool assemblages in Kutikina Cave, Franklin Valley, Tasmania.

Jones, R., D. Ranson, J. Allen & K. Kiernan 1983. The Australian National University – Tasmanian National Parks and Wildlife Service archaeological expedition to the Franklin River, 1982. A summary of results. *Australian Archaeology* **16**, 57–70.

Jones, R., R. Cosgrove, J. Allen, S. Lane, K. Kiernan, S. Webb, T. Loy, D. West & E. Stadler 1988. An archaeological reconnaissance of Karst caves within the Southern Forests region of Tasmania, September 1987. *Australian Archaeology* **26**, 1–23.

Kamminga, J. & H. Allen 1973. Report of the archaeological survey. Alligator Rivers Environmental Fact-finding Study, Canberra.

Kiernan, K., R. Jones & D. Ranson 1983. New evidence from Fraser Cave for Glacial age man in south west Tasmania. *Nature* **301**, 28–32.

Loeffler, E. 1972. *Geomorphology of Papua New Guinea*. Canberra: Australian National University Press.

Loy, T. H. & R. Jones in prep. Residue analysis and the identification of function of Late Pleistocene and Early Holocene stone tools from Tasmania.

McCarthy, F. D. & F. M. Setzler 1960. The archaeology of Arnhem Land. In *Records of the American–Australian Scientific Expedition to Arnhem Land*. Vol. 2: *Anthropology and nutrition*, C. P. Mountford (ed.), 215–95. Melbourne: Melbourne University Press.

Magee, J. W. & P. J. Hughes 1982. Thin-section analysis and the geomorphic history of the Colless Creek archaeological site in northwestern Queensland. In *Archaeometry:*

An Australasian perspective, W. Ambrose & P. Djerden (eds), 120–8. Canberra: Department of Prehistory, Research School of Pacific Studies, Australian National University.

Mountain, M. J. 1979. The rescue of the ancestors in Papua New Guinea. Institute of Archaeology, University of London, Bulletin **16**, 63–80.

Mountain, M. J. 1981. Digging into yesterday. *Paradise* **27**, 25–9. Port Moresby: Air Niugini.

Mulvaney, D. J. & E. B. Joyce 1965. Archaeological and geomorphological investigations on Mt Moffatt Station Queensland, Australia. *Proceedings of the Prehistoric Society* **31**, 147–212.

Oda, S. & C. T. Keally 1973. Edge-ground stone tools from the Japanese preceramic culture. *Busshitsu Bunka [Material Culture]* **22**, 1–26.

Pearce, R. H. & M. Barbetti 1981. A 38 000 year old archaeological site at Upper Swan, Western Australia. *Archaeology in Oceania* **16**(3), 173–8.

Ride, W. D. L. 1970. *A Guide to the Native Mammals of Australia*. London: Oxford University Press.

Rosenfeld, A., D. Horton & J. Winter 1981. Early man in north Queensland: Art and archaeology in the Laura area. *Terra Australis 6*. Canberra: Department of Prehistory, Research School of Pacific Studies, Australian National University.

Schrire, C. (formerly White) 1982. The Alligator Rivers: Prehistory and ecology in western Arnhem Land. *Terra Australis 7*. Canberra: Department of Prehistory, Research School of Pacific Studies, Australian National University.

Shawcross, F. W. & M. Kaye 1980. Australian archaeology: Implications of current interdisciplinary research. *Interdisciplinary Science Reviews* **5**, 112–28.

Smith, M. A. 1987. Pleistocene occupation in arid central Australia. *Nature* **328**, 710–11.

Smith, M. A. 1988. Central Australian seed grinding implements and Pleistocene grindstones. In *Archaeology with ethnography: An Australian perspective*, B. Meehan & R. Jones (eds). 94–108. Canberra: Department of Prehistory, Research School of Pacific Studies, Australian National University.

Veth, P. 1987. Martutjara prehistory: Variation in arid zone adaptations. *Australian Archeology* **25**, 101–22.

Veth, P. 1988. Islands in the interior: A model for the colonisation of Australia's arid zone. Paper presented to Australian Archaeological Association Conference, Armidale, 15–18 December.

White, C. 1967a. Plateau and plain. Unpublished PhD thesis, Australian National University, Canberra.

White, C. 1967b. The prehistory of the Kakadu people. *Mankind* **6**, 426–31.

White, C. 1967c. Early stone axes in Arnhem land. *Antiquity* **41**, 149–52.

White, J. P., K. A. W. Crook & B. P. Ruxton. 1970. Kosipe: A late Pleistocene site in the Papuan Highlands. *Proceedings of the Prehistoric Society* **36**, 152–70.

Wickler, S. & M. Spriggs 1988. Pleistocene human occupation of the Solomon Islands, Melanesia. *Antiquity* **62**(237), 703–6.

Woodroffe, C. D., J. M. A. Chappell, B. G. Thom & E. Wallensky 1986. *Geomorphological dynamics and evolution of the South Alligator tidal river and plains, Northern Territory*. Darwin: Australian National University North Australia Research Unit.

Wright, R. V. S. 1971. The cave. In *Archaeology of the Gallus site, Koonalda Cave*, R. V. S. Wright (ed.), 22–30. Canberra: Australian Institute of Aboriginal Studies.

15 Environmental history in southwestern New South Wales during the Late Pleistocene

HARRY ALLEN

Introduction

The major rivers of the Murray–Darling system, the Murray, Murrumbidgee, Lachlan, and Darling rivers, flow through the southern part of the Murray Basin and experience similar local conditions (Fig. 15.1). Their headwaters, however, are situated in different parts of the Eastern Divide, which follows a south to north arc along the coastal hinterland of eastern Australia. Variations in environmental conditions along this divide are sufficient to produce differences in the seasonal flow regimes and discharges of these inland-flowing rivers.

While each of these rivers clearly responded to the regional environmental changes that affected the entire Murray Basin at the end of the Pleistocene, the nature of their responses differed in timing and degree. Lakes fed by the different rivers also showed varying responses. For this reason it is appropriate to discuss the environmental histories of the Willandra Lakes, Lake Victoria, and the Darling River (Fig. 15.2) in separate sections, while drawing attention to any common elements which existed in the responses they exhibited.

The Willandra Lakes

The Willandra Lakes are the largest dry lakes in New South Wales. They occupy an area of 1000 km^2 of semiarid sand dune country between the lower Lachlan and Darling rivers. They are lunette lakes – dry, shallow, deflation basins, subelliptical in plan, with regular transverse crescentic dunes on their eastern margins (Bowler 1970, p. 106) (see Fig. 15.3).

These lakes were fed by the Willandra Creek, an overflow channel of the Lachlan River, which now carries water only during peak or flood discharges. Under today's conditions of low annual rainfall (c. 300 mm), high evaporation (2800 mm) and low river discharges, water does not even reach these lakes let alone fill them to overflowing.

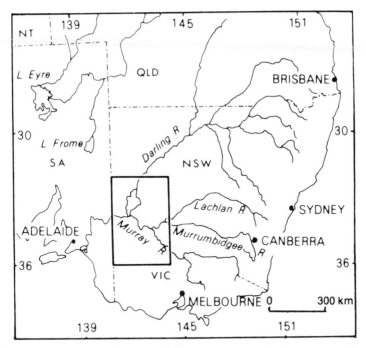

Figure 15.1   Location diagram: southwestern New South Wales and northwestern Victoria (from Bowler & Magee 1978).

Geomorphological work by Bowler has revealed that the Willandra Lakes have been through a number of hydrological cycles. The final one of these began towards the end of the last interglacial, 100 000 years ago or before. From 100 000 to 50 000 BP the lake system was dry. The Mungo Lacustral Phase covers the period 50 000–25 000 BP when the lakes were full and contained a freshwater fauna that attracted Aboriginal groups to their shores. The final phase, the Mungo–Zanci Arid Period (25 000–15 000 BP), was a time when the lakes formed a closed system and were in an oscillatory, highly saline phase, clay dunes were built up on most of the lunettes, and away from the lakes, linear and subparabolic dunes became mobile (Bowler 1980, pp. 22–5).

After that the entire lake system became inactive, the Willandra Creek ceased to flow and, as a result of recolonization by mallee vegetation, dune mobilization ceased. Mallee is a low scrub dominated by eucalpyts having many stems arising from a large, underground, woody swelling composed of stem tissue (Parsons 1981, p. 227). It is well suited to dry, sandy environments, particularly if subject to frequent fires.

Since c. 15 000 BP the area has been subject to erosion but no major geomorphic events have occurred to reshape the landscape, as Bowler notes: 'Despite many thousands of years of disuse the overflow channel through the dunes remains well defined, suggesting little or no aeolian modification since it was last active' (Bowler 1970, p. 106).

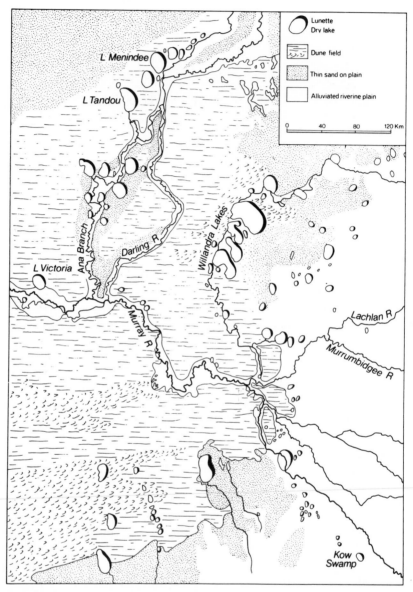

Figure 15.2 Geomorphological features in western New South Wales and Victoria (from Bowler 1971, in Hope 1978).

Archaeological sites in the Willandra Lakes area, 22 000–15 000 BP

Introduction

Two factors affect our knowledge of archaeological sites in the Willandra Lakes area during the 22 000–15 000 BP period. The first is the preservation and visibility of sites on the landscape. The second factor concerns the adequacy or otherwise of archaeological surveying in the area.

Deposition sequences associated with the lunette and mallee dune build-up have preserved many archaeological sites in datable contexts. Erosion, as a result of firing and the grazing of introduced animals on this landscape, occasionally uncovers these sites and thus increases their visibility, but in doing so exposes them to destructive elements. Sites are most visible and accessible around the lake shores and stream courses. Archaeological attention has focused on these areas, particularly where sedimentary sequences exist, such as on the lunettes. Only recently have surveys of areas away from these foci been undertaken, generally as part of an environmental impact study for a development project (McIntyre 1981).

The initial surveys by Allen and others during the period 1968–1972 concentrated on the lake margins and on scattered sites located over a huge area (Shawcross & Kaye 1980, pp. 116–19). Since then, Mulvaney, Shawcross, McBryde, and others (Shawcross & Kaye 1980, pp. 119–26) have carried out excavations and controlled surveying along the Lake Mungo Lunette. Systematic surveying of the area between Lake Mungo and Garnpung and other portions of the Willandra Lakes area has been undertaken by McIntyre since 1976.

A recurrent problem concerns the integrity of the archaeological material collected from eroded open sites which lack any stratigraphic association with the lunette depositional sequences. Dare-Edwards, McIntyre, and Hope (Dare-Edwards, 1980, pp. 37–8, Hope *et al.* 1983, pp. 45–53) have developed surveying and collecting techniques that are closely related to soil stratigraphic units in an attempt to overcome this problem. Clark is currently bringing together information on the 300 archaeological sites and 120 radiocarbon dates recorded from the Willandra Lakes to date (Hope 1985, p. 33, Clark pers. comm.). Although there has been some publication of the results of these latter surveys, the material from the first phase of archaeological work is still all that is available in any detail.

The archaeological sites surveyed during 1968–72 are listed below under three headings (a) midden sites; (b) quarry sites and artefact scatters; and (c) hearth or oven sites. Included within this listing is some discussion of the archaeological findings relating to the interpretation of site age, stratigraphy, or contents. Possible changes in Aboriginal subsistence and population numbers relative to the Late Pleistocene environmental changes are discussed later in this chapter.

In this region, dates on shellfish are likely to give a better indication of true age than do charcoal dates (Allen 1972, p. 319, Kefous 1983). All radiocarbon dates are uncorrected and are given in years BP.

While the field evidence discussed below concentrates on the Willandra Lakes area from 22 000–15 000 BP, it is necessary to know what happened in the area before and after this time-period, and what was happening in adjacent regions, in order to interpret the Willandra data. A comparison of the few sites older than 22 000 BP with those dating from 22 000 to 15 000 BP did not reveal significant differences in faunal or artefact contents, site types or their location (Allen 1972, pp. 329–38, Barbetti & Allen 1972, p. 48). As far as we can extend the evidence from the durable aspects on these sites and their internal relationships, we can speculate that there were no major changes in Aboriginal equipment and foraging patterns over the period that the lakes were operative (40 000–15 000 BP). The virtual absence of signs of Pleistocene human occupation in the Flinders Range, Strzelecki Desert, Cooper Basin, and the shores of Lake Frome and Lake Torrens, despite extensive surveying by Lampert & Hughes (Lampert 1983, p. 176), however, and an absence of human evidence from similar Pleistocene lunette lakes in semiarid southwestern Western Australia (J. Bowler pers. comm.) supports the conclusion that inland Australia was not universally occupied throughout the time-period in question (30 000–5000 BP).

From these pieces of evidence we can infer that the Willandra Lakes sites, dating between 30 000 and 15 000 BP, were probably used by a small localized population whose generalized hunting and gathering economy was focused on the exploitation of the lakes and nearby plains for at least some part of the year and possibly the entire year. The vagueness of this description is unfortunate, but it does draw attention to the lack of information about seasonal movements and settlement patterns during this early period.

The Mungo–Zanci Arid Period ended with the final drying of the entire lake system. This must have caused some disruption to the patterns of Aboriginal settlement and subsistence that had operated in the region during the period 40 000–c.15 000 BP. The virtual absence of dates and traces of Aboriginal occupation in the Willandra area between 15 000 BP and 5000 BP documented below supports the idea of less intensive settlement, if not total abandonment, after the lakes dried up. More recent surveys of dated sites confirm this observation (Clark pers. comm.). While the absence of deposition since 15 000 BP, when the local area reverted to semiarid plains and dunefield, may have decreased the chances of site survival during the period 15 000–5000 BP, this factor cannot explain why sites become more common after 5000 BP. Thus it is the very nature of the environmental changes that occurred in the period 15 000 BP to 5000 BP and the likely Aboriginal responses to them that makes it difficult for us to gather much evidence about these changes from the Willandra Lakes area alone.

The climatic events which led to the demise of the Willandra system also had their impact on lakes and rivers which continued to function elsewhere in the region. The period following 15 000 BP was characterized by lower discharges and a lower sediment-carrying capacity of the Murray and Darling rivers. The population previously supported by the resources in the Willandra Lakes could move to the rivers and lakes on the adjacent Lachlan, Murray and Darling rivers. The environments they encountered there would already be under some form of climatic stress. Shell-middens and sites near rivers and lakes that continued to function in the Murray–Darling Region after 15 000 BP often return dates within the 15 000–5000 BP period (Allen 1972, p. 332, Gill 1973, pp. 57–8, Kefous 1983).

In this climatic and cultural context we would expect a number of changes in Aboriginal subsistence and demography. However, we can only speculate about the impact of these environmental and demographic changes until we have information about the distribution and density of Aboriginal populations in the region, the seasonal pattern of movements being made, and the social relations which existed between the groups making them.

Detailed comparisons with regions where lakes and rivers did not entirely dry up over the past 15 000 years is needed to document possible changes in the exploitation of rivers, lakes, and their peripheral resource zones. Such studies are currently being pursued by Hope and co-workers on the Darling River (Hope 1981), on Talyawalka Creek by J. Balme, and on Lake Victoria, at the junction of the Darling and Murray rivers, by Kefous (1983).

Similarly, an understanding of the Aboriginal exploitation of the semiarid dunes and plains of the post-lacustrine Willandra area can only come from comparisons with regions that did not experience a lacustrine phase during the Late Pleistocene and consequently showed a degree of continuity of semiarid conditions. Such areas include the Victorian mallee (Ross 1981a) and the Cobar Peneplain (Ross 1981b, Bonhomme 1984). In the mallee and dune areas of northwestern Victoria evidence for aboriginal occupation of drier country prior to c. 5000 BP is rare (Ross 1981a, pp. 145–55, 1985).

While the vagaries of site preservation and the adequacy of archaeological surveys have clearly played some part in producing the pattern of dates discussed below, less intensive occupation of the semiarid Willandra region in the Post-Zanci to mid-Recent period compared to the previous Mungo Lacustral Phase and the Mungo–Zanci Arid Period is likely to be a contributing factor.

After 5000 BP archaeological conditions again seem to have changed. The number of hearths and ovens in the Willandra area that date to the period since 5000 BP suggests a recent increase in Aboriginal numbers and new abilities to exploit the limited resources of the region. This renewed or more intensive Aboriginal presence in the Willandra Lakes area during the recent period occurred despite the absence of local water runoff, when conditions were, if anything, drier than at present (Wasson 1976, p. 100). Because of the soil-drainage characteristics of most of the surrounding dune and plains country, the dry Willandra Lake basins were likely to be areas, first, where water was temporarily retained, and, secondly, where ephemeral grasses which require inundation for germination, such as *Panicum decompositum*, would flourish. These are circumstances in which we might expect the reoccupation, for quite different reasons, of some of the older Willandra Lakes sites. In such situations, seed-grinding stones and other stone artefacts could easily be incorporated with the older faunal and artefactual material, thus creating archaeological situations that are difficult to disentangle. These are some of the problems and potentialities of archaeological work in semiarid southeastern Australia.

Midden sites

From Figure 15.3 it can be seen that five major lake depressions, all now dry, make up the prehistoric Willandra Lakes system. These are Lakes Arumpo, Mungo, Leaghur, Garnpung, and Mulurulu. Nine midden sites on these lake depressions date, or have been assumed to date, between 22 000 and *c*. 15 000 BP. The sites are listed in order from the southernmost on Lake Arumpo/ Chibnalwood to the northernmost on Lake Mulurulu.

The middens are described in terms of their geographical position on these lake depressions whether near or on the lunette, generally the northeast shore away from the presumed direction of the prevailing winds during the Late Pleistocene at the time when the lunettes were formed, or on the backshore, generally the southwestern shore opposite the lunette and towards the presumed direction of the prevailing winds.

ARUMPO LUNETTE

Bowler (pers. comm.) reports a shell date from a midden on the Outer Arumpo Lunette, N–1664 equal to 22 600 ± 430 BP.

LEAGHUR BACKSHORE I

This site consists of eight small midden mounds of freshwater mussel (*Velesunio ambiguus*) situated on a sandy promontory extending into the western (backshore) margin of Pleistocene Lake Leaghur. Each mound is about 2 m in diameter, but only 15 cm thick. They are scattered over an area 45 m × 45 m. No other faunal remains occur at the site and there are only a few stone artefacts present. Although undated, the stratigraphic situation and appearance of these middens suggests an age similar to the Leaghur backshore II site, discussed below.

LEAGHUR BACKSHORE II

Two extensive areas of blown-out dune covered with scattered freshwater mussel (*V. ambiguus*) on the central northwestern margin of Lake Leaghur (Fig. 15.3). Only small sections of the midden are *in situ* in a grey-brown soil horizon. A shell sample (ANU-461) gave a determination of 15 690 ± 235.

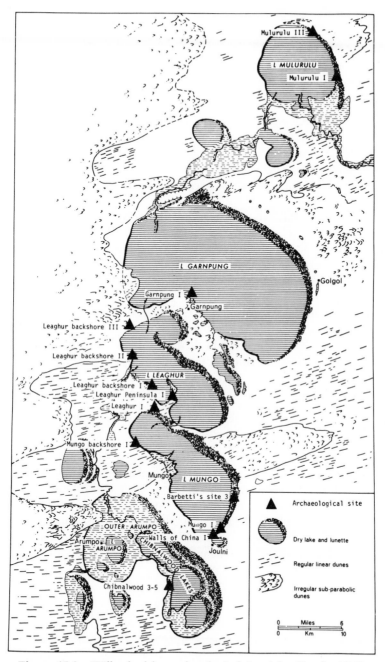

Figure 15.3 Willandra lakes archaeological sites (after Bowler 1971).

LEAGHUR BACKSHORE III

A thin layer of freshwater mussel shells, with no other fauna and few stone artefacts, located on the northwestern margin of the lake.

GARNPUNG I

Garnpung I is located on a sandy promontory that extends out into the western margin of Lake Garnpung. The midden occurs in a similar situation to the Leaghur backshore sites. Although there are seven exposures with stone artefacts, only a small part (30 m × 30 m) of the total area of one exposure (GN 1A and 1B, 90 m × 60 m) is covered with a scatter of freshwater mussel shells.

In a few parts of this exposure *in situ* midden is preserved in a layer *c*. 8 cm thick. ^{14}C dates for charcoal (ANU-373A, 13 920 ± 480 BP) and shell (ANU–373B, 15 480 ± 210 BP) collected from this layer indicate that the shellfish were gathered at about the same time as the final freshwater phase in the lake. *Velesunio ambiguus* require fresh to brackish water.

In addition to the estimated 50–100 m^3 of mussel shell that may have been originally present on the site, other evidence indicates that extensive, if somewhat specialized, collecting activities were carried out along this lake's windward shore. This evidence is in the form of gastroliths from freshwater crayfish (*Cherax destructor* – minimum number 27), otoliths from freshwater perch (*Plectroplites ambiguus* – minimum number 244, estimated mean length 400 mm and weight 1100 g), and eggshell fragments from an unidentified bird (not emu – 585 fragments) (see Table 15.1).

Artefacts (2473 in total) were collected from marked squares on areas GN 1A and 1B. These mainly consisted of unmodified flakes (73%) and cores (7%). The artefacts had a density of distribution of 20 per m^2 in the area collected. However, similar artefacts with a similar density of occurrence can be associated with a hearth dated to 3560 ± 85 (ANU–701) in an adjacent red-brown soil horizon. Consequently, it is not known whether any of the artefacts collected from the surface of the midden horizon can be definitely associated with the 15 000-year-old shell-midden. Backed flakes, adze flakes, and retouched scrapers are prominent elements in the Garnpung collections.

GARNPUNG SHORELINE SEDIMENTS

Although not a midden date, ANU–266, 15 400 ± 210 for Unionid shells excavated from a trench through lacustrine shoreline sediments in the inner (W) margin of Lake Garnpung Lunette, is of interest because as Bowler notes, the 'age ... is consistent with final drying of system. L. Garnpung is on upstream end of system and probably received freshwater inflow from waning discharge of Willandra Ck. After L. Mungo and L. Chibnalwood had already dried. Consequently final drying in L. Chibnalwood near 16 780 (ANU–320) occurs before that in L. Garnpung ...' (Polach *et al.* 1970, pp. 1–18).

Table 15.1 Faunal remains from archaeological middens at the Willandra Lakes and Lake Tandou, New South Wales (from Allen 1972, in Hope 1978).

Species	Mungo I	Leaghur I	Leaghur Peninsula I		Garnpung I	Mulurulu I	Mulurulu IIIA	Mulurulu IIIB	Mulurulu IIIC	Tandou III
years BP	26 000	26 000	15 000	no date	15 000	15 000	13 000–15 000	no date	no date	no date
cf. *Megaleia rufa*					1		1			
Macropus cf. *giganteus*			1	2			1			
Macropus cf. *robustus*						1				
Macropus cf. *cooperi*							1			
Large macropodid	4								1	
Lagorchestes spp.	4		2			9	37	14	3	2
Onychogalea cf. *fraenata*				2			1			1
Bettongia lesueur	1		1				7			
Bettongia penicillata	1					4	6	2		4
Bettongia spp.			1	2		3	3	3	1	1
Caloprymnus campestris			1				4			
Small macropodid	3	1					2	2		
Trichosurus vulpecula										
Lasiorhinus sp.	1									1
Perameles cf. *bougainville*	1					3	3		1	1
Isoodon obesulus							2			1
Sarcophilus harrisii							1	1		1
Dasyurus maculatus								2		
Dasyurus cf. *geoffroii*	2						1	1		
cf. *Dasycercus cristicauda*										
Rattus lutreolus	1						1		1	
Rattus sp.						1				
Leporillus conditor				1		2	3			2
cf. *Notomys* or *Pseudomys*				1		2	1			
Bird	3						3			4
Lizard	2	1					2	1		
Plectroplites ambiguus	130		1		244	172	12	14	1	1
Macullochella macquariensis						1				
cf. *Cherax destructor*					27				18	
Mussel shell	+	+	+		+	+	+	+	+	+
Eggshell	+	+		+	+	+	+		+	+

MULURULU I

 This site consists of ten small midden heaps of freshwater mussel shell scattered
along an area (135 m × 60 m) of sandy deposit on the southeastern end of the
Lake Mulurulu Lunette. Fish and mammalian remains are associated with
some of the middens. A series of samples of burnt and unburnt shell from
midden no. 2 (ANU–880A, 15 120 ± 235; ANU 880B, 15 450 ± 240)
indicate that these middens were deposited at about the same time as the
Garnpung and Leaghur backshore middens.

 Except for a few eroded pieces of grindstone, there were no stone artefacts
associated with these middens. A sample of material from the bone scatter
associated with middens 7–10 from an area c. 60 m^2 (one-third to a half of the
total area of scatter) included a minimum number of 25 mammals ranging in
size from the medium-sized wallaroo (M. robustus 38 ± 10 kg) to the tiny
hopping mouse (Notomys or Pseudomys sp. < 100 g). Small mammals c.
1–5 kg) such as hare-wallabies (Lagorchestes spp.), rat-kangaroos (Bettongia spp.
and Bettongia penicillata), and bandicoots (Perameles cf. bougainville) were the
most common. This is a pattern repeated at the other Mulurulu midden sites
(see Table 15.1 and below). In addition, otoliths indicated the presence of at
least 172 freshwater perch (P. ambiguus, estimated mean length 350 mm and
weight 640 g) and one Murray Cod (Macculochella macquariensis). There were
also a few fragments of emu eggshell.

MULURULU IIIA

Twelve small freshwater mussel middens dotted along a 1 km length of the
northern end of the Lake Mulurulu Lunette. ^{14}C samples taken from midden
6 (ANU–984A, 12 800 ± 990 BP – charcoal) and (ANU–948B, 15 560 ±
240 BP – shell) again indicate contemporaneity with the middens at Leaghur
and Garnpung. All middens at MLIIIA are located on a layer of quartz beach
sands independently dated to 15 490 ± 740 BP (ANU–882). Aeolian clay
lunette deposits, which are the most recent lunette deposits at lakes Garnpung,
Leaghur, Mungo, and Chibnalwood, are absent at Lake Mulurulu. This
suggests that the final lacustral phase at Mulurulu, the northernmost Willandra
Lake and the one closest to the Lachlan River water source, was different to
that of the other lakes. Possibly conditions changed abruptly at Mulurulu from
a high freshwater to a dry stage without any intervening, highly saline,
oscillatory, phase.

 Few stone artefacts, apart from grindstone fragments, were associated with
MLIIIA middens 1–5. A carbonate-covered bone point was included with a
sample of the faunal remains collected from midden 1. Similar bone points
have been recovered from lunette sites at Lakes Mungo, Menindee, and
Victoria (Fig. 15.2).

 Middens 6–12 at MLIIIA are located in a small deflation basin measuring
about 180 m × 90 m on which there was a surface scatter of stone
implements and bone fragments. Small test excavations showed in situ bones

and stone flakes (in small numbers) associated with patches of blackened sand, which were probably hearths. From an area of 260 m², 100 stone artefacts were collected. These were mainly flakes and cores (58% and 6% respectively). Depending on the typology used, retouched or use-worn artefacts could vary here from 7% to 32% and the proportions of flakes and cores without visible retouch or use-wear would have to be adjusted accordingly. In the absence of microscopic use-wear analysis, it is presently unwise to make the jump from listing the occurrence of artefacts to conclusions about site relationships or function on tool typology alone.

The faunal material at MLIIIA is shown in Table 15.1. This represents an estimated 40% of bone material associated with the 12 small middens.

MULURULU IIIB AND IIIC

Directly to the north of MLIIIA middens 3 and 4, and MLIIIA middens 6–12, are two areas where burnt animal bones and shells or fish bones have eroded out of the core of the lunette. These are sites MLIIIB and MLIIIC respectively. Their stratigraphic situation suggests that these two sites are older than MLIIIA and should probably be located at the upper end of the period under consideration here, c. 20 000 BP (Bowler pers. comm.).

MLIIIB consists of four small fireplaces surrounded by burnt animal bones and 37 artefacts, mainly flakes, cores, pebbles, and stones with bruising. The absence of shellfish remains from MLIIIB may be a result of preservation factors or the small area of the exposure, as freshwater fish bones are present on the site.

MLIIIC is also associated with the Mulurulu Lunette core sediments directly behind the MLIIIA middens 6–12 area. The site was badly eroded, no site features other than a scatter of bones, mussel-shell fragments, and crayfish gastroliths being present.

The faunal remains from MLIIIB and MLIIIC are listed in Table 15.1. The range of species present is similar to that recorded for the other Mulurulu sites.

Quarry sites and artefact scatters

The majority of stone artefacts associated with the Willandra Lake sites are manufactured from silcrete, an intensively indurated siliceous rock probably produced as a near-surface by-product of weathering during the Tertiary (Sullivan & Simmons 1979, p. 51). Exposures of silcrete occur as ridges on the backshore margins of lakes Chibnalwood and Mungo, and probably occur near the surface at Lake Leaghur. These structural features may have influenced the initial stage of lake formation in this area (Allen 1972, p. 286, Bowler pers. comm.). In any case, the silcrete exposures have had an impact on Aboriginal usage of the region even after the final drying phase of the lakes.

CHIBNALWOOD 3–5

The Chibnalwood Lakes consist of three small lake basins that formed inside the older Arumpo Lake basin during the period 20 000–15 000 BP (Bowler 1970, p. 142).

On the southwestern margin of Outer Arumpo there are two areas of exposed beach deposits, consisting of silcrete pebbles. Rolled artefacts in small numbers occur within these gravels. Excavations at locality 2 (CH3–5) recovered 45 artefacts from 4.5 m^3 of gravel. A ^{14}C date for a small sample of charcoal gave a minimum age of 14 630 ± 1100 BP (ANU–881) for these gravels. Nearby are exposures of silcrete boulders surrounded by quarry debris consisting of scattered large flakes and cores. The artefactual material in the gravels is probably quarry debris incorporated into the beach deposits during the high-water Zanci phase.

LAKE MUNGO SITES

Bowler (1970, p. 121) notes that rolled artefacts occur in gravels in the inner dune margin at the southern end of the Walls of China (Lake Mungo Lunette) in a situation similar to the Chibnalwood gravels discussed above. Apart from this, two other sites may date to the time-period under discussion.

The Walls of China I site is located 0.5 km to the southwest of the 26 000-year-old Mungo I site. It covers an area of 1100 m^2 where artefacts are thinly scattered on Zanci clay dune deposits. Apart from the eroded remains of a burial, 872 stone artefacts were collected here, consisting mainly of flakes (75%) and unmodified cores (9%), with a density of distribution of less than one artefact per m^2. Of the 116 artefacts with visible signs of edge damage, 44 (38%) were classified as horsehoof cores or steep-edged scrapers, but today would be placed in the core category, while there were 72 flakes or small scrapers with some form of retouch or use modification, with edges varying in shape from notched or concave to convex. Except for cores or larger flakes that may have suffered opportunistic use, these smaller retouched or use-modified flakes are the only likely implements on the site (*contra* the 'core tool and scraper tradition' of Jones & Allen, in Bowler *et al.*, 1970, p. 52).

The second site, Mungo backshore I, is located on top of the cliffed shoreline on the northwestern margin of Lake Mungo. It covers an area of 4200 m^2. Artefacts (1495) were collected from within a gridded area of 440 m^2. This gives a density of 3 per m^2. 1215 unmodified flakes and 80 cores were collected (if 32 steep-edged scrapers and horsehoof cores are included as cores) leaving 191 flakes with edge modification ranging from bruising to convex retouch. A few grindstone fragments and anvil stones were also present on the site. A hearth associated with this site was dated to 940 ± 50 BP (ANU–660) and at least seven of the artefacts collected (five adze slugs and two backed flakes) are probably younger than 5000 BP.

The difficulties in interpreting the evidence at sites such as Mungo backshore I raise questions that are of general significance for the study of deflated sites in semiarid environments. Given that the dated hearth, the backed flakes, and the adze slugs are definitely recent, the question becomes, what proportion of the remaining artefacts are also recent in age?

In 1972, I accepted that all artefacts on this site were less than 1000 years old (Allen 1972, p. 279). It was argued that similarities between this site and the older Mungo I (26 000 BP), and Walls of China (*c.* 15 000 BP?) sites, in terms of artefact content and sizes, could be interpreted as 'strong evidence for cultural continuity over the past 30 000 years in the Lake Mungo region' (Allen 1972, pp. 279, 353). Furthermore, it was suggested that, 'Despite the great age differences between Mungo I site and the other two, the implements from all three sites clearly belong to the same industrial tradition.' (Allen 1972, p. 279).

Apart from noting that the technological and cultural domains are combined here in an unsatisfactory manner, two other points should be made concerning these conclusions. First , if the sites do span a period of 26 000 years, as concluded in 1972, they do show a degree of technological similarity. However, apart from the horsehoof cores, which morphologically could reflect the semiarid environment or the use of silcrete as a raw material (see White & O'Connell 1982, p. 65, who follow Kamminga's 1978, pp. 309–16, interpretation of horsehoof cores), the cores, flakes, and retouched pieces on these sites are of so generalized a nature as to rob a conclusion of technological similarity of most of its potential meaning.

Only a few Australian flake artefacts correspond with the archaeologist's notion of formal types (Flenniken & White 1985, pp. 142–9). These appear relatively late on Australian sites. Most Australian cores, flakes, and retouched artefacts can be interpreted as the product of a single reduction sequence which involved simple percussion flaking techniques. Except for a general trend in the reduction of artefact size over time, discussed below, variations between most Australian assemblages in the shape and size of flakes and cores depended more on the availability of raw materials, the degree of reduction, and the immediate needs of the stoneworkers than on cultural variations (Flenniken & White 1985, pp. 132–6).

The stoneworking techniques of ethnographically documented Aboriginal groups conformed with the reduction sequence described above. However, their subsistence economies and perishable material culture varied widely from place to place. Documenting a degree of similarity in stone raw materials, cores, and flakes over a long period of time and interpreting this as cultural or technological continuity (in its wider sense) might, in these cases, be obscuring the changes in Aboriginal culture or technology that did take place (see Hutterer 1977, pp. 56–7 and White 1977, p. 23 for similar statements about New Guinean and Southeast Asian stone tools and their interpretation). Similar difficulties involved in sustaining a conclusion of long-term continuity in Aboriginal hunting and gathering patterns are discussed below.

An alternative interpretation is that most of the Mungo backshore I artefacts are old and that the hearths, backed flakes, and adze slugs are intrusive. Their presence might be the result of reoccupation of the site and possible reutilization of the older artefacts as a raw-material source during the recent period.

Reinterpretation of the artefact assemblages from recent, stratified sites such as Burke's Cave and Meadow Glen suggests that considerable artefactual change has occurred in the region in the past 5000 years. Lorblanchet & Jones (1979), as part of their analysis of implements from Skew Valley, Western Australia, documented a general trend towards the miniaturization of cores, flakes, and implements over time in Australian stone tool assemblages (Fig. 15.4). The proportions of different classes of artefacts and the sizes of horsehoof cores and steep-edged scraper/cores are similar for Mungo I (26 000 BP), Walls of China I (c. 15 000 BP), and Mungo backshore I(?). If artefact size is any indication of relative chronological age, as Lorblanchet & Jones suggest, then the three sites could all relate to the period when the lake system was still operative. In which case, the technological similarities they exhibit could be a reflection of similarities of site function location, and proximity in time.

LEAGHUR PENINSULA I

LPI is located on a long peninsula which juts into the southwestern part of the now-dry Leaghur Lake basin. The peninsula is probably structurally determined by the presence of a ridge of silcrete. Large numbers of stone artefacts, mainly large silcrete flakes and cobbles but also some (presumably intrusive) backed flakes, are strewn about the wind-blown exposures on this peninsula. Although no *in situ* boulders of silcrete were seen, the site can be interpreted as a quarry site with more than one phase of use.

Bones, otoliths, eggshell [not emu], freshwater mussel shells, and flaked stone material are now all located on the same erosional surface.

The faunal remains can be roughly sorted into two groups. These are listed in Table 15.1 and are:

(1)   Bones which have a heavy carbonate encrustation indicative of burial during a period of soil formation, plus those animals that can reasonably be associated with lake-full conditions, such as fish. These are likely to be older than 15 000 BP.
(2)   Bones which lack any chronological indications and may be older or younger than 15 000 BP.

The stone artefacts did not allow this chronological division to be made except that backed flakes elsewhere in Australia are generally younger than 4500 BP (White & O'Connell 1982, p. 111). The same problems of interpretation as discussed for the Garnpung I and the Lake Mungo sites also affect this site.

Hearth or oven sites

Following Barbetti (1973, p. 5), ovens can be defined as cooking stones (or lumps of baked clay) arranged on top of a thin band of ash and charcoal in a shallow depression; and hearths are small areas of blackened earth without cooking stones, which may result from a small, open fire.

As part of a study of sites selected for archaeomagnetic determination,

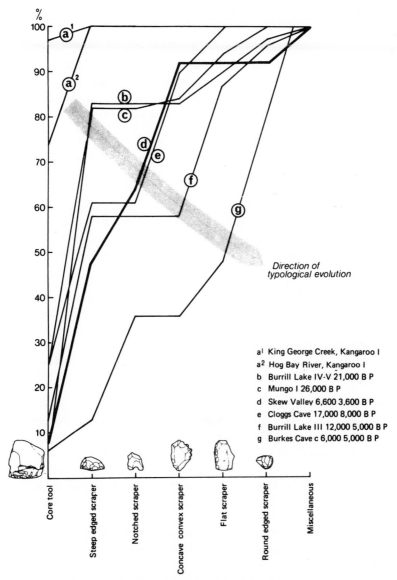

Figure 15.4 Direction of typological evolution in Australian core tool and scraper industries (After Lorblanchet & Jones 1979, in Lampert 1981).

Barbetti dated 27 hearths or ovens from the Willandra Lakes (Barbetti & Polach 1972, pp. 241–51). Some of the dates came from single ovens within an area where up to 20 small ovens might be located. Artefact scatters were associated with some hearths and ovens. Except in particular stratigraphic circumstances, such as in the carbonate-rich Mungo deposits, faunal and plant remains were not preserved, despite the presumed function of these features for the cooking of food.

Of the 27 dated hearths or ovens, only two related to the 22 000–15 000 BP time-period. These were:

ANU–668   19 420 ± 360   charcoal from an oven on the Mungo Lunette covered by Zanci deposits
ANU–684   12 490 ± 550   charcoal from a hearth near the top of the Zanci deposit at Lake Mungo

Small sample size is probably responsible for a younger than true age for this second date. Polach *et al.* (1970, pp. 1–18) report a date from charcoal from a hearth – ANU–330, 17 670 ± 550 BP – in Zanci deposits in the central part of the Lake Mungo Lunette.

Of the 28 age determinations on hearths or ovens, eight relate to the latter part of the Mungo Lacustral Phase (i.e. 30 000–22 000 BP), three to the period 22 000–15 000 BP, none were dated between 15 000 and 5000 BP, while 17 were more recent than 4000 BP [most (11) were younger than 1500 BP]. Barbetti comments:

> The apparent absence of oven sites in the Willandra Lakes area between 5000 yr and 19 000 yr B.P. may reflect either a lack of preservation of these sites (assuming they once existed), or an abandoning of the area by the Aboriginal population because of unfavourable conditions . . . it is not at all unreasonable to expect that sites exposed on the open plains would be unlikely to survive intact for more than 5000 yr. (Barbetti 1973, p. 6).

In opposition to Barbetti's hypothesis that the relative absence of dates between 5000 and 15 000 BP reflects site survival, it should be noted that a similar dearth of dates from this period shows up in Clark's much larger sample (Clark pers. comm.). As with the Willandra Lakes data, the general increase in site numbers in southwestern New South Wales in the post-5000 BP period cannot be demonstrated to be solely a function of geomorphic changes or site preservation (Ross 1985, pp. 84–5), though these factors cannot be entirely dismissed.

Discussion

Artefact scatters and hearths

During the Mungo–Zanci Arid Period there was quarrying of silcrete exposures for artefact raw materials. This has left extensive scatters of cores, flakes, and a small proportion of retouched or use-worn implements at a number of sites. Except for a few pieces of ochre, raw materials seem to be mainly local in origin. There is no evidence for large-scale trading networks in these durable materials at least. A few hearths and ovens can also be dated to this final lake period.

Midden contents, dates, and population fluctuations

Most of the middens discussed above can be dated to the final drying phase of the Mungo Zanci Arid Period. Their contents can be related:

(a) to their location on each lake, whether on the shallow backshore or on the lunette; and

(b) to the position of the lake on which they occur in the sequence of lakes from south to north.

There is no evidence for shell-middens at the southernmost lakes, Mungo and Arumpo/Chibnalwood during the period 20 000–15 000 BP. By contrast, the more northerly lakes, Leaghur, Garnpung and Mulurulu, all have middens dating close to 15 500 BP.

Middens on the backshore of Lake Leaghur contain only mussels. Slightly to the north, on the backshore of Garnpung, middens contain shellfish, fish, crayfish, and birds' eggs. Those on the northernmost Mulurulu Lunette contain a range of food items from the lake (fish, shellfish, crayfish) and the surrounding lunette and plains (mammals, birds, reptiles, and birds' eggs). [The Mulurulu sites, MLI and MLIIIA–C, are most like the older Mungo I site (26 000 BP), which was similarly situated on quartz-sand lunette beach deposits and can also be associated with a high freshwater phase in the lake.]

Bowler (1970:120) notes that unionid freshwater mussel shells and stone artefacts (horsehoof cores and steep-sided scrapers/cores?) are being eroded throughout the Zanci unit on all lakes from Mulurulu to Lake Mungo, with the single exception of the Chibnalwood Lunette. The implication is that Chibnalwood, the southernmost lake, had already entered a saline phase and was therefore an unattractive locality at the time when Aborigines were still gathering freshwater shellfish from the other lakes.

The increasing range of food items shown between sites on Lake Leaghur to the south and Mulurulu to the north, which were all occupied at about 15 500 BP (the final part of the Mungo–Zanci Arid Period), may indicate that there was a gradation in the local lake environment at that time with Lake Leaghur being more brackish while Lake Mulurulu still held a considerable volume of freshwater. Brackish conditions could mean that only the salt- and drought-tolerant freshwater mussels would be available in Lake Leaghur. This is not the whole story, however, as backshore middens generally show a more restricted variety of faunal contents than lunette middens, even when the lakes were in a full freshwater phase (see, for example, the 27 000 BP Leaghur I midden, Allen 1972, p. 284). The backshore areas were likely to be shallow and could have been better suited to shellfish exploitation than to other pursuits.

The only site that might go against both these patterns is the undated Leaghur Peninsula I site, which shows a wider range of material remains than the other backshore sites.

The site types, their location, and faunal and artefact contents are similar in range to that documented for the later part of the Mungo Lacustral Phase (32 000–25 000 BP, Barbetti & Allen 1972, p. 48).

The faunal contents of the Mungo I, Mulurulu I, and Mulurulu IIIA–C middens suggest that fishing and shellfishing were the principal subsistence activities carried out here. The large range but low frequency of small mammals on these sites indicate a pattern of generalized foraging, possibly allied with the quest for (the unrepresented) vegetable foods. The only exception to this is the higher than expected proportion of hare-wallabies (*Lagorchestes* spp.). Hare-wallabies are not so prominent in Late Pleistocene non-midden faunal collections from Lake Victoria (Marshall 1973, p. 164) and Lake Tandou (Merrilees 1973, pp. 179–80). This led Hope to conclude:

The mammal assemblages from the Willandra middens, even at the height of the Mungo freshwater phase, consist almost entirely of arid species, some of which, such as *Lagorchestes* spp., are proportionally far more common than they are in the Darling sites. These midden assemblages certainly reflect hunting practices rather than the actual proportions of the species in the environment.' (Hope 1978, p. 79).

European records of animal distributions and observations of Aboriginal activities in the Murray–Darling region were first made in the middle of the 19th century. These records showed that Aborigines living then were capturing many of the same species as those preserved in the Pleistocene Willandra shell-middens. Krefft noted that *Lagorchestes leporides* was 'Common upon the level country between the Murray and Darling; strictly nocturnal and solitary in its habits; it is seen during the daytime only, and is generally found asleep under some saltbush, or in any other sheltered locality.' (Krefft 1866, p. 20.)

Many of the mammalian species in the 19th century were adapted to a semiarid environment and to vegetation consisting of a mosaic of patches at different stages of succession produced by small-scale sporadic Aboriginal burning (Allen 1983, pp. 42–6).

Lagorchestes hirsutus, a central Australian species, requires spinifex grass at different fire stages for shelter and food. Aborigines earlier this century used fire to drive these animals towards lines of hunters armed with clubs (Finlayson 1935, pp. 64–7). While it is possible that similar hunting techniques were responsible for the numbers of *Lagorchestes* spp. at the Mulurulu middens, such a conclusion requires detailed faunal analysis from Recent and Pleistocene middens, information that is not yet available.

Revision of comparisons between the 19th century AD Ba:gandji economy and the Late Pleistocene mode of subsistence in the Willandra area.

In 1972, and in the subsequent publications (Allen 1972, 1974, 1980), the similarities in species composition between the Pleistocene middens from the Willandra Lakes area and the ethnohistoric description of hunting and gathering techniques of Ba:gandji-speaking peoples, who inhabited both the dry Willandra area and the lakes and rivershores associated with the Darling River in the mid-19th century, were taken as indicating:

(a)   that while the Willandra Lake system dried up and ceased to function at c. 15 000 BP, the dune environment away from the immediate vicinity of the Willandra Lakes had not changed significantly over the past 30 000 years; and

(b)   except for a shift in location of fishing and shellfishing from the Willandra Lakes to the Darling River when the lakes dried up, there had been little change in Aboriginal subsistence activities in the Darling River region since 30 000 BP.

One exception to this latter generalization was allowed. The arid phase, which caused the drying of the lakes and thereby lowered the region's productivity and carrying capacity, was thought to have stimulated the growth of wild grasses and indirectly steered the Aboriginal population towards the utilization of new resources or to intensifying the collection of previously minor resources, in this case seeds of the wild millet, *Panicum decompositum* (Allen 1980, p. 42).

Since 1980, I have dealt with this evidence in a more cautious and critical fashion. First, the continuity of semiarid conditions and of Aboriginal hunting patterns can be questioned.

The presence of bettongs and hare-wallabies at the Mungo I site almost certainly represents the interaction of Aboriginal hunting and burning with a local environment which was not humid. . . . Whether the remains represent generalised or specialised hunting and extensive or intensive burning in conjunction with an environment which might be arid/semi-arid or semi-arid/sub-humid we are unable to say from the midden evidence above. Different combinations of the above factors could produce very similar midden contents . . . On the available evidence we are not justified in pushing the ethnographically documented situation of complex social and economic relations and specialised hunting and burning techniques in the semi-arid Darling region back into the late Pleistocene. . . . Claims for environmental continuity over the past 12 000 years . . . are on stronger ground . . . (Allen 1983, p. 53).

Secondly, the claims for an antiquity of *c.* 15 000 BP for seed grindstones rested on Bowler's statement that he had recovered carbonate-coated grinding stones eroding out of Zanci lunette deposits, and also on their surface association with shell-middens at Leaghur backshore I, Mulurulu I and Mulurulu IIIA, 'sites where there is no evidence of intrusive (presumably recent) stone artefacts' (Allen 1972, p. 338).

At the Tandou Lunette I site, on the Darling River system, grindstone fragments occurred in situ in the same deposits as a human cremation dated to 12 530 + 1630/ − 1350 BP (ANU–705). An associated shell-midden, dated during a more recent archaeological and stratigraphic survey of this site, gave an age of 25 920 ± 560 BP (ANU–2754) (Hope *et al.* 1983, p. 49). This survey revealed that the sequence of deposition, erosion, and soil formation at Lake Tandou was complex. The possibility that the Tandou Lunette I grindstones were in a reworked sedimentary layer cannot be dismissed.

At the nearby Tandou Creek I midden, carbonate-encrusted grinding stones occur as surface finds. The midden returned a shell date of 12 350 ± 170 (ANU–702), while charcoal from an oven dug through this midden was dated to 105 ± 65 BP (modern, ANU–449) (Allen 1972, pp. 236–7). Finally, at Rat-catcher's Lake on Talyawalka Creek, an anabranch of the Darling River, grinding stones, freshwater mussels, and fish bones occurred together on a single erosion surface. A shell date from an exposed section of freshwater mussel shells was dated to 7170 ± 110 BP (ANU–949).

Smith has recently examined the above specimens and concluded that most were amorphous grindstones: 'On morphological criteria none ... can be positively identified as seedgrinding implements. The Pleistocene grindstones differ in overall form and in the morphology of the functional surface from Central Australian seedgrinders' (Smith 1985, p. 36). Although Shawcross & Kaye report the presence of a steep-sided scraper at Mungo I with 'signs of polish as if the tool had been used as a rubber or grindstone' and add, 'it is at least a hint of the possibility of tracing cereal grinding technology as far back as this early site so that the sense of continuity ... becomes stronger still' (Shawcross & Kaye 1980, p. 125), there is now no firm evidence for specialized seed grindstones prior to 5000 BP in the Willandra area or elsewhere in Australia. The cumulation of a lot of poor evidence cannot, in this case, make up for the absence of a single securely dated seed grindstone of any antiquity in western New South Wales.

In the light of Smith's reanalysis, the evidence for the conjunction in time of the final phase of the Mungo–Zanci Arid Period and the presence of specialized seed grindstones put forward by Allen (1974, pp. 315–18) cannot be sustained.

Finally, the question of continuity in the use of fishing nets remains open. Kefous (1977) used the limited size-range of freshwater perch at the Mungo I site [also repeated at Mulurulu and Garnpung (Allen 1972, pp. 331–5)] to suggest the use of specialized equipment, such as nets or traps, as far back as 30 000 BP. However, the breeding requirements of the golden perch, *Plectro-plites ambiguus*, in combination with the seasonal changes in water height envisaged for the Pleistocene Willandra Lakes, plus the effects of Aboriginal and bird predation, are likely to result in a restricted size and range of adult fish being present in the lakes at any one time. The midden contents will probably reflect such a pattern irrespective of the hunting techniques used by the Aborigines.

Thus there is insufficient evidence to justify projecting the 19th century Aboriginal fishing and foraging economy back on to the Late Pleistocene sites discussed above. The historically recorded Ba:gandji depended on the use of fire and an extensive array of traps and nets, the large-scale gathering, processing, and some storage, of wild cereals, a well-developed sexual division of labour, and communal residential and gathering practices to exploit the region (Allen 1972, pp. 41–98, 1974, pp. 309–22, 1980, pp. 33–43). The only point of direct contact between the ethnohistorical evidence and the archaeological evidence from the sites dating between 15 000 and 30 000 BP lies in the animal, fish, and shellfish species being exploited. As these species can be captured in a variety of ways they are poor indicators of any specific Aboriginal mode of subsistence. The present-day ecological requirements of the relevant species range from subhumid to arid environments in the case of the mammals, and throughout the Murray–Darling river system in the case of the fish and shellfish. These requirements are so wide as to preclude any definite statement on the continuity of local conditions, on this evidence alone. The presence of the lunette dune itself might be the crucial habitat element in the case of the burrowing *Bettongia lesueur*. Previous arguments about a high degree of continuity in stone-implement manufacture as discussed above must also be discounted. Finally, we know little to nothing about the development of cereal-based subsistence economies in semiarid western New South Wales.

The virtual absence of any knowledge of what Aborigines were doing in the Willandra area during the post-Zanci to mid-recent period (15 000–5000 BP) means that any generalization about continuity in hunting and gathering practices between the Late Pleistocene and Recent period must depend on detailed midden analyses carried out elsewhere.

The arguments about the continuity of Aboriginal modes of subsistence are of greater concern than can be conveyed by these expressions of doubt about the adequacy of midden analyses or the overenthusiastic projection of ethnohistoric information on to the archaeological data. In 1972, the following position was advanced:

The main impression gained from an archaeological study of the economy and stone implements on sites in the Darling Basin, together with an ethnographic study of the Darling River Bagundji, is one of a single continuous cultural tradition. Changes took place in this tradition during man's 32 000 year history in the area, but these were not so great as to destroy the impression of continuity.

This is most apparent in the Darling River stone industry which, despite quite drastic environmental changes at the end of the Pleistocene, continued as a recognisable regional component of the Australian core tool and scraper tradition from 30 000 B.P. to 2000 B.P. After 2000 B.P. new stone implements were added to the industry which still continued as a recognisable unit.

More change is apparent in the prehistoric economy. At the end of the Pleistocene, the collection of cereals was added to the basic riverine and Lacustrine economy that had been practised from 30 000 B.P. The addition of cereals to the diet, at about 15 000 B.P., produced the type of economy that continued in the Darling Basin until the ethnographic present. By the 19th century, the Bagundji had developed a remarkably efficient and sophisticated riverine economy.

It seems the Bagundji were the inheritors of an old and complex cultural tradition in the Darling Basin. (Allen 1972, pp. 356–7.)

Against this picture of relentless continuity, timelessness and changelessness (which is the traditional description and explanation of conservative hunting and gathering societies and which has the unfortunate feature of incorporating the notion of a cultural and environmental determinism that is unresponsive to cultural and environmental changes), I would now advance a simpler proposal.

As noted earlier, the sites around the Willandra Lakes dating from *c.* 30 000–15 000 BP can be interpreted as sites where a small localized population practised a generalized hunting and gathering way of life. The environmental and sociocultural circumstances prevailing at that time are unlikely to represent a close analogue to any recent ethnographic or environmental situation.

The environmental changes that took place in the Willandra area at about 15 000 BP, particularly the drying of the lakes removed the conditions necessary to sustain even this level of Aboriginal occupation. We do not know the fate of the inhabitants of the area affected by these changes. If people were present in the Willandra area during the period 15 000–5000 BP, the material remains they left, given our present knowledge, are below the level of archaeological visibility.

Sometime after 5000 BP, traces of a renewed Aboriginal occupation become abundant in the archaeological record. This reoccupation of the now semiarid dunefields and plains does not coincide with any amelioration of environmental circumstances, in fact local conditions may have been worse than at present. It can be concluded that this reoccupation represents new abilities on the part of the Aboriginal population to exploit a virtually waterless environment.

There appears to be a general increase in the number and distribution of archaeological sites in southeastern Australia (including the semiarid zone) during the middle to late Holocene (Ross 1985, pp. 81–9). This has been interpreted as indicating an increase in Aboriginal populations and/or the complexity of Aboriginal sociopolitical organizations. It coincides with changes in stone artefact manufacturing practices. At present there is considerable debate about these changes and their interpretation amongst Australian archaeologists (Murray & White 1985) but these considerations lie outside the scope of this chapter.

Acknowledgements

I would like to thank D. Brown and K. Kefous for comments on this chapter and K. Kereszturi and I. Penny for typing it.

References

Allen, H. 1972. Where the crow flies backwards: man and land in the Darling Basin. Unpublished PhD thesis, The Australian National University, Canberra.

Allen, H. 1974. The Bagundji of the Darling Basin: cereal gatherers in an uncertain environment. *World Archaeology* **5**, 309–22.

Allen, H. 1980. Aborigines of the western plains of New South Wales. *Parks and Wildlife* **2**, 33–43.

Allen, H. 1983. 19th Century faunal change in western NSW and NW Victoria. Working Papers in Anthropology, Archaeology, Linguistics and Maori Studies, No. 64. Department of Anthropology, University of Auckland.

Barbetti, M. 1973. Archaeomagnetic and radiocarbon studies of Aboriginal fireplaces. Unpublished PhD thesis, The Australian National University, Canberra.

Barbetti, M. & H. Allen 1972. Prehistoric man at Lake Mungo, Australia, by 32 000 yr BP. *Nature* **240**, 46–8.

Barbetti, M. & H. Polach 1972. ANU radiocarbon date list V. *Radiocarbon* **15**, 241–51.

Bonhomme, T. 1984. Bunda Lake – a study in site location. Unpublished BA (hons) thesis, Macquarie University, Sydney.

Bowler, J. M. 1970. Late Quaternary environments: a study of lakes and associated sediments in south-eastern Australia. Unpublished PhD thesis, The Australian National University, Canberra.

Bowler, J. M. 1971. Pleistocene salinities and climatic change: evidence from lakes and lunettes in southeastern Australia. In *Aboriginal man and environment in Australia*, D. J. Mulvaney & J. Golson (eds), 47–65. Canberra: The Australian National University Press.

Bowler, J. M. 1980. Quaternary chronology and palaeohydrology in the evolution of mallee landscapes. In *Aeolian landscapes in the semi-arid zone of south eastern Australia*, R. R. Storrier & M. E. Stannard (eds), 17–38. Australian Society of Soil Science, Riverina Branch.

Bowler, J. M. & J. W. Magee 1978. Geomorphology of the mallee region in semi-arid northern Victoria and western New South Wales. *Proceedings of the Royal Society of Victoria* **90**, 5–26.

Bowler, J. M., R. Jones, H. Allen & A. G. Thorne 1970. Pleistocene human remains from Australia: a living site and human cremation from Lake Mungo, western New South Wales. *World Archaeology* **2**, 39–60.

Dare-Edwards, A. J. 1980. Potential of soil stratigraphy. In *Aeolian landscapes in the semi-arid zone of south eastern Australia*, R. R. Storrier & M. E. Stannard (eds), 37–8. Australian Society of Soil Science, Riverina Branch.

Finlayson, H. H. 1935. *The red centre*. Sydney: Angus and Robertson.

Flenniken, J. J. & J. P. White 1985. Australian flaked stone tools: a technological perspective. *Records of the Australian Museum* **36**, 131–51.

Gill, E. D. 1973. Geology and geomorphology of the Murray River region between Mildura and Renmark, Australia. *Memoirs of the National Museum of Victoria* **34**, 1–99.

Hope, J. H. 1978. Pleistocene mammal extinctions: the problem of Mungo and Menindee, New South Wales. *Alcheringa* **6**, 65–82.

Hope, J. H. (ed.) 1981. Darling surveys 1. Occasional Papers in Prehistory 3, Department of Prehistory, Research School of Pacific Studies, The Australian National University, Canberra.

Hope, J. H. 1985. A regional environmental plan for the Willandra Lakes World Heritage Region. *Australian Archaeology* **20**, 32–7.

Hope, J. H., A. Dare-Edwards & M. L. McIntyre 1983. Middens and megafauna: stratigraphy and dating of Lake Tandou Lunette, western New South Wales. *Archaeology in Oceania* **18**, 45–53.

Hutterer, K. L. 1977. Reinterpreting the Southeast Asian Palaeolithic. In *Sunda and Sahul: prehistoric studies in Southeast Asia, Melanesia and Australia*, J. Allen, J. Golson & R. Jones (eds), 31–72. London: Academic Press.

Kamminga, J. 1978. Journey into the microcosms: a functional analysis of certain classes of prehistoric Australian stone tools. Unpublished PhD thesis, University of Sydney, Sydney.

Kefous, K. 1977. We have a fish with ears, and wonder if it is valuable? Unpublished BA (hons.) thesis, The Australian National University, Canberra.

Kefous, K. 1983. Riverain: Water availability and Aboriginal prehistory of the Murray River, Lake Victoria area, western New South Wales. Unpublished MA thesis, The Australian National University, Canberra.

Krefft, G. 1866. On the vertebrated animals of the lower Murray and Darling, their habits, economy, and geographical distribution. *Transactions of the Philosophical Society of New South Wales* **I**, 1–38.

Lampert, R. 1981. The great kartan mystery. *Terra Australis 5*. Department of Prehistory, Research School of Pacific Studies, The Australian National University, Canberra.

Lampert, R. 1983. The Kartan mystery revisited. *Australian Archaeology* **16**, 175–7.

Lorblanchet, M. & R. Jones 1979. Les premierès fouilles à Dampier (Australie occidentale), et leur place dans l'ensemble australien. *Bulletin de la Société Préhistorique Française* **76**, 463–87.

McIntyre, M. 1981. An archaeological survey of the Mildura–Broken Hill Electricity Line Corridor. In Darling Surveys I, J. Hope (ed.), 9–32. Occasional Paper in Prehistory 3, Department of Prehistory, Research School of Pacific Studies, The Australian National University, Canberra.

Marshall, L. G. 1973. Fossil vertebrate faunas from the Lake Victoria region, SW New South Wales, Australia. *Memoirs of the National Museum of Victoria* **34**, 151–72.

Merrilees, D. 1973. Fossiliferous deposits at Lake Tandou, New South Wales, Australia. *Memoirs of the National Museum of Victoria* **34**, 177–82.

Murray, T. & J. P. White 1985. Trends towards social complexity in Australia and Papua New Guinea. *Archaeology in Oceania* **20**, 41–65, 73–89.

Parsons, R. F. 1981. *Eucalyptus* scrubs and shrublands. In *Australian vegetation*, R. H. Groves (ed.), 228–53. Cambridge: Cambridge University Press.

Polach, H. A., A. J. Lovering & J. M. Bowler 1970. ANU radiocarbon datelist IV. *Radiocarbon* **12**, 1–18.

Ross, A. 1981a. Holocene environments and prehistoric site patterning in the Victorian mallee. *Archaeology in Oceania* **16**, 145–55.
Ross, A. 1981b. An archaeological survey of Bunda Lake, Belarabon, western New South Wales. *Australian Archaeology* **12**, 17–26,
Ross, A. 1985. Archaeological evidence for population change in the middle to late holocene in southeastern Australia. *Archaeology in Oceania* **20**, 81–9.

Shawcross, F. W. & M. Kaye 1980. Australian archaeology: implications of current interdisciplinary research. *Interdisciplinary Science Reviews* **5**, 112–28.
Smith, M. A. 1985. A morphological comparison of central Australian seedgrinding implements and Australian Pleistocene-age grindstones. *The Beagle, Occasional Papers of the Northern Territory Museum of Arts and Sciences* **2**, 23–38.
Sullivan, M. E. & S. Simmons 1979. Silcrete: a classification for flaked stone artefact assemblages. *The Artefact* **4**, 51–60.

Wasson, R. J. 1976. Holocene aeolian landforms in the Belarabon Area, S.W. of Cobar, N.S.W. *Journal of the Royal Society of New South Wales* **109**, 91–101.
White, J. P. 1977. Crude, colourless and unenterprising: Prehistorians and their views on the stone age of Sunda and Sahul. In *Sunda and Sahul: prehistoric studies in southeast Asia, Melanesia and Australia*, J. Allen, J. Golson & R. Jones (eds), 13–30. London: Academic Press.
White, J. P. & J. F. O'Connell 1982. *A prehistory of Australia, New Guinea and Sahul.* Sydney: Academic Press.

Afterword
Minitime and megaspace in the Palaeolithic at 18 K and otherwise

H. MARTIN WOBST

In *The world at 18 000 BP* a distinguished group of Palaeolithic archaeologists writes about the Palaeolithic without talking only about Western or Central Europe. Both volumes are truly international in scope, but perhaps North American archaeologists stand to gain the most from this Palaeolithic International, because it allows them to compare the Palaeolithic commonly chronicled in their textbooks with Palaeolithic data from east of Rhine and Rhône, and from south of the Mediterranean.

No change without change

The world at 18 000 BP is an attempt to use a chronometric date as a point of departure for worldwide comparison and contrast. This deviates considerably from the standard practice of international symposia. There the reference points tend to be *boundaries* (biological, geological, or cultural), *origins* of behaviours or levels of cultural complexity (e.g. language or *Homo sapiens*), or archaeologically (stylistically) defined *time slices* (e.g. Perigordian or Aurignacian). Upon closer inspection, such markers of contemporaneity or shared time often turn out to be chronologically evanescent. Events that had been assumed to share dates are usually discovered to have been considerably time-transgressive.

Time-transgressiveness tends to confound the study of change in a number of ways. Obviously, experts talking about different points in space will usually end up talking about different points in time. However, they will also usually talk about different sets of processes. There are two reasons for this: (a) in the place where the time-transgressive phenomenon first develops the dynamics of change are bound to differ from those that are observed later on (in the places to which the phenomenon is seen/expected to have spread); and (b) what is spreading itself confounds the dynamics of the places it is spreading to, even before it gets there. Thus, it generates many different processual settings along the way. The result is usually so multidimensional that the central question of the given symposium tends to remain unresolved or achieve only weak (re)solution

If experts are asked about the state of culture and nature at a given point in time, they should all be talking about that same point in time. This should control for one of the confounding variables: assuming the chronometry works, only space should vary. At the interregional scale, contemporaneous variation and variability should then be revealed. That sounds trite and straightforward. For the discipline, however, such knowledge is vital. If we want to elicit what is responsible for change, action, process, and evolution, we need to arrange our data so that they track the ability of variables to vary, and we need to lay out the shapes of the resulting variation. We can evaluate our ideas about change, process, action, and evolution only against data that vary.

The usual archaeological rationale groups things (artefacts, fauna, plants, geomorphological data), first and foremost, by similarity in form, time, and space. This creates internally homogeneous entities, such as 'type', 'culture', and 'horizon'. These entities are then contrasted (in space or time) with other such creations. In this methodology, change between entities is entirely 'make believe', rather than observed along transects, because data about change are explicitly removed when the entities are first constructed. Those parts of the range of variation that potentially link the entities are explicitly sorted out and discarded, before questions are raised about transition or change.

To understand change worldwide, even the data *within* regions need to be laid out in ways that expose the range of variability and the shape of variation. Only then will we be able to link a given region along transects with adjacent ones. This, of course, contrasts sharply with the 'lowest common denominator' approach of traditional archaeological practice, in which space is thrown together into a region because it shares (some, arbitrary) form. Only that form is selected which is shared spatially. The regional boundary occurs where that form is shared no longer. Form is selected so as to be shared within the given regions, and so as to be surrounded by a hiatus at the regional boundaries. Laying out the *internal* variation of the different regions, in addition to interregional variation, is all the more important since the arena of hunter–gatherer behaviour (and of the environmental risks or rewards that may articulate with human behaviour) is rarely regional. It tends to be subregional and often relatively local in scope. To analyse worldwide variations in hunter–gatherer behaviour, we need information about change and variation along spatial scales of behavioural relevance to hunter–gatherers, that is, at scales smaller than the region, along transects that are not arbitrarily aborted at regional boundaries, and with population units as operating variables that are significantly smaller and more sensitive than regional maximum bands.

There has not been enough devil's advocacy about the ethnographic record to resolve whether claimed regional boundaries, or other sharply defined behavioural or ecological boundaries, are the artefacts of culture contact or of poor ethnographic field method (cf. Wobst 1978). Until the ethnographic images of bounded hunter–gatherers have been aggressively evaluated, archae-ologists must consider any boundaries in the world of hunter–gatherers to be arbitrary and to present no obstacle to the continuity of environmental or cultural process.

The world at 18 000 BP should stimulate a series of Palaeolithic studies that focus on other worldwide marker horizons. For instance, climatological cold or warm maxima, such as interglacial peaks; geophysical events, such as the Brunhes–Matuyama boundary or the Brno or Laschamp events; and chron-ometric points, such as every 10 000 years in the last glaciation. Such an exchange of information should expose interesting variables and measures of change and allow us to ask sensitive questions about the processes of variation. For example:

(a) How do the range of variability and the shape of variation differ, by region or worldwide, through successive cold maxima, for a given cultural variable or constellation of different variables?

(b) How does the shape of variation for a given variable or constellation of variables change, along a transect from the equator to the poles, along gradients of continentality or other environmental variables?

(c) How do the scales of covariation differ among different environmental variables?

(d) What is the shape of spatial correlation in cultural variables, through time over successive environmental peaks, or through space along environ-mental gradients (such as continentality, variance, richness, diversity, 'edgeness')?

(e) What happens at the extremes of the range of cultural variables environmentally? What happens at the extremes of the range of environ-mental variables culturally?

18 K hunter–gatherers

If one looks beyond the limelight and surveys the Palaeolithic at 18 000 BP along interregional, continental, and even intercontinental spatial transects, one gains a new appreciation of variability that is easily lost when the spatial focus is too narrow. The monolith 'Upper Palaeolithic' is then seen to have been dynamic in space as well as time. Like the stereotyped hunter–gatherers of modern times, our 18 000 BP ancestors were adaptable, flexible characters when viewed over the total space they occupied. This broad perspective also gives us a good sense of the relative uniqueness of the periglacial behavioural package (such as portable 'art', cave painting, rapid change in lithic assemblage types, narrow stylistic standards, lots of concern for non-utilitarian features of tools), compared with the remainder of the world. At 18 000 BP, all people are classified as *Homo sapiens*. But only a very few are involved in the behaviours our textbooks write about (i.e. the periglacial behavioural package) in their chapters on the Upper Palaeolithic 'of the world', or the origins of *Homo sapiens*, or the speed-up of 'cultural evolution' in the period from 40 000 to 10 000 BP.

Of course, a transect across hunter—gatherers in the ethnographic present, from equator to permafrost, would have very similar features at the periglacial margins as in the Upper Palaeolithic, 18 000 years ago. For example, in the ethnographic present and in the Palaeolithic, the northern margins of the population distribution have produced highly stylized and easily 'typed' material culture, high intensity of decorative art, curative technology, and impressive facilities (for example, shrines and mammoth bone structures in the past and drive lines tens of miles long in the present). Although the data are not easily accessible yet, I would not be very much surprised if we were to find similar constellations at the southern margins also (see Jones Vol 2 Ch. 14).

European Palaeolithic data or Inuit material culture are apparently not evidence for the emergence of a new set of sapient abilities at 18 000 BP along the arctic periphery of humanity. Instead, what we see there at this time is an early and highly visible archaeological *expression* of these behaviours, in places and under circumstances where they are situationally appropriate. The vast majority of humans then and now have always been capable of expressing such behaviours, but for situational reasons did not feel compelled to engage in them.

Please, do not mistake this comment as simple, straightforward, environmental determinism or environmental possibilism. It is not meant to be so. Yet it is my sense, that – at 18 000 BP and in the ethnographic present – the behaviour of hunter—gatherers was patterned. It articulated with a number of different variables and, certainly, some of these variables reached their extremes toward the poles. But I would not be at all surprised if, on a map of time and space, similar constellations of variables appeared in places more temperate, or less marginal, and thus facilitated the occasional rise of similar behavioural packages. To conclude that latitude (or any of the variables that covary with it) was the cause of this correspondence between the archaeological and ethnographic record is premature, mechanical – rather like saying that 'shoe-size correlates with intelligence' – and hence processually vacuous.

Studies of different regions at the same point in time also reveal that humans were not successful in many places. They may, on occasion, have temporarily retreated, disappeared, or experienced considerably higher levels of morbidity than elsewhere. Information about human absence or lack of success is elicited mostly during systematic interregional comparison, as in these pages. Where else would there be any good reason to talk about regions devoid of people? Even the periglacial package, which our textbooks stress as the ultimate demonstration of Pleistocene human success, often actually failed. We should be careful in pointing to the behaviour at the periglacial margins (or to any other set of human behaviour) as demonstrating 'an advance in human evolution' when, quite frequently, that behaviour plainly failed, in similar areas and habitats and at the same time.

I have argued elsewhere (Wobst 1989) against confounding the expression of a behaviour with the emergence of the ability for that behaviour. Questions about the emergence of the ability for the periglacial behavioural package need to be logically separated from questions about where and when that ability finds its first and subsequent expression. In terms of process, they relate to each other only marginally (the emergence of the *ability* for a behaviour needs to precede its first *expression*). The absence of the periglacial behavioural package elsewhere tells us nothing about the *abilities* of the people involved; all it does tell us is that such behaviours apparently did not make sense there. And questions about the emergence of the *ability* for a type of behaviour are notoriously difficult to resolve.

18 K nature and culture

There are a number of pitfalls in trying to cut a slice across the time continuum worldwide in order to make regional comparisons. Such an approach, for example, invites unbridled environmental determinism, a disease that may be diagnosed by a careful reading of some of the chapters in these volumes. Where time is held constant so that only space varies, the following argument is very tempting:

(a) Nature is easier to measure and observe than human behaviour.
(b) For whatever reasons, both nature and behaviour will vary if they are measured at points far enough apart. This applies to the regional comparisons in these volumes.
(c) Differing measurements invite the jump from associated change in nature and behaviour, to correlated change and to causation in which all human behavioural change and variation are attributed to environmental stress or to avoiding environmental risk.

This chain of logic seems to be very inviting because, on first approximation, the more remote in time our ancestors are from us, the more we expect them to have been slaves of nature. If we measure human evolution in millions of years, that might very well be true at a general level (so general in fact that we are liable to lose all sense of operation and process). On the other hand, I cannot suppress the hunch that, even 18 000 years ago, *Homo sapiens* was not merely such a slave. There are several reasons for this.

First, by the Upper Pleistocene, humans had become the most widely distributed mammal worldwide. They had taken up residence at the top or close to the top of every regional food chain. In that position, they must have been important in restructuring these food chains. In other words, they had become a highly significant variable in their own environment. Even where they were proximately reacting to 'natural' variables, the humans themselves had become one of the most important of these, because of their impact on the restructuring of 'natural' variables.

Secondly, in many areas and through time, humans spent a major part of their tool-making activities not in changing the working edges – those parts of the tool used for extracting, processing, and consuming activities – in order to more effectively interact with the environment, but in changing that part of the tool that was *not* the working edge. For example, the major changes that allow French archaeologists to define and recognize a number of Perigordian, Aurignacian, or Magdalenian stages do not relate to working edges as such (which remain pretty constant), but to those parts of the tool which provide the context for the working edge (i.e. the piece of raw material on which the working edge is located). Whether standardization in *that* part has anything to do with the environment remains to be reasoned and evaluated. The argument about 'time-stressed' environments (Torrence 1983) and their effect upon tools has failed to demonstrate that anything but the *environmentally* active part of the tool should show any correspondence with environmental variables.

Thirdly, as we know from such places as the periglacial belt, from cave paintings, mobile art, and other decorative media, humans had thoroughly enculturated nature or naturalized culture (cf. Orgel 1987). Thus, nature could be painful or potentially painful, primarily for one reason: because humans had constructed nature so that they ended up interacting with it through a select few channels in a select few, highly rule-bound ways. In other words, even (or may be, especially) where humans suffered from nature, they did not merely suffer from the independent variable 'nature out there', but from a cultural construction of their own making. Aside from helping to avoid stress and/or making it sufferable, Nature – the human construction – has the potential at times to actually amplify stress, relative to 'nature out there'. This is because culture selects and defines the channels with which to interact or not to interact with nature. These channels limit human behavioural flexibility and variability.

Even at 18 000 BP, in my evaluation, it is too simplistic (and not very operational) to treat humans as dependent and nature as independent. Certainly, there can be no doubt that variables of the 'natural' environment are strongly articulated with behavioural ones. The suggestion is that both are interacting dependently and independently, and that we need to know some of the context and the history of both in order to unravel and explain the mismatches between them, even at 18 000 BP.

Contemporaneity

If we pretend to be talking about the same point in time at 18 000 BP or 700 000 BP, on a regional, continental, or worldwide basis, we are obviously not kidding anybody. Our ability to identify that point, defined as it is chronometrically, depends too much upon the accuracy of our dating methods. Twenty years ago, I gathered all the then extant ^{14}C dates between 10 000 BP and 20 000 BP. At that time the dates were distributed such that one could attribute interstadial or stadial conditions convincingly to any 500-year period (my Do-It-Yourself-Curve of the Upper Pleistocene). I don't think that dating methods have improved enough over the past 20 years to assign one's regional data, on the basis of chronometry alone, confidently to a *point* in time.

By grouping chronometrically, we will end up with considerably more than a year in our data pile. Simple counting statistics alone generates a range of time of at least plus or minus a few hundred years around 18 000 BP. The more data we throw into our comparisons, the more actual years they will contain, and the more we will tend to lose control over the time that we were trying to hold constant. If we only used chronometrically selected data, my guesstimate would be that our worldwide 'point in time' would expand to 18 000 BP, plus or minus 2000 years. In that case, and holding everything else constant, deviations from the chosen point in time should be fairly random, or cancel themselves out over the expanse of the compared distribution. We would have virtually nothing to discuss if we actually limited ourselves to our archaeological data from the year 18 000 BP. Given the known site-densities in that time-range, the interregional comparison of sites dating from 18 000 BP would be senseless. But isn't that what most people had in mind and haven't I just extolled the virtues of that kind of comparison?

In *The world at 18 000 BP* our ability to identify the same point in time depends largely on the accuracy of climatological markers, of course. These markers will be sufficient for our purposes only if climatological theory is correct and the extreme at 18 000 BP actually happened worldwide and simultaneously, if our proximate measures of that point are sensitive enough so that all of us can identify it, and if the characteristics that we use to identify it are interregionally simultaneous.

Even assuming that climatological theory is correct, i.e. that the cold extreme occurred at the same time around the world, we are still the slaves of our proximate data. Pollen, fauna or microfauna distributions, and sedimentologies, for instance, are usually time-transgressive, and those data most often used by archaeologists tend to be particularly so. The archaeologically or palaeoenvironmentally inferred low will lag behind the actual low by a considerable time. However, compared with the counting statistics of ^{14}C dates, such a deviation from 18 000 BP is relatively systematic and patterned, although, as noted above, it will introduce problems of a processual kind. Even if we were to use semi-instantaneous palaeomagnetic reversals as time markers, they would look like a wide range of time in most archaeologically tracked sediment, after 18 000 years of fossilization.

Thus, we must admit that we are actually talking about a considerable time-range in these volumes, optimistically, say 18 000 BP plus or minus 1000 or 2000 years, as the editors acknowledged in their advice to authors.

Most of the contributors to these volumes have resolved the problem by writing about ranges of time, sometimes many millennia long (Gamble & Soffer, Vols 1 and 2, Introduction, Table). Unless we are very careful with the ways in which we choose to slice time, this introduces new problems. If we look at Pleistocene climatic process, we see cycles in the general shape of sine curves. This should alert us. We want to slice time so that climatic process proceeds in the same direction: getting colder and drier, or warmer and more humid, for example. This would imply slicing the pie from the optimum of the interstadial (interglacial) to the temperature minimum of the stadial (glacial), or vice versa.

In practice, climatological process tends to get cut another way, which is parallel to the way cultural remains are grouped. Periods of similar climate (rather than of similar climatic process) are combined into an archaeological data pile, as in 'the data from the ... interstadial' or 'the data from the ... glaciation'. Particularly, archaeologists who expect variables of the habitat to have been Palaeolithic driving forces should be wary of slicing the diachronic pie in this way since it will group archaeological data generated on the way towards an environmental extreme (the period preceeding the environmental maximum, minimum, or optimum) with those generated on the way out of that same environmental extreme. In terms of environmental process and potential environmental driving variables, archaeological data grouped in this way will be contradictory. The processual insensitivity of such grouping may condemn subsequent inquiries into the interface between human behaviour and habitat to a weak resolution.

Some of the authors in these volumes raise questions about the effect of the temperature extreme upon various phenomena. Unfortunately their data often derive from 'around that extreme'. It is very difficult, if not impossible, to be certain on which side of that extreme a particular data set sits, given our proximate data, the vicissitudes of chronometric and palaeoenvironmental method, and our customary *archaeological* method of grouping which puts phenomena into groups if they look alike. Unless we can say cleanly and clearly that the data are all 'from along the way towards that extreme' or all 'from the period after that extreme', we may never be able to resolve the issue.

This discussion suggests that future studies of the interface between behaviour and nature may focus on data from the periods either leading up to or away from the environmental extreme in order to make worldwide comparisons. Only then will we be able to increase our understanding, winnow our explanations, and begin to discard unsupported claims, metaphysics, and mechanistic relationships between variables.

Peak form

Present wisdom treats hunter–gatherers as slaves of their situation, the more so, the further back in time we go. This assumption makes for trouble when the period that encompasses our data gets longer. As yet, no theory or methodology allows us to accommodate a changeable environment, change-able humans, and a long period of time within the same hypotheses. Their implications for our data would be so equifinal that virtually any scenario would be plausible.

If this creates problems for approaching the data 'deductively', it also creates problems for raising one's head above the data 'inductively'. Collective data from a given time-range are usually interpreted in terms of the most common measurement within a range of artefact measurements, the most common shape within a range of artefact shapes, and the most frequent behaviour within a range of behavioural variation. That peak frequency becomes equated with normalcy, norm, or standard. Bell-shaped curves are fitted around the data pile to mark by their peaks what was striven for and desirable, or what was working.

Less frequent parts of a given range of formal or behavioural variation are viewed as deviations and failures, in contrast to the most frequently occurring parts of the formal or behavioural range. Models or explanations are then invented that allow us to retrodict the behaviour at the peak. Of course, such models are unlikely to be contradicted by the data because they were invented so that they would not be contradicted. This is a very dangerous procedure, processually speaking, for several somewhat contradictory reasons:

(a) If hunter–gatherers are actually situational in their behaviour, 'in tune with environmental variation', then the less frequently occurring behaviours or artefact forms, over the range of the given behaviour or artefact form, tell us as much about environmental driving forces or adaptation as the more frequently occurring ones. A rather complex argument is required to interpret the frequency distribution over a given range of behaviour or artefact form in terms of which parts of that range are adaptively better than others. We must assume that the entire frequency distribution testifies to the fact that the hunter–gatherers once dealt situationally with environmental exigencies, whether we are talking about the distributional peaks or valleys.

(b) Somewhat in contradiction, if we are trying to chronicle adaptation to the natural habitat, we should be searching out the *extremes of variation*. That is where pain and penalty reside, where variables are stressed and strained beyond the breaking point, where selection happens, and *where most change occurs*. In other words, the rare outliers on a range of behavioural or formal variation will tell us more about the relation between humans and nature than the main body of points in between. What is in between is adapted, that is, explicitly uncoupled from the environmental stressor. The stuff between the extreme points of the range avoids most stress and is, thus, the worst place in one's data to look for a neat articulation between stressor and response.

(c) We do not know yet, whether behaviour that is associated – for the purpose of this argument and in normal archaeological practice – with pain or penalty at the extreme points of its range will generate a bell-shaped curve of data in the middle A much simpler expectation would be that any point away from where such pain starts would be as good a place as any other in avoiding that stress. This would make at least two distributions more probable as behavioural outcomes than normal curves: (i) a *random* location for the point of greatest frequency, anywhere between the two extremes; or (ii) a bimodal distribution, generated by avoidances of the two extremes, away from the midpoint towards the extremes of the range.

Even data that are internally contradictory over their range, generated by process that was moving all over creation, or completely random, will have frequency peaks. The simple existence of a frequency peak in diachronic distributions of artefact form or behaviour does not mean that much in itself. Its significance depends on our research questions. Since peaking can occur randomly, or for unknown or 'wrong' reasons, it is dangerous to innocently and routinely take the peaks in the distribution of behavioural data as the starting and end points for one's explanations.

18 K panopticum

Globally, our knowledge of the hunter–gatherer at the height of the last glaciation is limited and excessively uneven. We know, too, that there have been vast differences in the regional intensity of research. For example, it is quite conceivable that more archaeologists have worked on the Palaeolithic of southwestern France than on all the rest of the Palaeolithic world put together. Surely, the odd juxtaposition of emptiness and cluster that is conspicuous when one looks at the peak of the last glaciation primarily reflects the state of research rather than the state of nature.

As has often been pointed out, human absence is difficult to demonstrate conclusively without a problem-directed survey that is correct about the human behaviour that is sought for but not found. Given weaknesses in our behavioural models of hunter–gatherers as well as in survey methodology, my hunch is that false models have guided the survey in most cases of surveyed emptiness, rather than that prehistoric occupants actually were absent from the survey area.

Sometimes we can completely exclude people from regions for sound environmental reasons, such as the presence of a glacier covering the area in question or a polar desert that left it devoid of food. But for many parts of the globe that are supposed to have been uninhabited at 18 000 BP we need much more fine-grained data than we presently possess to rule out hunter–gatherers for environmental reasons.

Archaeologists do not get much pleasure out of demonstrating that something was not there – they prefer to spend their time on excavations that lead to exciting discoveries. Thus the reality of the vast realms of emptiness at 18 000 BP is liable to remain unevaluated for some time to come. Of course, it is also next to impossible to demonstrate conclusively that humans were continuously present in an area (as is claimed, for example for much of France during the last glaciation). Given the notoriously low sedimentation rates in most caves and rock shelters, it is very difficult to prove decisively that local populations have not been absent for a few centuries.

Let us assume that only 10% of that empty space at 18 000 BP is real (and that only 10% of the claimed regional continuities in Upper Palaeolithic settlement turn out to have been false). This should help us to replace our textbook stereotype of gradual cumulative progression towards bigger and better things, of an inevitable worldwide process towards more occupied land and more population. The new picture is a bit more processual, with a lot more waxing and waning, population expansion and contraction, and cyclicity in cultural behaviour. At times, in places, hunter–gatherer societies socially rearticulated, reorganized up and down the ladders of social complexity, and even failed. This makes the hunter–gatherers of the Upper Pleistocene a little more like Neolithic or Archaic and Woodland people and, thus, a little bit more human.

The worldwide distribution of hunter–gatherers at 18 000 BP indicates apparently that many of the known regional site arrangements are quite linear. To a large extent, this only shows how easy it is for archaeologists to survey along lines such as coasts, rivers, forest edges, and lake sides. These same lines of relative ease of archaeological movement were also the areas of the most intensive groundwork during the 19th century (road and railroad construction and sand and gravel pitting) when most of our ideas about Palaeolithic sites were first formed. The location of the sites found by early investigations has thus to some degree foreshadowed the linearity of Palaeolithic sites found much later. Again, if only 10% of these linear patterns survived problem-directed survey to look for sites beyond the boundaries of the known lines (i.e. no sites would be found there), this would have considerable implications for Palaeolithic social organization which demand further research.

A final point deserves some comment. When one takes a broad view of the Palaeolithic world of 18 000 BP, the overall similarity of the record despite the many variations noted in these volumes is striking, particularly in contrast to the archaeological records of most later periods. Of course, where we have fewer data, we also have fewer means to generate subdivisions, contrasts, and contradictions. That is, the impression of a relative lack of variation is, to some extent, caused by the remoteness of the data in time, and not by the conditions at 18 000 BP or earlier. This impression of uniformity is also a product of the methods and theories favoured by the archaeologists themselves.

Methodologically, if all archaeologists summarize the variation in their data in the same shallow way, the data cannot show much variation. For too long, Palaeolithic variation has been presented in terms of the 'lowest common denominator'. Such an approach suppresses variation between regions and stresses what they have in common. The schemes of lithic typology which were in fashion until very recently, must have contributed significantly to the impression of a relatively invariable – if not boring – Upper Palaeolithic record.

The expectation that lithic variation will expose the major axes of behavioural variation among hunter–gatherers is, of course, not very convincing. The method which our research and analysis emphasizes – lithic analysis – has not been demonstrated to track behavioural variation among hunter–gatherers, and among other populations at other times, particularly well. Thus, the choice of method (and of raw material category) allows us to predict limited behavioural variation as a result of our lithic games, regardless of the actual behavioural ranges involved.

The real explanation for the apparent lack of variation at the LGM and at other times in the Upper Pleistocene is probably to be found somewhere between the deficiencies of our extant method and theory. Implicitly, archaeologists expect from ancestors who are somewhat remote in time, as at 18 000 BP, less of an ability to vary than from more recent forebears. Since the populations at 18 000 BP have been placed into the category of 'hunter–gatherers', moreover, they are thought to have been closer to nature and, thus, less able to vary, in contrast to the humans after the Neolithic revolution, who are thought to have finally thrown off the shackles of nature.

Thus more archaeologists are quite content with the limited inter- and intraregional range of variation at 18 000 BP that their stone artefacts project. There is no need for them to be concerned about the lack of sources for variation across regions, or about how to make past behavioural variation more visible in their archaeological data.

Vast behavioural realms still need to be described, compared, and contrasted across regions. For example, we must describe and examine 'culture' as it is reflected in the rule-bound treatment of plants and animals as food and raw material, in spacing behaviours and proxemics, in the dumping of rubbish and in sweeping rules, in the order, logic, and complexity of rule structures, and the like. The range of variation, behavioural realm by behavioural realm, needs to be exposed, explained, and evaluated in a problem-directed way. The authors of *The world at 18 000 BP* have made remarkable progress towards this goal. Once the task has been accomplished, our rather monotonous image of the hunter–gatherers of the world at 18 000 BP may be transformed, and they may turn out to have been as varied and dynamic as modern *Homo sapiens*. Then we will be able to explain with more confidence why various groups of humans were at different points on the behavioural range, and we will have the knowledge to talk with some authority and security about how humans at 18 000 BP were scoring on the scales of evolution and adaptation.

Acknowledgements

This chapter is dedicated to those who have laboured in the non-glamorous Palaeolithic. I need to make amends to Jude, Natalia, Gregory, and Woozl for granting me temporary leaves-of-absence from the household routines. This chapter would not have been possible without the intellectual environment at the University of Massachusetts. Over the years, the students in my Prehistoric Cultural Ecology and European Prehistory seminars have watched patiently and a bit perplexed as I was releasing trial balloons with similar ideas into the clouds, and quite often have forced me to become Earthbound more rapidly than I had anticipated. I hold the sole copyright to the flaws of this chapter.

References

Orgel, M. 1987. Upper Paleolithic cave artists as ritual elites. *NEAA 1987. Program and Abstracts*, 12.

Torrence, R. 1983. Time budgeting and hunter–gatherer technology. In *Hunter–gatherer economy in prehistory*, G. Bailey (ed.), 11–22. Cambridge: Cambridge University Press.

Wobst, H. M. 1978. The archaeo-ethnology of hunter–gatherers or the tyranny of the ethnographic record in archaeology. *American Antiquity* **43**(2), 303–9.

Wobst, H. M. 1989. Discussant's comments. In *The human revolution*, P. Mellars & C. Stringer (eds). Edinburgh and Princeton: Edinburgh University Press and Princeton University Press, in press.

Geographical index

Africa 121–61
  north 25, 41–53
  south 131, 170–84, 189–202, 214–27
ACH/84/1 285
Abri Alain 46
Abu Madi I 73
Afalou bou Rhummel 45, 46
Ain Mallaha 114
Ainchwara 242, 243
Aladi Springs 153
Aldan, R. 33
Alexandersfontein Pan 174
Ali Kosh 132
Altai region 29
Amadzimba 142
Apollo 11 Cave 138, 173, 180, 182, 183, 220, 221, 223
Arumpo Lunette 302
Asia, central 25
  south 231–5
Australasia 266–91
Ayme 46
Azraq sites 91, 108
  Azraq 61 67, 70, 112
  Azraq 17 86
  Azraq 18 91, 92

Baghaikhor 245
Ballawinne Cave 289
Bambata 142
Beginner's Luck Cave 276
Belan-Seoti Valley 238, 239, 240, 241, 245, 250, 252
Bir Tarfawi 25
Bluff Cave 287–8
Blydefontein Shelter 194
Boluma-Isoku 137
Bone Cave 285, 286, 288, 289
Boomplas Cave 173, 174, 180, 183, 195, 200, 201, 202, 220, 222
Border Cave 178, 182
Breekbeenkolk 174
Buffelskloof 173
Burke's Cave 309
Burzahmon 233
Bushman Rock Shelter 173, 222
Butapathri 233
Buur Heybe 152, 153
Byneskranskop 180

Campion site 154
Cango Caves 173, 195
Cape Fold Belt 223, 225

Cape Fold Mountain Belt 192, 193, 195, 197
Cape York Peninsula 275
Cave Bay Cave 276, 283
Cbar Penplain 301
Cherangani Hills 132
Chifubwa Stream 145
Chopani-Mando 251
Colless Creek 274
Cornelia 174
Cottage Cave 173
Cracroft River 277
Craigrossie 174
Cuddapah 252, 253

Daiya 240, 242
Darling, R. 264, 296, 301
Darwin Crater 285, 286
Deena-Reena 284, 287
Depression Cave 138, 159
Devil's Lair 264
Dikbosch I 190, 202
Drakensberg Mountains 192, 197, 199, 223
Drotsky's Cave 136, 138
Duncombe Farm 143, 144, 209
Dundo 136

E71K13 50
E71P1 50, 52
E71P2 50, 52
E71P7 50
E71K13 52, 53
E71K9 49
Ein Gev I 63, 66, 70, 72, 108, 109, 111
  Ein Gev III 70
  Ein Gev IV 69
El Guettar 42
El Hamel 43
El Haouita 43
El Oncor 43
El-Kowm 61, 67, 70
Elands Bay Cave 173, 175, 180, 214, 216–20, 222, 223, 224
Es Sayar 43

F/82/6 285
Far East 30
Fazael III 72
Florentine Valley 276, 277
Franklin, R. 276, 279, 285
Franklin sites 286
  Franklin-Gordon Caves 288

Gaap Escarpment 174, 224

Gambles Cave 150
Garibaldi Complex *see* K'one Complex
Garnpung 306, 316
    Garnpung I 304, 310
Ghaggar Valley 232
Gi 135, 136, 138, 160
Gobedra rockshelter 153
Gogoshii Qabe (Gure Makeke) 152, 153
Gombe Point 137, 157
Grotte Rassel 42, 45, 46, 47
Grotte des Contrebandiers 43
Guli Waabayo 152
Gure Makeke *see* Gogoshii Qabe
GvJm 16 151
GvJm 22 151
GvJm 46 151

Haaskraal 174
Hagfet et Tera 48, 49
Hamifgash IV 69
Haon II 103
Haua Fteah 42, 47, 48, 49
Hayonim/Sefunim 29
Hefsibah 70
Heuningneskrans 173, 180, 200
Hoezar Oost 174
Hora Mt rockshelter 7, 147
Howiesons Poort 173, 176, 177
Huon 272

Imbonga 137
Ishango 137, 155, 159
Isna 50
Itaha 242
Iwo Eleru 161

Jaita II 62, 65, 72
Jalgaon 252
Japan 29, 30, 272
Jebel Sahaba 51
Jerico 112
Jordan Valley sites 59
Jordanian Desert 78–93
Jos Plateau 158
Juba, R. 153
Judd's Cavern 289, 290

K'one (Garibaldi) Caldera Complex 152
Kaimur Range 242, 252
Kalahari 135, 138
Kalambo Falls 136, 144, 145, 150
Kalemba 145, 146, 147, 159
Kalinjar 242, 243
Kamoa 136
Kamoa Valley 156
Kangkara 180
Kannikwa 174
Karin Heegan 153
Karoo 174, 223
Karwi 242

Kashmir 29
Kathu Pan 174
Kathu Vlei 195
Kebara 63
    Kebaran Complex 61, 64
    Kebara Cave 111
    Kebara/Qafseh 29
Kenniff Cave 272
Khami 142, 160
Kharaneh *see* Wadi Kharaneh
Khenzira Caves 46
Khor Musa 50
Kiese II 147, 148
Kilu Cave 265
Klasies, R. 173, 182, 183, 201
Koobi Fora 107, 112
Koonalda Cave 275
Korea 30
Kosipe 272
Kota Tampan 258
Kow Swamp 288
Ksar Akai 62
Ksar Akil 29
Kurnool 252
Kutikina Cave 276, 278, 279, 280, 281,
    278–84, 285, 286, 287, 289

Lake Abhe 133
L. Anchar 233
L. Arumpo 302, 313
L. Baringo 133
L. Besaka 152, 153, 154
L. Bogorio 133
L. Bosumtwi 133
L. Chad 133
L. Chesi 133
L. Chinalbwood 307, 308, 313
L. Didwana 232
L. Eyasi Basin 149
L. Garnpung 302, 313
L. Ionnina 61
L. Hokarsar 233
L. Ishiba Ngandu 133
L. Kivu 133
L. Leaghur 302, 307, 310, 313
L. Lisan 60, 97
L. Mahoma 132
L. Makgadi 133, 135
L. Malawi 133
L. Manyara 133
L. Menindee 306
L. Mobutu 133
L. Mungo Lunette 312
L. Mulurulu 302, 313
L. Mungo 264, 302, 306, 307, 308–12, 313
L. Naivasha 133
L. Nakuru 150
L. Nakuru-Elmentaita 133
L. Rukwa 133
L. Tandou 314

L. Tanganyika 133
L. Turkana 133
L. Van 60
L. Victoria 133, 296, 306, 314
L. Zeribar 60, 61
L. Ziway 152, 153
L. Ziway-Shala 133
Lac Tumba 136, 137, 157
Laga Oda rockshelter 152
Laharia-dih 245, 246
Lakhanpur 242
Leaghur 306
Leaghur Backshore I 302, 316
Leaghur Backshore II 302
Leaghur Backshore III 303
Leaghur Peninsula I 310, 313
Leang Burung 2, 261
Lekhahia 245
Leopard's Hill Cave 145, 146, 147, 159,
    160
Lukenya Hill 147, 150

M86/2 288
MLI 313
    MLIII 313
Madai-Baturong 258, 261
Magosi 151
Mahuackachcha 242
Malakunanja II 270
Malangangerr 270, 272, 273
Mallaha 62
Manahill 275
Mashonaland 208, 209
Matenkupkum Cave 265
Matopos 207, 208, 209
Matopos Hills 141
Matupi Cave 137, 154, 155, 160
Maxwell, R. 288
Mayo Louti 158
Meadow Glen 309
Mediterranean Levant 58–74
Melikane 173, 174, 180
Melkhoutboom 180
Middle Orange River Valley 192, 193
Midhishi 2 153
Mongolia 29
Montagu 173
Morhana Pahar 245
Mt Darwin 281
Mt Elgon 132
Mt Hoyo 136
Mt Kenya 132
Mt Kilimanjaro 132
Mufulwe 145, 146, 147
Mulurulu I 306, 314, 316
    Mulurulu III 306, 307, 314
Mumba 147, 148
Mumba-Hohle 149, 159, 160
Mumbwa Cave 145
Mundva 242

Mungo 272
    Mungo Backshore I 308, 310
    Mungo I 309, 310, 313, 314, 316
Munyama Cave 147, 151
Mura-Gurjhia hills 245
Murray, R. 301
Muscat 231
Mushabi XIV, 111
Mwambacimo 145, 146, 147
Mwelu Rocks 145

Near East 25
Nachifuku shelter 143
Nahal Hadera 72
Namib 136
Namib Desert 174
Nanwoon Cave 288
Nasera rockshelter 148, 149
Nauwalabila I 270, 273, 274
Nawamoyn 270, 272, 273
Nazlet Khater-4 49
Nderit Drift 150
Negev 71, 122
Nelson Bay Cave 173, 174, 180, 220, 222,
    223, 224
Neveh David 780
New South Wales 296–319
Ngarulutra 112
Niah Cave 258, 260
Nos 173, 180
Nsalu Cave 145
Nswatugi 141
Nyarunazi 154
Nyazonga 209

Odo Ogun 158
Oenpelli rockshelters 270
Olduvai Gorge Naisiusiu Beds 147, 148, 151
    Olduvai Ndutu Beds 148
Old World 24–33
Orwa 242

Pahiha 242
Palmyra 61
Patne 253
Payakumbuh Caves 258
Pfupi rockshelter 143, 209
Phillipon Tenaghi 61
Poggenbank 138, 173, 180
Pomongwe Cave 142, 143, 159, 208
Puritjarra 274
Pushkar 252

Rachgoun 45
Ras an Naqb 112
Ratcatcher's Lake 316
Redcliff 142, 143
Reniguntа 252
Rift Valley 98
Rocky Cape 283, 284

Rocky Caves 280
Rose Cottage Cave 190
Rossing Cave 136
Ruiki 157
Rutonde site 154
Ruwenzoris 132
Rwanda 132

Sahara Desert 41
Saharo-Arabian belt 60, 61
Samarkanda 29
Sawmills 208
Seacow Valley 192
Seekoei Valley 224
Sefunim 67
Sehonghong 173, 180, 194, 202, 220, 223
Semlike Valley 156
Sepik, R. 289
Shashabugwa Shelter 142, 208
Shongweni 173, 180
Shuwikhat 49
Sibebi 173
Siberia 30, 31
Siddhapur 242
Sidi Mansour 44
Sinhor 245
Sitanda Dam 208
Skew Valley 310
Sonanchi Crater 148
Sunda continental shelf 255
Sundaland 255–61

Tabon Cave 258, 261
Taforalt 225, 42, 43, 45, 47
Tamar Hat 27, 42, 43, 45, 46, 47, 48
Tamara 27
Tandou Creek I 316
Tandou Lunette I 316
Tasi, no. 3614, 289
Tenere 25
Thar Desert 232, 253
Tianko Panjang Cave 259
Tingkayu Valley 258
Toshmaidan 233
Tshangula 142, 159
Twilight Cave 147, 150, 151
Twin Rivers Kopje 144

Ultenhage 195
Umhlatuzana 180

Upper Cave, Zhoukoudian 30
Uttar Pradesh 237–53

Wadi al-Hammeh 97–115
    Wadi Hammeh 9 113
    Wadi Hammeh 12 113
    Wadi Hammeh 22 113
    Wadi Hammeh 23 113
    Wadi Hammeh 25 100
    Wadi Hammeh 26 100, 102, 103, 104, 106,
        107, 108, 109, 111, 112
    Wadi Hammeh 27 64, 99, 100, 106, 107,
        109, 111, 112, 113, 114
    Wadi Hammeh 31 101, 106, 107, 108
    Wadi Hammeh 32 101, 106, 107
    Wadi Hammeh 33 100, 106
Wadi Fazael 109
Wadi Halfa 28
Wadi Hasa 64
Wadi Jilat 66, 81, 83, 91
    Jilat 6 65, 67, 69, 90, 91, 92, 93, 111
    Jilat 8 111
    Jilat 9 86
    Jilat 10 91
Wadi Kharaneh 66
Wadi Kharaneh 4 66, 70, 93
Wadi Kubbaniya 50, 51, 52, 53
Wadi Mushabi 71
Wadi Sayakh 66, 70
Wadi Uwaynid 81, 86, 90, 91, 93
    Wadi Uwaynid 18 86
Wadi Ziqlab 98
Wadi al-Hasa 98
Walls of China 309
    Walls of China I 308, 310
Webi Shebelli 153
Weld, R. 277
Willandra Lakes 296, 297
Willandra, R. 264
Wolkberg Caves 173
Wonderkrater 174
Wonderwerk 190, 202

Yabrud III 67, 72
Yenisey, R. 33

Zagros mountains 61
Zaire Basin 132, 137
Zimbabwe 206–11
Zombepata Cave 143, 209

General index

abandonment 13, 141, 160, 300
Acheulian 81–94, 238–53
acorn 67
adaptation 1, 2, 5, 6, 9, 12, 14, 15, 18, 53, 72,
    74, 93, 255, 261, 342
  adaptive strategy 5, 12
aeolian silt 86, 90
Afontavo 31
agate 242, 288
Ainchwara 243–53
Albany 222–7
almond 103, 111
amelioration, Lipovo-Novoselovsk 32
animal size 58, 133, 174, 175
antelope 159, 181
Anthrospermum 132
arctic fox 32
aridity 7, 8, 13, 17, 25, 28, 41, 73, 104, 132,
    135, 137, 138, 159, 160, 174, 195, 201,
    224, 226, 253
  hyper-aridity 53
  semi-aridity 7, 196, 253
art 16, 91, 182, 184, 211, 275, 288, 334, 336
  mobiliary 17, 155, 333
    painted slab 17, 180, 182, 184
  parietal 17, 18, 91, 106, 147, 153, 275,
    288–90, 333, 334
  ritual 182
artefact
  bone 65, 141, 142, 143, 207
    awl, 146, 283, 286
    harpoon 155, 241
    head, 180
    reamer 283
    sickle 111
    spatula 286
  cluster 242
  Darwin Glass see also exotic material,
    industry, lithic assemblage, raw
    material 282–8
  density 67, 92, 104, 106, 112, 155, 242, 273
  obsidian 148, 150, 152
  palette and grinder 149, 219
  tortoise carapace container 86
  shell 141, 143, 207
    ostrich water-flask 189, 222
  stone see also lithic assemblage 264, 265,
    282, 284, 287
    anvil 69, 308
    bored 142, 143, 145, 146, 147, 155, 160
    bowl 66, 67
    'cup-holes' 66
    drill 155

grindstone 51, 52, 67, 70, 90, 91, 93,
    108, 146, 219, 220, 275, 306, 308, 316
    mano 66
    mining 106
    mortar 49, 66, 67
    pestle 66, 67
    pounding stone 69, 112, 178, 278, 284,
    285, 286, 287, 288, 302, 304, 307, 308,
    313
    whetstone 219, 220
  torch-stick 275
  tortoise-shell bowl 180, 182
  wood
    weighted digging stick 160
Artemisia 132
Arterian 25–33, 43, 45
Aurignacian, Levantine 29
aurochs 32

Ba:gandji see also ethnography 315, 317, 318
baboon 143
Bambata 141–61, 207
bandicoot (Perameles cf. bougainville) 283
Baradostian 29, 306
Barbary sheep (Ammotragus lervia) 46, 48,
    53
bead 83, 91, 182, 183, 184
  bone 219, 222
  ostrich shell 141, 144, 150, 155, 177, 180,
    182, 184, 219
  shell 91, 93
behaviour 12, 45, 147, 237, 331, 334, 335,
    339, 342
Bembesi 141–61
Besaka 154–61
bettong 315
biological extinction 257
biomass 12, 196, 199, 200, 201, 261
bird 51, 149, 152, 159, 283, 288
  marine 219
  water 52
  game 92
bison (Bos bison) 32
blesbok (Damaliscus dorcas albifrons) 138
blood see also art
  human 289
  mammalian 289
bone see artefact, industry 67, 69, 104, 216,
    278, 283, 309, 264
  burnt 109, 264, 307
  density 282–3, 286
  element frequency 109
  gnawed 109

boneworking *see* artefact, industry, ornamentation
boundary *see also* territoriality 331, 332, 333
bovid 147, 152, 216
buckthorn 103
burial *see also* cemetery, cremation, grave goods, hominid 17, 50, 66, 70, 92, 93, 106, 112, 149, 182, 184, 226, 308
bushbuck 151
butchery 142

calorie 47, 67
Capsian escargotiere 109
carnivore 133, 143, 149, 257, 286
cemetery *see also* burial, cremation, grave goods, hominid 45, 51
cereal exploitation *see also* domestic crop 11
chalcedony *see also* raw material 178, 242, 286, 288
Chalcolithic 81–94
Charaman 141–61
charcoal 109, 150, 152, 155, 173, 195, 216
    oak, 111
    tamarisk 51
Chenopodiaceae 155
chert *see also* raw material 106, 107, 148, 178, 242, 242, 243, 282, 286, 288
chimpanzee 149, 150
CLIMANZ 6, 265
CLIMAP 4, 6, 42
clothing manufacture 284
COHMAP 6, 7
Compositae 231
core 106, 219, 242, 243, 245
    area 259
    reduction *see also* industry, lithic assemblage 112, 184, 245, 260, 261, 280, 282, 286, 309, 310
crab freshwater 156
cremation *see also* burial, cemetery, grave goods, hominid 264, 316
crypto-crystalline silica 241, 242
crystal quartz 178, 286, 288
culture 6, 13, 261, 331, 333, 336
curative technology 334

Dabarosa 27
Dabban 27, 47–53
Daiya 252
Darwin Glass *see also* lithic assemblage 281–8
dassie 216
dasyurid 286
dating 215–16, 220–2, 337
    bone apatite 121, 146
    C14, 29, 121, 136, 142, 208, 215
    calcrete 121, 135
    cave sinter 131, 135, 136
    deep-sea core 58, 59
    fission-track 29
    relative chronology 62

shell carbonate 121
travertine 131
typological analysis 29–30, 32
decision-making 13
deer
    fallow (*Dama dama*) 72
    red (*Cervus elaphus*) 32
    roe 72
deglaciation *see also* glaciation, interstadial, stadial 233, 234
desert 73, 136, 174, 232, 275
    scrubland 265
diet 47, 67, 109, 142, 211
Diuktai 30
Djokocian 157
Doian/Eibian 153
dom-palm 51, 52
dometic animal 78
domestic crop *see* cereal exploitation 78
duck 92
duiker 142

Eburran 150–61
economy 49, 53, 114, 300
    development 257
    marine-based 222
    specialisation 156
elephant, 257
elk 32
environment
    change 257, 261
    continuity 20, 315, 317
    deterioration 210, 220
    reconstruction 58–61, 98, 137–8
    selection 6
    variable 2
equid 216
Ericacea 132
Ethiopian Blade Tool Tradition *see also* lithic assemblage 152
ethnography *see also* Ba:gandji, Inuit, San 182, 183, 184, 189, 315, 317–18
Eucalyptus obliqua 286
exchange *see also* exotic material 66, 91, 92, 93, 112, 288
exotic material, procurement of *see also* exchange, lithic assemblage 52, 53, 90–1, 92, 112, 148, 282, 286
extinction 72, 143, 160
    through hunting 257

Fakhurian 28, 50–3
fauna 58, 337
feature *see also* house 226
fern 155
figurine *see also* art
    bone 241
fish 149, 152, 155, 219, 264, 306, 310, 313, 316

fish *cont.*
    freshwater
      catfish 52, 53, 149, 152, 156
      crayfish (*Cherax destructor*) 304, 307, 313
      perch (*Plectroplites ambiguus*) 304, 306, 316
      golden perch 316
    marine 47, 265
      Murray cod (*Macculochele macquariensis*) 306
fishing 130, 314
    net 316
flora 83
food
    charred plant remain 111
    collection *see also* foraging, gathering 52, 53, 67, 71, 93, 184
    management 3, 53, 72, 73, 146, 219–20, 265, 301
    preparation, drying or smoking 51
    production 17, 18, 52, 71, 281
foraging *see also* food collection, gathering 73, 147, 300, 314
fox 92, 93, 106, 109
fruit 67, 70, 72

gallery forest 137, 155
gathering *see also* food collection, foraging 108, 160, 211, 300, 304
gazelle 49, 51, 70, 72, 86, 91, 92, 93, 109
geology 98, 240
gift exchange *see also* exchange 182, 183
glaciation 24, 42
    Mungo Lacustral phase 297, 301, 312
    Sartan 30, 31, 32
    Zyrianka 30
Graminae 155
grass bedding 216
grassland 136, 200
grave goods *see also* burial, cemetery, cremation, hominid 16, 70, 112
groundsels (*Dendrosenecio*) 133
grysbok 216

hackberry 103, 111
haematite 146, 155
hafting 64
Halfan 28, 49
Harappan 233
hare 70, 86, 91, 92, 93, 109, 142, 143, 147, 159
hare-wallaby 306, 314, 315
Hargeisan 153–61
hartebeest 46, 51, 52, 151
hawthorn 103
hearth 46, 67, 70, 86, 91, 103, 104, 106, 109, 112, 264, 270, 278, 282, 301, 304, 307, 310, 311, 312
hedgehog 143
herbivore 149

herding 46
hippopotamus 152
Hoabinhian 258
hominid *see also* burial, cemetery, cremation, grave goods 151, 155, 184
    Mechtoid 45–53
    Mungo I 288
    Negrito 259
hornfels 193, 194, 286, 288
horse 32
house 46, 66, 70, 91, 108
Howiesons Poort 149, 183, 176–84
hunting 46, 52, 53, 59, 108, 143, 147, 159, 181, 183, 184, 283, 300, 309, 314
hxaro *see* gift exchange
hyrax 142, 143, 160

Iberomaurusian 25–33, 42–53
Iberomaurusian, Eastern 27, 44, 47–53
ibex (*Capra ibex*) 70
ice
    pack 266
    Vistulian 33
    sheet 268
ideology 182, 184
Idfuan 28, 49–53
impala 151
industry *see also* artefact
    bone 83, 91, 106, 147, 180, 219, 222, 241, 281, 286
    lithic *see also* core
      assemblage 47, 48, 62, 69, 71, 73, 86, 90, 91, 93, 101, 106, 107, 111, 121, 138, 140, 141, 143, 145, 147, 148, 149, 150, 151, 152, 153, 154, 155, 156, 158, 159, 160, 175, 177, 178, 180, 181, 183, 184, 192, 193, 194, 195, 201, 207, 209, 219, 220, 222, 224, 226, 238, 240, 242, 243, 245, 248, 250, 251, 257, 258, 260, 261, 264, 265, 272, 273, 276, 279, 280, 281, 284, 285, 286, 287, 288, 304, 307, 310, 312, 333, 336
      Darwin Glass 282–8
      debitage 69, 70, 100, 104, 105, 112, 143, 220, 222, 226, 242, 245
      technotypological analysis 64–5, 73, 238, 240, 341–2
      tool discard 112
      workshops 241–5, 252
    wood 281
Indu 232
innovation
    blowpipe 260
    bow and arrow 260
    digging-stick weight *see also* artefact 211
    hunting and trapping technique 260
    technology 181, 183
INQUA 6
insolation 7, 8
interaction 13, 70

interstadial *see also* glaciation
    Bolling–Allerod 60
    Karga 30, 31, 32
interval *see also* glaciation
    Kibangian 157
    Leopoldvillian 157
    Douroumain 158
Inuit *see also* ethnography 334
iron-ore 288
Ishangian 155–61

jasper 286
jewellery 16
Juniperu 132

'Kalahari' sand 137, 157
Kalinian 157
Kalinjar 245
kangaroo 288
    grey (*Macropus giganteus*) 286
Kebaran 29, 58–73, 97–115
    Geometric 29, 61–74, 103–15
Kenyan Capsian 150–61
Khami 141–61
Khormusan 28
kinship 183, 184
klipspringer 142
knapping 64, 241–2, 252, 253
Krukowski microburin 69
Kubbaniyan 28, 49–53
Kubu 259 *see also* ethnography
kudu 159

Lagaman 62
Laharia-dih 251
lake-level 6, 7, 8, 101, 133, 135, 137, 149, 174
landbridge 276
landsnail 46, 49, 53, 160
lemming 32
leopard 257
Leopoldvillian 157
Levallois 153
    cores 175
    flakes 157
Levallois-Mousterian 27–33, 102–3
lithics *see* industry
lizard 147, 149
lobster 219
Lockshoek 193–202, 224–7
loess 24, 233, 235
Lupemban 144–61
lunates Helwan 71
Lupembo-Tshitolian 156–61

macrobotany 79
macropod 283, 286
Magosian 147
Malayan tapir 257
Maleme 208
Malta-buret 30–1

mammoth 32
mangrove colony 256
marine resources 43, 45, 219, 265, 313
    molluscs 47, 48, 66
        Achatina 149
        Homalopoma 47
        Nerita 66
        Melanopsis praemorsa 109
marriage 183
Menelikia lyrocera 149
microburins Krukowski 69
microfauna 83, 173, 195, 337
micromammals 138
MNI 142, 147, 283, 304, 306
mobility *see* population movement
mole-rat 175, 216
mollusc, freshwater *see also* marine resources
    Unio abyssinicus 42, 50, 51, 52
    mussel (*Velesurio ambiguus*) 302, 304, 306,
        307, 310, 313, 316
mouse hopping (*Notomys or Pseudomys sp.*) 306
Mungo Lacustral phase 301, 312
Mungo–Zanci Arid Period 297, 300, 301,
        312, 316
murids 283
Mushabian 61–73
musk ox (*Ovibos*) 32

Nachifukan 143–61, 209
Naseran 148–61
Natufian 62–73, 97–115
nutshell 92

oak 103, 111
obsidian *see also* artefact, exotic material, raw
        material 148, 150
ochre 90, 91, 93, 146, 264, 288, 312
onager 32
optimality 13
Oranian, Eastern *see* Iberomaurusian, Eastern
organic residues on artefacts 111, 184, 265,
        275, 280, 316
ornament *see also* art, beads, jewellery 16
    bone 65, 106, 241
    shell 90, 92, 106, 180, 182, 183, 220, 222
oven *see* hearth

Pacitanian 257, 258
palynology *see also* pollen 28, 58, 60, 145,
        159, 231, 234, 279
pig, bushy 149–50
pigment 146, 147
Pinus Nigra 42
pistachio 71, 103, 111
pit 112
platypus (*Ornithorhynchus*) 288
Podocarpus 136
points *see also* artefact, industry
    bone 65, 70, 90, 141, 144, 169, 189, 283
    bone, polished 177–8, 182, 183, 184

points *cont.*
    Rocky Cape 283, 284
    stone
    Falita 65
    Kebara 65
    La Mouillah 71, 90, 91
    Lupemban 156
    Ramon 71
pollen *see also* palynology 6, 25, 28, 42, 92,
        103, 104, 130, 132, 133, 136, 137, 155,
        156, 173, 195, 231, 232, 233, 235, 337
Polungu 145
polyphony 20
Pomongwe 141–61
population
    density 7, 111, 112, 113, 160, 181, 182, 183,
        196, 202, 208, 210, 223, 227, 242, 252,
        260, 301
    movement 66, 73, 257, 260, 288, 301
porcupine 143
pottery 143, 149, 150, 153, 158, 209, 248
pre-Harappan 233
protein 67
Punan 259

Quadan 27
quarry 220, 307–10
quartz *see also* raw material 148, 149, 155,
        193, 279, 280
quartzite *see also* raw material 240, 242, 250,
        272, 279, 280, 284, 286

r-selection 53
rainfall 12, 14, 25, 28, 41, 42, 60, 61, 79, 98,
        132, 135, 136, 141, 142, 174, 175, 195,
        196, 197, 198, 199, 201, 224, 225, 232,
        234, 235, 253, 255, 257, 266
rainforest 18, 257, 258, 259, 276
rat-kangaroo (*Bettongia spp.*) 306
raw material procurement 52, 66, 79, 148,
        193, 195, 240, 242, 250, 252, 279, 280,
        282, 284, 286, 288, 307
refugia 13, 14, 154, 161
refuse disposal 112
reindeer 32
reptile 149, 152
rhinoceros
    black 149
    Javan 257
    woolly 32, 33
risk 332
    avoidance 17, 335
ritual *see also* art 16, 17, 112, 182, 289
Robberg 178–84, 193–202, 209, 222–7
rodents 109

sable 142
San *see also* ethnography 182–4, 189, 200
sandstone *see also* raw material 250, 284
savanna 155, 265

sea-going capacity 265
sea-level 13, 25, 30, 175, 196, 219, 220, 232,
        238, 256, 257, 260, 261, 265, 270, 276,
        279
Sebilian 27
seeds 51, 70, 72, 92
settlement *see also* site 3, 13, 17, 32, 42, 70,
        72, 114–15, 216, 223, 226, 237
    continuity 20, 29, 317
    density 7, 223, 253
    seasonality *see also* population movement
        48, 70, 92, 108
Shabarakh 29
shale *see also* raw material 219, 220
shamans 184
shell 310
    bird 304, 313
    conus *see also* burial, grave goods 182
    emu 288, 306
    ostrich 147, 148, 149, 152, 156, 222
shell-midden 45, 46, 52, 149, 216, 258, 260,
        264, 265, 273, 301, 302–7
shellfish 220
shellfishing 314
'shrine' 112
sieving 83
silcrete 178, 219, 307
silica *see also* raw material 242, 243, 250
Siszya 145
site *see also* settlement
    distribution 48, 67, 181, 183, 252
    function 220, 226
    open-air 46, 136, 138, 155, 215, 223, 224,
        239, 251, 264
    seasonality *see also* population movement
        52, 220, 258, 288
    size 66, 108, 137, 273
'Smithfield A' *see* Lockshoek
snow cover 14
    line 279
social organisation 2, 3, 12, 14, 18, 45, 69,
        72, 114, 181, 182, 211, 226, 275, 301,
        318
Somaliland Wilton 153
springbok 206
springhare 142, 143
stadial *see also* glaciation, interstadial
    Gydanian 32
    Younger Dryas 60
steenbok 142, 216
steppe-desert 73
steppe-tundra 32
storage 112
    pits 73
stratigraphy 238, 272–3
stress 16, 260, 275, 335
structures 106, 108, 112
subsistence strategies 3, 5, 58, 67, 72, 108–11,
        202, 265, 301, 314
symbolism 112

taiga 32
Tasmanian Devil (*Sarcophilus harrissii*) 283
technocomplexes 5–6
tell 114
temperature 25, 28, 41, 42, 60, 79, 104, 132,
    136, 137, 145, 173, 175, 198, 201, 233,
    255, 265, 266
territoriality 18, 72, 181, 199
time-transgressive 331, 337
Tingkayu 261
tool *see* artefact, industry
tortoise 86, 91, 93, 109, 142, 149, 160, 216,
    219, 220
trade *see* exchange
trapping 159
tsessebe 142
Tshangulan 141–61, 207–11
tuber, club-rush and nut-grass 51
tundra 32

Umgazan 141–61

wallaby 284
    red-necked (*Macropus rufogriseus*) 283, 285,
        288
wallaroo (*Macropus robustus*) 306
warfare 51
warthog 147, 152, 159
wild ass 86, 91, 92, 93
wild banteng cattle 261
wild cattle 51, 52, 91, 92, 93
wild dog (*Cuon sp.*) 257
wildebeest 142, 147, 151
windbreaks 46
wolf 91, 92, 93
wombat (*Vombatus ursinus*) 283, 286, 288
woodland savanna 137

Zarzian 29
zebra 46, 142, 147, 148, 151, 159, 174